INTERACTIONS IN MAGNETICALLY ORDERED SOLIDS

Interactions in Magnetically Ordered Solids

KRITYUNJAI PRASAD SINHA
AND
NARENDRA KUMAR

OXFORD UNIVERSITY PRESS

1980

PHYSICS

Oxford University Press, Walton Street, Oxford OX2 6DP

OXFORD LONDON GLASGOW
NEW YORK TORONTO MELBOURNE WELLINGTON
KUALA LUMPUR SINGAPORE JAKARTA HONG KONG TOKYO
DELHI BOMBAY CALCUTTA MADRAS KARACHI
NAIROBI DAR ES SALAAM CAPE TOWN

© *Oxford University Press* 1980

British Library Cataloguing in Publication Data

Sinha, Krityuryai Prasad
  Interactions in magnetically ordered solids.
  1. Solids – Magnetic properties
  2. Electromagnetic interactions
  3. Nonmetallic materials
  I. Title   II. Kumar, Narendra
  530.4′1   QC176.8.M3   79-41619

  ISBN 0-19-851423-9

Photoset and printed in Malta by Interprint Limited.

TO PROFESSOR M. H. L. PRYCE

PREFACE

Magnetically ordered solids exhibit a wide range of interesting phenomena involving the nature of magnetic ordering and the dynamical interaction between various elementary excitations of the system. The present monograph is addressed to a microscopic treatment of these phenomena with emphasis on the underlying interaction mechanisms and various relaxation effects associated with them. From this point of view it differs distinctly from the existing texts. This field is extremely rich in possibilities, both for theorists and experimentalists, and has grown immensely over the past few decades and the rapid expansion still continues. In a short monograph one is therefore severely restricted in the scope and choice of topics to be covered. We have therefore been selective and confined our attention to magnetic insulators and semiconductors where magnetic ordering is due essentially to the spatial correlation of the spins of the unpaired electrons that are fairly localized in the vicinity of the paramagnetic ions.

As the basic magnetic constituent of the systems in question is an isolated paramagnetic ion whose state is determined by the surrounding diamagnetic ligands, we have given an elementary discussion of the ligand field theory in the introductory Chapter 1. In Chapter 2 we describe the phenomena of resonance and relaxation in magnetically dilute (paramagnetic) systems as they complement the discussion on concentrated systems in subsequent chapters. Chapters 3 and 4 deal with a detailed treatment of the origin and nature of exchange interactions, namely direct as well as various indirect mechanisms. After presenting the standard treatment of quantized spinwaves—the magnons and their thermodynamics in Chapter 5, the following chapters (7 to 12) are concerned with magnon-magnon and the magnon-phonon interaction mechanisms and the associated kinetic phenomena—relaxation and heat transports. In view of the importance of interactions with neutrons, photons, and conduction electrons acting as probes for the magnetic systems, we have included a discussion of these topics in Chapters 11, 13, and 14 respectively. Further, a few words about the inclusion of chapter 6 on criticial phenomena in magnetic systems will be in order. The recent development of the renormalization group-theoretic concepts have revolutionized our thinking on this topic and we felt that readers should be given a flavour of the essential ideas.

The list of topics covered may appear to be fairly comprehensive and yet we have left out many important areas such as itinerant (or band) magnetism and the developing field of amorphous magnets, spin glasses, etc., to name a few. The reason has already been given.

This monograph is intended for postgraduate students contemplating research in magnetism or related areas of solid-state physics. It is hoped that active research workers in this general area will also find the book sufficiently useful. One of us (K. P. S.) is grateful to the Science Research Council, U.K. for the award of a visiting Professorship (1977–78) at the H. H. Wills Physics Laboratory, University of Bristol, where the book received the final touches. The other (N. K.) is also thankful to the Science Research Council, U.K., for the award of a visiting Professorship (1978–79) in the Department of Physics, University of Warwick, where the manuscript was finalized. Finally, we are indebted to all the authors who have graciously permitted us to make use of figures from their publications.

K. P. S.

Bangalore 1978   N. K.

CONTENTS

1

INTRODUCTION

There is now a rich variety of magnetic materials that exhibit spontaneous long-range ordering of localized magnetic moments below a critical temperature which is characteristic for each substance. These magnetic systems have been broadly classified into four categories according to the nature of long-range order. These are called ferromagnetic, antiferromagnetic, ferrimagnetic, and helimagnetic systems and correspond, respectively, to parallel, antiparallel, uncompensated antiparallel, and spiral alignment of magnetic moments. Some substances show even more complicated arrangements. We shall, however, confine our attention to the first three categories. Further, we address ourselves to magnetic systems which are insulators or semiconductors. For such systems the magnetic moment resides in and around the paramagnetic ions which are ditributed over special crystallographic positions in the matrix of diamagnetic ions. This is to be contrasted with metallic systems where magnetism may arise from itinerant or band electrons. The spatial disposition and relative energies of the electrons which are responsible for the atomic moments (i.e. those belonging to the partially filled d or f atomic shells) are determined by their interaction with the diamagnetic ions. This lies within the domain of the ligand field theory (see Griffiths 1961), and will be discussed in §1.2.

1.1. Some physical characteristics of magnetically concentrated systems

In this section, we shall adumbrate some important physical properties of (a) ferromagnetic, (b) antiferromagnetic, and (c) ferrimagnetic systems.

(a) *Ferromagnets*. Some typical examples of ferromagnetic insulators are EuO, $CrBr_3$, etc. The nature of the internal exchange field in ferromagnets is such that below the critical (Curie) temperature T_c the individual atomic moments are aligned parallel to one another resulting in a large spontaneous bulk magnetization of the sample in some arbitrary direction if the system is isotropic. When the sample is placed in an external magnetic field, the magnetic moments point along the direction of the field. In real materials, however, there is also an internal anisotropy field along some direction which removes the orientational degeneracy in the absence of an external field and the bulk magnetic moment **M** points along this axis (direction of easy magnetization). The spontaneous magnetization $\mathbf{M}(T)$ is a function of temperature T and vanishes at and above the critical temperature. Its temperature dependence near and below T_c simulates the behaviour

$$\mathbf{M}(T) \sim \mathbf{M}(0)\left(1 - \frac{T}{T_c}\right)^{\beta} \quad \text{for } T \to T_c^- \tag{1.1}$$

where $\mathbf{M}(0)$ is the saturation magnetization and corresponds to complete alignment of moments and β is the critical exponent and close to 0.36. In the low-temperature region, i.e. for $T \to 0$, the dependence has a power law form given by

$$\mathbf{M}(T) = M(0)(1 - a_1 T^{3/2} - a_2 T^{5/2} - \ldots) \tag{1.2}$$

(the absence of the $T^{1/2}$ term is worth noting) where the a's are some constitutive constants. At the Curie temperature T_c a transition from the ferromagnetic to the paramagnetic phase occurs. This phase transition is of the second order in the absence of an external magnetic field. In the paramagnetic phase $(T > T_c)$ the response of the system to an external magnetic field, i.e. the paramagnetic isothermal susceptibility, obeys the Curie–Weiss law

$$\chi = \left(\frac{\partial M}{\partial h_{\text{ext}}}\right)_T = \frac{\text{constant}}{T - T_c}. \tag{1.3}$$

The above is based on the mean-field approximation. Experimentally, one observes some departure from the above behaviour for T close to T_c where

$$\chi \propto (T - T_c)^{-\gamma}$$

γ being another critical exponent close to 1.33.

(b) *Antiferromagnets.* Some typical examples are $RbMnF_3$ and $KNiF_3$ (cubic perovskite structure), MnF_2, FeF_2, NiF_2 (rutile structure), and MnO and NiO (rocksalt structure).

An antiferromagnetic system consists of two or more interpenetrating equivalent magnetic sublattices. The nature of the internal field is such that below the transition temperature T_N (the Néel temperature) the two sublattices are ordered with the moments of one sublattice pointing in the opposite direction to the moments of the second sublattice (Néel 1932). In the absence of an external magnetic field the resultant magnetization is zero, although the spontaneous magnetization of each sublattice has a temperature dependence similar to that of a ferromagnet. Thus there is a complete orientational degeneracy in the system which cannot be removed by an external magnetic field alone. There is, however, an alternant anisotropy field which plays an important role in fixing the direction of the magnetic moments of the magnetic sublattices with respect to the crystal axes.

An important feature of antiferromagnets is that the magnetic susceptibility has a maximum at the Néel temperature T_N beyond which it shows the same behaviour as a paramagnetic system. Below T_N the average susceptibility decreases, reaching a finite value at $T=0$. In fact the susceptibility shows different behaviour for the following two situations. When the external field is parallel to the direction of sublattice magnetization the susceptibility $\chi_\parallel$ goes to zero at $T=0$. This is because the moments on the spin-down sublattice cannot turn over owing to the strong internal field. On the other hand, when the external field is normal to the magnetization, the sublattices respond feebly and $\chi_\perp$ has a constant value from $T=0$ to $T=T_N$. The above behaviour of $\chi_\parallel$ and $\chi_\perp$ has an interesting consequence for an antiferromagnet—the so called spin-flop transition. Consider an antiferromagnet at $T=0$ K in a parallel field $\mathbf{B}$ and let the alternating anisotropy field $\mathbf{B}_{AN}=0$ for the moment. Since $\chi_\perp > \chi_\parallel = 0$, the system can lower its energy by going over to a perpendicular configuration with slight canting of the spins to take advantage of the Zeeman energy via $\chi_\perp$. When $\mathbf{B}_{AN} \neq 0$, the external parallel field $\mathbf{B}$ must, of course, exceed a critical value to cause this spin-flop transition. Above T_N the susceptibility follows the law $\chi = \text{constant}/(T + \theta)$, where it is expected that $\theta = T_N$. This holds when the inter-sublattice interaction only is considered. Experimentally, it is observed that θ/T_N deviates from unity which may be accounted for by intrasublattice interaction effects.

The fact that, unlike a ferromagnet, an antiferromagnet shows no divergence of susceptibility at $T=T_N$ is readily explained by the following argument. In both cases what is measured experimentally is the response of the system (magnetization) to an external uniform magnetic field. For a ferromagnet the nature of order is such that a uniform magnetic field is conjugate to the magnetization (the order parameter). In the case of an antiferromagnet, however, a uniform field is not conjugate to the order parameter—which is staggered magnetization. For this, response to an alternant magnetic field will diverge. However, such a field is not accesible in the laboratory. If one were to measure the wavevector ($\mathbf{q}$)-dependent susceptibility $\chi(\mathbf{q})$, then for a ferromagnet $\chi(\mathbf{q})$ will diverge at T_c for $\mathbf{q}=0$ (centre of the Brillouin zone) but for an antiferromagnet $\chi(\mathbf{q})$ will diverge at T_N for $\mathbf{q}$ at the surface of the Brillouin zone.

(c) *Ferrimagnets.* Typical examples of this type of ordering are ferrites $MnFe_2O_4$, $NiFe_2O_4$ etc. which have cubic spinel structure) and magnetic garnets (e.g. yttrium iron garnet $Y_3Fe_3O_{12}$ (YIG) which has a complex cubic structure).

Néel (1948) generalized his concept of antiferromagnetic ordering to a situation where two or more magnetic sublattices are not equivalent. For example, in a two sublattice situation, if the atomic moments on the two sublattices are unequal, there will not be exact cancellation of the magnetizations and we shall have a resultant spontaneous magnetization as in a ferromagnet. This kind of ordering was referred to as ferrimagnetic by Neel. Above the transition temperature ferrimagnets show paramagnetic behaviour; however, the susceptibility is described by the Curie–Néel law

$$\frac{1}{\chi} = \frac{1}{\chi_0} + \frac{T}{C} - \frac{D}{T - T_c} \qquad (1.4)$$

where χ_0, C, and D are constants.

If we are dealing with more than two sublattices in a ferrimagnet, the system may display some interesting features. Below the transition temperature T_c the magnetization of different sublattices may vary differently with temperature. As a consequence, the resultant magnetization may vanish at a temperature much lower than T_c and again increase to vanish completely at T_c. The intermediate temperature is called the compensation temperature. This kind of behaviour has been observed in ferrites and garnets.

In the foregoing we have discussed some physical characteristics of the magnetically ordered systems without specifying the nature of the atomic magnetic moment and the origin of the internal Weiss field. The atomic magnetic moments arise from the unpaired electron spins and unquenched orbital moments. The strength B_i of the internal field in these systems is known to be of the order of 10^6–10^7 G as estimated from the transition temperature T_c. Thus the field cannot arise from the magnetic dipole–dipole interaction which gives much lower fields of approximately 10^3 G. In Chapter 3 we shall discuss the quantum mechanisms of the exchange interaction between paramagnetic atoms which leads to their spin coupling through the spin-correlated electrostatic interaction.

In a classical picture a system of electrons in equilibrium in a static external magnetic field and with arbitrary but fixed boundaries has zero magnetic susceptibility and hence no magnetization. This theorem due to Van Leeuwen (see Van Vleck 1932) is a consequence of the fact that the external magnetic field can be incorporated through a redefinition of the canonical momentum $\mathbf{p} = m\mathbf{v} + e/c \, \mathbf{A}$, where $m\mathbf{v}$ is the mechanical momentum and $\mathbf{A}$ is the vector potential. Thus, the vector potential disappears altogether when performing momentum integration to the partition function or the free energy. Since magnetic response involves the derivative of the free energy with respect to the external field, it vanishes identically. But when treated quantum-mechanically one indeed gets non-zero orbital magnetism. The dominant contribution to magnetism however comes from the intrinsic spin of electrons that has no classical counterpart. The spin and the associated antisymmetric statistics for electrons give rise to a spin-dependent interaction whose strength is coulombic.

(d) *Behaviour near the critical point in magnetic systems.* In this section we shall briefly describe the behaviour of the magnetic systems in the vicinity of the critical point i.e. the Curie temperature T_c or the Néel temperature T_N as the case may be) where the system undergoes a second-order phase transition. The high-temperature phase (i.e. the paramagnetic phase) goes to the ordered phase below the critical temperature. Various thermodynamic derivatives become singular at the critical point. The singularities are, in general, of the power-law type and the indices are called critical exponents. For example, the specific heat $C(T)$, the spontaneous magnetization $M(T)$, and the susceptibility $\chi(T)$ of a ferromagnet behave as follows:

$$C(T)_{h_{ext}=0} \sim (T - T_c)^{-\alpha} \qquad T \to T_c^+$$

$$M(T)_{h_{ext}=0} \sim (T_c - T)^{\beta} \qquad T \to T_c^-$$

$$\chi(T)_{h_{ext}=0} \sim (T - T_c)^{-\gamma} \qquad T \to T_c^+.$$

Experimentally, it is found that the values of the exponents α, β, and γ are independent of the details of the microscopic interaction Hamiltonian of the system, e.g. lattice structure etc. Indeed, they depend only on the symmetry of the interaction, the spatial dimensionality d, and the index of isotropy n, where n refers to the number of independent components of the order parameter, namely magnetization or staggered magnetization. This behaviour is often referred to as the universality hypothesis. Thus widely differing systems exhibit similar critical behaviour. For example, the critical index γ is observed to have values close to 1·36 for isotropic ferromagnets such as Ni and Fe, but close to 1·22 for anisotropic materials such as $CrBr_3$ and liquids. Similarly, $\alpha \sim +0·1$ for anisotropic magnets and fluids but $\alpha \sim -0·1$ for isotropic magnets. Also, $\beta \sim 0·42$ for isotropic ferromagnets and $\beta \sim 0·36$ for anisotropic systems (e.g. $CrBr_3$). The mean-field theory of Landau predicts the so-called classical values $\gamma = 1$ and $\beta = \frac{1}{2}$ and a discontinuity in the specific heat, in complete disagreement except for cases where interactions are long range (e.g. dipolar interactions). A rational understanding of the universality is provided by the recent theory of renormalization groups as developed by Wilson (1973) and Fisher (1974). A more detailed discussion of the critical point phenomenon and renormalization group theory will be given in a separate chapter. However, the important physical point to note is that the Landau theory neglects the intermediate-wavelength fluctuations of the order parameter. This is remedied in the renormalization group theoretical approach. Table 1.0 gives some selected data.

TABLE 1.0

*Data for some selected ferro- antiferro-, and ferrimagnets
prepared by using references: Anderson (1963), Keffer (1966), and
Kittel (1971)*

	Substance	Structure	T_c	T_N
			in deg. K	
Ferromagnets	$CrBr_3$	Hexagonal layer	37	
	EuO	Rock salt	69	
	EuS	Rock salt	16	
	Cd Cr_2S_4	Normal spinel	84·5–97	
	$CdCr_2Se_4$	Normal spinel	129·5–142	
Antiferromagnets	MnO	Rock salt		116
	NiO	Rock salt		525
	MnF_2	Rutile		67
	FeF_2	Rutile		79
	NiF_2	Rutile		78.5 − 83
	$RbMnF_3$	Perovskite		54·5
	$KNiF_3$	Perovskite		253·5
Ferrimagnets	$MnFe_2O_4$	Inverse spinel	573	
	$FeFe_2O_4$	Inverse spinel	858	
	$NiFe_2O_4$	Inverse spinel	858	
	$Y_3Fe_5O_{12}$	Garnet	560	
	$Gd_3Fe_5O_{12}$	Garnet	564	
	$Eu_3Fe_5O_{12}$	Garnet	566	

Anderson (1963) has tabulated the energy $E_J = |J| S^2$ for a large number of compounds. An approximate idea of a single interaction J can be obtained from the Néel or Curie temperature by the relation $J = 3k_B/2ZS(S+1)(T_N$ or $T_C)$, Z being the number of nearest neighbours interacting with a given ion with spin S.

1.2. Electronic states of paramagnetic atoms in crystals

Before discussing the various mechanisms of exchange coupling, it is desirable to have some idea of the state of the paramagnetic ions in a crystalline solid and the special features of the unpaired electrons which are responsible for the magnetic moments. These electrons usually belong to the partially filled d or f shells of such atoms.

The electronic state of a free hydrogen-like atom is denoted by the ket symbol $|n, l, m_l, m_s\rangle$, where n, l, m_l, and m_s represent the principal, azimuthal, magnetic and spin quantum numbers respectively. While the first three take integral values, e.g. $n = 1, 2, 3, \ldots$, $l = 0, 1, 2, \ldots, n-1$, $m_l = -l$, $-l+1, \ldots, 0, \ldots, +l$, the spin quantum number m_s takes the values $\pm\frac{1}{2}$. By convention the states with $l = 0, 1, 2, 3$, etc. are designated as s, p, d, f, etc., the states being $2(2l+1)$-fold degenerate in the absence of an external magnetic field. The corresponding one-electron orbital functions expressed in polar co-ordinates are given by

$$\Psi_{n,m_l}(r, \theta, \phi) = R_n(r)Y_{l,m_l}(\theta, \phi)$$

where $R_n(r)$ is the radial part of the function and $Y_{l,m_l}(\theta, \phi)$ is the spherical harmonic and describes the angular variation. As m_l spans the $(2l+1)$ values noted above, the Y_{l,m_l}'s constitute the base functions of a $(2l+1)$-dimensional function space. Sometimes it is convenient to use a suitable linear combination of these functions to display the spatial disposition of these functions with respect to the Cartesian axes. Thus the angular part of the three p orbitals having equivalent lobes in the x, y and z directions is given by

$$p_z = Y_{1,0} \equiv |1, 0\rangle$$

$$p_x = \frac{1}{\sqrt{2}}(Y_{1,1} + Y_{1,-1}) \equiv \frac{1}{\sqrt{2}}(|1, 1\rangle + |1, -1\rangle) \qquad (1.5)$$

$$p_y = \frac{-i}{\sqrt{2}}(Y_{1,1} - Y_{1,-1}) \equiv \frac{-i}{\sqrt{2}}(|1, 1\rangle - |1, -1\rangle).$$

Similarly, for the five d orbitals we can write

$$d_{z^2} = Y_{2,0} \equiv |2, 0\rangle$$

$$d_{x^2-y^2} = \frac{1}{\sqrt{2}}(Y_{2,2} + Y_{2,-2}) \equiv \frac{1}{\sqrt{2}}(|2, 2\rangle + |2, -2\rangle)$$

$$d_{xy} = \frac{-i}{\sqrt{2}}(Y_{2,2} - Y_{2,-2}) \equiv \frac{-i}{\sqrt{2}}(|2, -2\rangle - |2, -2\rangle)$$

$$d_{yz} = \frac{-i}{\sqrt{2}}(Y_{2,1} - Y_{2,-1}) \equiv \frac{-i}{\sqrt{2}}(|2, 1\rangle - |2, -1\rangle) \qquad (1.6)$$

$$d_{zx} = \frac{1}{\sqrt{2}}(Y_{2,1} + Y_{2,1}) \equiv \frac{1}{\sqrt{2}}(|2, 1\rangle + |2, -1\rangle).$$

For atoms having more than one electron, the total orbital and spin angular momenta **L** and **S** are defined as the vector sums of the individual angular momenta l_i and s_i respectively. Their components along the axis of quantization are given by $M_L = \Sigma_i(m_i)$ and $M_S = \Sigma_i(m_{si})$. The total angular momentum **J** is obtained by adding **L** and **S**, i.e. J takes the values $L + S$, $L + S - 1, \ldots, |L - S|$. The atomic states (terms), obtained by inclusion of the Coulomb interaction between the electrons, are designated by the general symbol ^{2S+1}L, where $2S + 1$ denotes the spin multiplicity. These states are $(2S + 1)(2L + 1)$-fold degenerate. When the spin–orbit interaction, i.e. $\lambda \mathbf{L} \cdot \mathbf{S}$, where λ is the coupling coefficient, is taken into account the different atomic states are denoted by $^{2S+1}L_J$ and are $(2J + 1)$-fold degenerate. Thus for an ion with an outer configuration d^2, the inclusion of interelectronic repulsion yields, in ascending order of energy, the states ^3F, ^1D, ^3P, ^1G, and ^1S corresponding respectively to L values of 3, 2, 1, 4, and 0. Further, on the inclusion of the spin–orbit interaction, the lowest state ^3F splits into the multiplets $^3F_2$, $^3F_2$ and $^3F_4$. This is described in another scheme by saying that the energy matrix of the free ion without spin–orbit coupling is diagonal in the representation $|SLM_LM_S\rangle$. When the spin–orbit interaction is included, it is diagonal in the representation $|SLJM_J\rangle$ (see Griffiths 1961).

In group-theoretical language, the Hamiltonian H_0 of the free ion has the full symmetry of the rotation group (spherical symmetry). Therefore the eigenfunctions of this Hamiltonian are simultaneously the eigenfunctions of the angular momentum operator **L**. The corresponding base functions Ψ_{LM_L} belong to the irreducible representation D_L (of dimension $2L + 1$; hence $(2L + 1)$-fold orbital degeneracy).

If the above system is subjected to a perturbation V_c having a symmetry lower than H_0 (e.g. that of a point group G), the symmetry of the Hamiltonian

$$H = H_0 + V_c \tag{1.7}$$

will be that of the perturbation V_c. As a result, the degenerate energy levels of the central ion will be split and the base functions of the split manifold will belong to the various irreducible representations of the point group G of H.

To fix ideas, let us consider an ion at the centre of an octahedron and a ligand (an ion or a group of ions) at each corner of the octahedron. The perturbation V_c due to the six ligands has the symmetry of the octahedral group O_h. The different manifolds of the rotation group are now split into submanifolds, each belonging to an irreducible representation Γ_i of the group. Some of these are shown in Table 1.1.

In this table Mulliken's notation has been used. The one-dimensional (non-degenerate) irreducible representations are denoted by A_1 and A_2, the two-dimensional (doubly degenerate) representations by E, and the three-dimensional (triply degenerate) representations by T_1 and T_2. The sub-

TABLE 1.1

D_L	$\Gamma(O_h)$	Base functions
S	A_{1g}	$f_o(r)$
		$f_4(r)(x^4 + y^4 + z^4 - r^4)$
P	T_{1u}	x
		y
		z
D	E_g	$3z^2 - r^2$
		$x^2 - y^2$
	T_{2g}	xy
		yz
		zx
	A_{2u}	xyz
F	T_{1u}	x
		y
		z
	T_{2u}	$z\sqrt{3}(x^2 - y^2)$
		$x\sqrt{3}(y^2 - z^2)$
		$y\sqrt{3}(z^2 - x^2)$

scripts 1 and 2 refer to those representations which are symmetric and anti symmetric respectively under one of the two-fold rotations about an axis perpendicular to the principal axis. Finally, g and u denote *gerade* (even) and *ungerade* (odd) under the inversion operation I, i.e. under the transformation $(x, y, \overset{.}{z}) \rightarrow (-x, -y, -z)$.

The crystal-field perturbation at the point (r, θ, ϕ) due to the ligand is usually expanded as

$$V_c = \sum_{l=0}^{\infty} \sum_{m=-1}^{l} C_{l,m} r^l Y_{l,m}(\theta, \phi) \tag{1.8}$$

where $Y_{l,m}$ are the normalized spherical harmonics and the coefficients $C_{l,m}$ are to be ascertained from the positions and the charge distributions of the ligands. For ligands treated as point charges these are expressed as

$$C_{l,0} = \left(\frac{2\pi}{2l+1}\right)^{1/2} \frac{q_k}{R_k} P_l(\cos \theta_k) \delta(1/R^l) \tag{1.9}$$

$$C_{l,\pm m} = \left\{\frac{2(l-m)!}{(2l+1)(l+m)!}\right\}^{1/2} \frac{q_k}{R_k} P_l^m(\cos \theta_k) \exp(\pm im\phi_k) \tag{1.10}$$

where $P_l^m(\cos \theta)$ are the associated Legendre polynomials, and q_k and $(R_k,$

θ_k, ϕ_k) are the charge and co-ordinates of the kth ligand. These expressions are summed over all ligand positions. The presence or the absence of the various terms in the above expression is determined by the point symmetry group of the system and certain group-theoretical considerations. For d electrons one need not consider terms higher than $l=4$ in that these terms subtend vanishing matrix elements within the d manifold. To be more specific, the crystal field at the centre ion of the octahedron with six equivalent point-charge ($q_k=q$) ligands is given as

$$V_c = V_R + \frac{7}{3} \frac{q\sqrt{\pi}}{R^5} \left\{ r^4 Y_{4,0} + \sqrt{\left(\frac{5}{14}\right)} r^4 (Y_{4,4} + Y_{4,-4}) \right\} \qquad (1.11a)$$

or in cubic harmonics

$$= V_R + \frac{35}{4} \frac{q}{R^5} \left(x^4 + y^4 + z^4 - \frac{3r^4}{5} \right). \qquad (1.11b)$$

As can be seen from Table 1.1, the form suggests that it belongs to the totally symmetric representation A_{1g} of the O_h group. This is true for V_c relevant to all point groups inasmuch as the Hamiltonian must remain invariant under symmetry transformations of the corresponding point group.

Before discussing the electronic configuration of ions in the presence of a ligand field, it is appropriate at this stage to draw a distinction between the various coupling schemes in the theory.

(1) The weak-field scheme in which the ligand field is feeble compared with the mutual Coulomb interaction between the electrons of the ion. Accordingly, the electronic configurations of the ion are first determined by considering the effect of the interelectronic Coulomb and spin–orbit interactions (free-ion states). Next, the influence of the ligand field is taken into account as a perturbation which splits the level structure and in some cases mixes various configurations.

(2) The strong-field scheme in which the ligand field is sufficiently strong to decouple the electrons from the usual Hund rule pairing. The various states are first described in terms of ligand-field configurations. The effect of Coulomb repulsion is treated after putting electrons in the ligand-field orbitals and finally the spin–orbit coupling is introduced.

(3) The intermediate coupling scheme which lies in between the above two. Here the forces due to the ligand field and the correlative interactions are comparable in magnitude.

For the $3d$ ion series the interelectronic repulsion energy is of the order 10^4–10^5 cm^{-1} and the crystal-field strength is about 10^4 cm^{-1}. The spin–orbit interaction comes next and is of the order of 10^2–10^3 cm^{-1}. For rare-earth ions, where the partially filled $4f$ shells are shielded by $5s$ and $5p$ shells, the crystal-field strength at the f electrons is feeble and the weak-field scheme is suitable. On the other hand, for incomplete $3d$ shell ions intermediate- or strong-field schemes seem appropriate depending on the strength of the ligand field. The differences between these two schemes become apparent for ions with low spin–orbit coupling in the presence of a strong crystal field.

Let us discuss a few specific cases to illustrate the concepts described above. Consider an ion having a closed shell plus a single d electron (e.g. Ti^{3+}) exposed to a purely electrostatic field of cubic symmetry produced by negatively charged ligands. The five-fold degenerate d orbitals in this field are split into a doublet

$$d\gamma : d_{2z^2 - x^2 - y^2}, \; d_{x^2 - y^2}$$

and a triplet

$$d\varepsilon : d_{xy}, \; d_{yz}, \; d_{zx};$$

i.e. the atomic ^2D term is split into ^2E_g and $^2T_{2g}$ terms.

For an octahedral field V_c the $d\gamma$ orbitals lie higher than the $d\varepsilon$ orbitals (the sequence is reversed for a tetrahedral arrangement of the ligands). The strength of the field is measured in terms of the energy separation between these two sets of orbitals. The difference is denoted by the symbol Δ or 10 Dq. The angular dependence of the orbitals is such that the lobes of the two $d\gamma$ orbitals point towards the z axis, and the x and y axes respectively. The $d\varepsilon$ orbitals have their lobes pointing midway between the co-ordinate axes. Thus for ligands with negative charges, the energy of an electron in the central metal ion in the $d\gamma$ orbitals is pushed up because it then directly faces the repulsive charges. On the other hand, an electron in the $d\varepsilon$ orbitals points between the charges thus avoiding the repulsive interaction and its energy is lowered. The case of $Cu^{2+}(d^9)$ in a cubic field can also be treated as a one-particle system, i.e. a 'hole' in the completed d shell (d^{10}). Since a hole is to be imagined as having a positive unit of charge, the sequence of levels is inverted and the triplet $^2T_{2g}$ lies higher than the doublet ^2E_g. The ground-state configurations of $3d$ ions in a cubic crystal field are given in Table 1.2. A schematic representation of crystal-field splitting of a transition-metal ion in an octahedral field is given in Fig. 1.1.

However, a purely electrostatic point-charge model for the crystal field is an idealization. The charge is distributed over the ligands and there is appreciable overlap between the metal-ion and ligand charge clouds. One therefore expects a covalent admixture between the metal-ion and ligand orbitals. In fact, there are now experimental results (e.g. electron spin resonance) which give unambiguous indications for covalent bonding and electron transfer in magnetic compounds. They also lead to a reduction of

TABLE 1.2

Number of d electrons	Free-ion ground state	Intermediate-field scheme	Strong-field scheme	Some typical ions
$3d^1$	^2D	$^2T_{2g}(d\varepsilon)$	Same	Ti^{3+}
$3d^2$	$3F$	$^3T_{1g}(d\varepsilon^2)$	Same	V^{3+}, Ti^{2+}
$3d^3$	^4F	$^4A_{2g}(d\varepsilon^3)$	Same	Mn^{4+}, Cr^{3+}, V^{2+}
$3d^4$	^5D	$^5E_g(d\varepsilon^3 d\gamma)$	$^3T_{1g}(d\varepsilon^4)$	Mn^{3+}, Cr^{2+}
$3d^5$	^6S	$^6A_{1g}(d\varepsilon^3 d\gamma^2)$	$^2T_{2g}(d\varepsilon^5)$	Fe^{3+}, Mn^{2+}
$3d^6$	^5D	$^5T_{2g}(d\varepsilon^4 d\gamma^2)$	$^1A_{1g}(d\varepsilon^6)$	Fe^{2+}
$3d^7$	^4D	$^4T_{1g}(d\varepsilon^5 d\gamma^2)$	$^2E_g(d\varepsilon^6 d\gamma)$	Co^{2+}
$3d^8$	^3D	$^3A_{2g}(d\varepsilon^6 d\gamma^2)$	Same	Ni^{2+}
$3d^9$	^2D	$^2T_{2g}(d\varepsilon^6 d\gamma^3)$	Same	Cu^{2+}

the interelectronic Coulomb repulsion energy and of the spin–orbit interaction parameter (see Koide and Oguchi 1963).

Two approaches have been used to describe the covalency effects.

(a) The configuration interaction method in which one adds to the totally ionic configuration of the metal and the ligand ions a small amount of a configuration wherein a ligand electron is transferred to the metal ion.

(b) The molecular orbital (MO) method in which the electrons of the system do not reside in pure metal-ion or ligand-ion orbitals but in

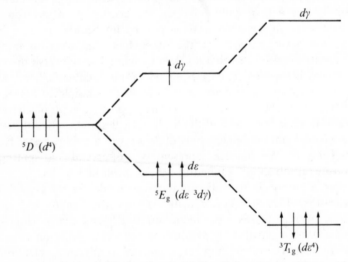

FIG. 1.1. A schematic representation of crystal-field splitting of a transition-metal ion (e.g. Mn^{3+} or Cr^{3+}) in an octahedral field.

molecular orbitals which are appropriate linear combinations of atomic orbitals (LCAO). This method has been extensively used in the calculation of the electronic properties of metal-ion complexes and compounds (Stevens 1953). In this context, it is referred to as the ligand-field theory to distinguish it from the crystal-field theory.

We shall illustrate the ligand-field approach by discussing an octahedral complex ML_6, where the metal ion M is at the centre of the octahedron and the ligands (e.g. O^{2-} or F^- ions) occupy the corner sites. A few words on notations and convention will be in order. The two ligand ions on the $\pm X$ axis are numbered 1 and 4, the two on the $\pm Y$ axis are numbered 2 and 5, and the two on the $\pm Z$ axis are numbered 3 and 6. Those orbitals which have even and odd symmetry under rotation by 180° about the axis joining the metal ion and a ligand ion are denoted σ and π respectively. It is assumed that the core electrons of the metal ion (e.g. the core $1s^2\ 2s^2\ 2p^6$ $3s^2\ 3p^6$ in transition-metal ions) are not involved in covalent bonding. Thus the orbitals on the metal ions important for mixing with ligand ions are the valence orbitals, namely nd, $(n+1)s$ and $(n+1)p$. Likewise the ligand orbitals which have an appreciable overlap with the appropriate metal-ion orbitals and which will be involved in the bonding and antibonding orbitals are $2p_x$, $2p_y$, $2p_z$ and $2s$. In order to determine the specific orbital of the metal ion that combines with a ligand orbital, it is helpful to classify them according to the symmetry transformation of the octahedral point group O_h. For this purpose linear combinations of the ligand orbitals that form the base functions of the various irreducible representation of the group in question are taken. These are given in Table 1.3 for the system ML_6 which has a point group O_h.

Once these symmetry orbitals are constructed, we have to consider the admixture between the metal orbitals and ligand symmetry orbitals belonging to the same irreducible representation, or symbolically between $\phi_M(\Gamma)$ and $\phi_L(\Gamma)$, where Γ denotes the particular irreducible representation. For each such pair there will be two molecular orbitals, one bonding and the other antibonding, which are mutually orthogonal. The bonding molecular orbital concentrates the electronic charge between the metal and the ligand ions, whereas the antibonding orbital depletes the electronic charge in this region. Thus the former makes use of the attractive field of the nuclei involved and lies lower in energy than the latter. Also, the bonding molecular orbitals involving σ orbitals (e.g. $d_{2z^2-x^2-y^2}$ of the metal ion and $2p_z$ of the ligand) will be of lower energy than those involving π bonding (d_{yz} with $2p_y$) owing to larger (end-on) overlap in the former case than in the latter case (sideways overlap).

The electronic configuration of the complex ML_6 now consists of completely filled bonding orbitals and partially filled or empty antibonding

TABLE 1.3

Irreducible representation	Metal-ion orbitals ϕ_M	Ligand symmetry orbitals ϕ_L
a_{1g}	s	$\frac{1}{\sqrt{6}}\{\sigma(x_1)-\sigma(x_4)+\sigma(y_2)-\sigma(y_5)+\sigma(z_3)-\sigma(z_6)\}$
e_g	$d_{2z^2-x^2-y^2}$	$\frac{1}{\sqrt{12}}\{2\sigma(z_3)-2\sigma(z_6)-\sigma(x_1)+\sigma(x_4)-\sigma(y_2)+\sigma(y_5)\}$
	$d_{x^2-y^2}$	$\frac{1}{2}\{\sigma(x_1)-\sigma(x_4)-\sigma(y_2)+\sigma(y_5)\}$
t_{2g}	d_{yz}	$\frac{1}{2}\{\sigma(z_2)-\sigma(z_5)+\sigma(y_3)-\sigma(y_5)\}$
	d_{zx}	$\frac{1}{2}\{\sigma(x_3)-\sigma(x_6)+\sigma(z_1)-\sigma(z_4)\}$
	d_{xy}	$\frac{1}{2}\{\sigma(y_1)-\sigma(y_4)+\sigma(x_2)-\sigma(x_5)\}$
t_{1u}	p_x	$\frac{1}{\sqrt{2}}\{\sigma(x_1)+\sigma(x_4)\}$
		$\frac{1}{2}\{\pi(x_2)+\pi(x_5)+\pi(x_3)+\pi(x_6)\}$
	p_y	$\frac{1}{\sqrt{2}}\{\sigma(y_2)+\sigma(y_5)\}$
		$\frac{1}{2}\{\pi(y_1)+\pi(y_4)+\pi(y_3)+\pi(y_6)\}$
	p_z	$\frac{1}{\sqrt{2}}\{\sigma(z_3)+\sigma(z_6)\}$
		$\frac{1}{2}\{\pi(z_1)+\pi(z_4)+\pi(z_2)+\pi(z_5)\}$
t_{1g}		$\frac{1}{2}\{\pi(z_2)-\pi(z_5)-\pi(y_3)+\pi(y_6)\}$
		$\frac{1}{2}\{\pi(z_4)-\pi(z_1)+\pi(x_3)-\pi(x_6)\}$
		$\frac{1}{2}\{\pi(y_1)-\pi(y_4)-\pi(x_2)+\pi(x_5)\}$
t_{2u}		$\frac{1}{2}\{\pi(x_2)+\pi(x_5)-\pi(x_3)-\pi(x_6)\}$
		$\frac{1}{2}\{\pi(y_1)+\pi(y_4)-\pi(y_3)-\pi(y_6)\}$
		$\frac{1}{2}\{\pi(z_1)+\pi(z_4)-\pi(z_2)-\pi(z_5)\}$

orbitals. In this scheme, using group-theoretical notation, the ground-state configuration can be described as $(a_{1g}^2\ t_{1u}^6\ e_g^4\ t_{2g}^6\ 2t_{1u}^6\ 3t_{1u}^6\ t_{1g}^6\ t_{2u}^6)$ $2t_{2g}^{*m},\ 3e_g^{*n}$, where the antibonding orbitals are denoted by starred symbols and bonding ones by unstarred symbols. Higher antibonding orbitals such as $3a_{1g}^*$, $4t_{1u}^*$, etc, are normally empty. Owing to the formation of the bonding and the antibonding orbitals, there is a net stabilization of the entire system relative to the ionic configuration.

To illustrate this we shall briefly discuss the partially filled antibonding e_g^* and t_{2g}^* orbitals involving the $d\gamma$, $d\varepsilon$ orbitals of the metal ions and the p orbitals of the ligands. These turn out to be important for the magnetic behaviour of the system:

$$\psi_u(e_g^*) = N_\sigma\left[d_{3z^2-r^2} - \frac{\lambda_\sigma}{\sqrt{12}}\left\{2\sigma(z_3) - 2\sigma(z_6) - \sigma(x_1)\right.\right.$$

$$\left.\left. + \sigma(x_4) - \sigma(y_2) + \sigma(y_5)\right\}\right]$$

$$\psi_v(e_g^*) = N_\sigma\left[d_{x^2-y^2} - \frac{\lambda_\sigma}{2}\left\{\sigma(x_1) - \sigma(x_4) - \sigma(y_2) + \sigma(y_5)\right\}\right]$$

$$\psi_\xi(t_{2g}^*) = N_\pi\left[d_{yz} - \frac{\lambda_\pi}{2}\left\{\pi(z_2) - \pi(z_5) + \pi(y_3) - \pi(y_6)\right\}\right] \qquad (1.12)$$

$$\psi_\eta(t_{2g}^*) = N_\pi\left[d_{zx} - \frac{\lambda_\pi}{2}\left\{\pi(x_3) - \pi(x_6) + \pi(z_1) - \pi(z_4)\right\}\right]$$

$$\psi_\zeta(t_{2g}^*) = N_\pi\left[d_{xy} - \frac{\lambda_\pi}{2}\left\{\pi(y_1) - \pi(y_4) + \pi(x_2) - \pi(y_5)\right\}\right]$$

where N_σ and N_π are, respectively, the normalization constant given by

$$N_\sigma^{-2} = 1 - 4\lambda_\sigma S_\sigma + \lambda_\sigma^2$$

$$N_\pi^{-2} = 1 - 4\lambda_\pi S_\pi + \lambda_\pi^2 \qquad (1.13)$$

with the overlap integrals defined as

$$S_\sigma = -\langle d_{x^2-y^2}|\sigma(x_1)\rangle$$

$$S_\pi = \langle d_{xy}|\pi(y_1)\rangle. \qquad (1.14)$$

The admixture coefficients λ_σ and λ_π are related to the matrix elements of the one-electron Hamiltonian

$$h = -\frac{\hbar^2\nabla^2}{2m} + V_M + V_L \qquad (1.15)$$

connecting the relevant metal and ligand orbitals, e.g. $\langle d_{x^2-y^2}|h|\sigma(x_1)\rangle \equiv$

$h_{d_\sigma} p_\sigma$. In eqn (1.15) the first term is the kinetic energy operator of the electron, and the second and third terms represent, its potential energy operator in the field of the metal-ion field and the ligand-ion field respectively. For example (see Owen and Thornley 1966),

$$\lambda_\sigma \approx \frac{\langle d_{x^2-y^2}|h|\sigma(x_1)\rangle}{(E_d - E_p)} + S_\sigma \tag{1.16}$$

where E_d and E_p represent the unperturbed energies of the metal-ion d orbital and the ligand-ion p orbitals respectively.

A second-order perturbation calculation gives an upward shift of the antibonding orbital by

$$\Delta E = \frac{|\langle d_{x^2-y^2}|h|\sigma(x)\rangle|^2}{E_d - E_p} \tag{1.17}$$

relative to E_d and a downward shift of the bonding orbital by the same amount ΔE relative to E_p. Inasmuch as there are two electrons in each bonding orbital and only one in each partially occupied antibonding orbital, we obtain a net stabilization of the system. In order to distinguish these configurations from the purely ionic configuration in the crystal field, as noted earlier, they are denoted in terms of the occupancy of these antibonding orbitals, e.g. Ni (II) is assigned $d^8(t_{2g}{}^{*6}e_g{}^{*2})$ and Cr (III) is assigned $d^3(t_{2g}{}^{*3})$.

The ligand-field parameter $\Delta \equiv 10$ Dq is identified with the difference of the energies $E(e_g{}^*)$ and $E(t_{2g}{}^*)$. This can be decomposed as

$$\Delta = \Delta(\text{ionic}) + \Delta(\text{covalent}) \tag{1.18}$$

where $\Delta(\text{ionic})$ represents the part which is usually calculated on the basis of the electrostatic (point-ion) model. Although $\Delta(\text{ionic})$ is of the right sign, it is smaller than the experimental value. Attempts have been made to calculate $\Delta(\text{ionic})$ on some improved ionic models for the octahedral complex $Cr^{3+}O_6{}^{2-}$. The model takes account of the fact that the d electrons of the Cr^{3+} ion see the attractive field of the ligand nucleus O^{2-} and the repulsive field of the ligand charge cloud. Calculations carried out by making the d-electron wavefunctions orthogonal to the core functions of the ligand (e.g. $2s$, $2p$ of O^{2-}) gave a result nearly the same as that obtained using the point-ion value (Tanabe and Sugano 1956). The reason for this similarity is that the orthogonalization procedure is tantamount to including the repulsive overlap potential of the ligand electrons. It so happens that this 'effective' (overlap) repulsive potential nearly cancels the attractive potential of the ligand nucleus and exchange potential as was shown by Phillips (1959).

$\Delta(\text{covalent})$ is the contribution arising solely from the covalent admixture.

Including the effect of mixing the d orbitals with the $2s$ orbitals of the ligands, this is given by

$$\Delta(\text{covalent}) = \{(\lambda_\sigma^2 - S_\sigma^2) - (\lambda_\pi^2 - S_\pi^2)\}\,(E_d - E_p)$$
$$+ (\lambda_s^2 - S_s^2)(E_d - E_s) \tag{1.19}$$

Here, we have subtracted the overlap contribution in that this is contained in $\Delta(\text{ionic})$. Computations of $\Delta(\text{ionic})$ and $\Delta(\text{covalent})$ for the complex $Ni^{2+}F_6^-$ in $KNiF_3$ have been carried out by several authors (for details see Owen and Thornley 1966). They obtain $\Delta(\text{ionic}) \sim 2300 \pm 300$ cm^{-1} and $\Delta(\text{covalent}) \sim 5000$ cm^{-1}. The experimental value of. Δ is approximately 7250 cm^{-1}. This shows that the dominant contribution to Δ comes from covalency effects. The agreement between the calculated and the experimental values should not be overemphasized in that some important effects have not been considered.

The ligand-field splitting parameter $\Delta(\text{covalent})$ gives a measure of certain parameters connected with exchange interaction between magnetic ions as we shall see later. As remarked earlier, the magnetic properties of the individual complexes are associated with the number of unpaired spins present in the antibonding orbitals. This would seem to suggest that a small amount of unpaired spin resides in the ligand orbital owing to the covalent admixture. A careful analysis by some authors has shown that the unpaired spins should be connected with the holes in the antibonding orbitals because the electron-transfer effects in the bonding and antibonding orbitals pertaining to the same kind of occupied spin (say spin-up) cancel except for the overlap effects. Therefore, the transfer effects are connected with spin-down electrons in the bonding orbitals or spin-up holes in the antibonding orbitals.

The calculation of the ligand-field parameter for the complex $Ni^{2+}(F^-)_6$ in $KNiF_3$ by the configuration interaction method (Rimmer 1965) also gives results in good agreement with the experimental value. Thus the two methods give equally good results provided of course that reasonably realistic estimates of the parameters are made.

At this stage, we shall give a brief account of the determination of the covalency parameters for the systems discussed above. Direct evidence for and a method of measurement of the covalency effect in transition-metal complexes is provided by the hyperfine interaction between the unpaired electrons of the paramagnetic ion and the ligand ions having non-zero nuclear spins I. This involves a fractional occupancy of the appropriate ligand orbitals owing to spin transfer and covalent admixture from the metal ions. This in turn leads to coupling of the unpaired electron spin with the nuclear spin resulting in hyperfine splitting of the paramagnetic or nuclear resonance levels. The hyperfine interaction Hamiltonian involving an s-type ligand orbital is given by

$$A_s^0 \mathbf{s} \cdot \mathbf{I} \qquad (1.20)$$

where $\mathbf{s}$ and $\mathbf{I}$ are the electron and the nuclear spins respectively and A_s^0 is the isotropic Fermi-type contact interaction constant, i.e.

$$A_s^0 = \frac{16\pi}{3} g_N \mu_B \mu_N |\psi(0)|^2 \qquad (1.21)$$

where g_N is the nuclear spectroscopic splitting factor, μ_B and μ_N are the electron and the nuclear Bohr magnetons, and $\psi(0)$ is the amplitude of the wavefunction at the ligand nucleus. In an actual complex there is only a fractional λ_s^2 occupancy of the ligand orbital in question giving the modified hyperfine coupling constant

$$A_s = \frac{\lambda_s^2 A_s^0}{2S} \qquad (1.22)$$

where S is the total ionic spin of the metal ion. Thus we see that an experimental measurement of the hyperfine splitting will give the value of λ_s^2 (see Owen and Thornley 1966 for details). A detailed discussion of the hyperfine splitting to ascertain covalency effects will be given in a separate chapter dealing with paramagnetic resonance.

2

INTERACTIONS IN PARAMAGNETIC SYSTEMS

In this chapter we shall consider a magnetically dilute system (paramagnetic solid) in which the atoms which have magnetic moments are sufficiently far apart to preclude ordering at temperatures of interest. However, such atoms can interact with external magnetic fields. In addition, there will be weak perturbations due to dipolar interactions between different spins and also with the lattice modes predominantly via spin–orbit coupling. For an exhaustive account of subjects dealt with in this chapter, reference may be made to Abragam and Bleaney (1970).

2.1. Magnetic resonance

In a classical description an isolated magnetic dipole $\boldsymbol{\mu} = g\mu_B \mathbf{S}$ in the presence of a static magnetic field $\mathbf{B}$ will precess with a Larmor frequency $\omega_L = \gamma_B$, where γ is the gyromagnetic ratio and is equal to $g(e/2mc)$, g being the spectroscopic splitting factor (g factor). Quantum mechanically, the dynamics is described by a spin Hamiltonian

$$H = -\boldsymbol{\mu} \cdot \mathbf{B} = -g\,\mu_B\,\mathbf{S} \cdot \mathbf{B}. \tag{2.1}$$

The allowed energy levels are separated by (for the spin 1/2 case)

$$\Delta E = g\,\mu_B\,B \equiv \hbar\omega_0. \tag{2.2}$$

A weak transverse oscillating field will cause a transition between the two Zeeman levels if the applied frequency equals ω_0. This is the resonance condition which will be infinitely sharp in the absence of any dissipative interaction. For a paramagnetic atom or ion, the magnetic moment can be written as $\mu_j = g_J\,\mu_B\,J$, where J is the total angular momentum 'good' quantum number ($\mathbf{J} = \mathbf{L} + \mathbf{S}$), $\mathbf{L}$ being the orbital angular momentum, and g_J is the spectroscopic splitting factor given by

$$g_j = \frac{J(J+1)(g_L+g_s) + \{L(L+1) - S(S+1)\}(g_L-g_s)}{2J(J+1)} \tag{2.3}$$

g_L and g_s being the g-factors for the orbital and spin angular momenta respectively. When $g_L = 1$ and $g_s = 2$, we obtain the well-known Landé formula from (2.3).

For a paramagnetic ion in a crystal, there are groups of nearly degenerate levels which are separated by energies much larger than those involved in paramagnetic resonance, typically of the order of 1 cm^{-1}. In resonance experiments one is interested only in the lowest group of levels and transitions between them in the presence of a static magnetic field. Hence, it has been expedient to define a fictitious (effective) spin $\tilde{S}$ such that the spin multiplicity $2\tilde{S}+1$ is equal to the degeneracy of the group.

Accordingly, one can define an effective spin Hamiltonian (Pryce 1950)

$$H_{\text{eff}} = g\mu_B(\mathbf{B} \cdot \tilde{\mathbf{S}}). \tag{2.4}$$

Here the g factor can be different from the pure spin or pure orbital value. The quantum of energy for an allowed transition is $\hbar\omega = g\mu_B B$. In general, the effective spin interaction is anisotropic and can be written in the dyadic form

$$H_{\text{eff}} = \mu_B(\mathbf{B} \cdot g \cdot \tilde{\mathbf{S}}). \tag{2.5}$$

$$\equiv \mu_B \, \Sigma_{i,j=x,y,z} \, g_{ij}(B_i)\tilde{S}_j.$$

Except for low-symmetry situations, the g tensor is generally symmetric and it is possible to transform to the principal axes in which the interaction is diagonal, i.e.

$$H_{\text{eff}} = \mu_B(g_{xx}B_x\tilde{S}_x + g_{yy}B_y\tilde{S}_y + g_{zz}B_z\tilde{S}_z). \tag{2.6}$$

If the external magnetic field has direction cosines l, m, n with respect to the principal axes, the energy splitting is given by (2.5) with

$$g^2 = l^2 g_{xx}^2 + m^2 g_{yy}^2 + y_{zz}^2. \tag{2.7}$$

It should be noted that for cubic symmetry $g_{xx} = g_{yy} = g_{zz}$ and thus the splitting is isotropic. On the other hand, for the axial case $g_{xx} = g_{yy} = g_{\perp}$ and $g_{zz} = g_{\parallel}$. Thus (2.7) reduces to

$$g^2 = g_{\parallel}^2 \, cos^2\theta + g_{\perp}^2 \, sin^2\theta$$

where θ is the angle between $\mathbf{B}$ and the z axis, which is parallel to the axis of symmetry. In paramagnetic resonance experiments one can directly measure the components of the g tensor.

A closely related problem is the interaction of the electron spin with the nuclear spin ($I \neq 0$) in a paramagnetic system. This hyperfine (hf) interaction can be derived simply from classical electrodynamics, where the interaction is given by

$$H_{\text{hf}} = g_N \, \mu_N \, \mathbf{I} \cdot \frac{1}{c} \int \nabla\left(\frac{1}{r}\right) \times \mathbf{j} d^3 r \tag{2.8}$$

where $\mathbf{j}$ is the current due to an unpaired electron in the quantum state described by the wavefunction Ψ, μ_N is the nuclear Bohr magneton, and g_N is the nuclear g factor. Explicitly,

$$\mathbf{j} = 2\mu_B c \ \text{curl} \ (|\Psi|^2 \mathbf{S}) \tag{2.9}$$

where $\mathbf{S}$ is the electron spin. Straightforward integration gives for s electrons, with the origin chosen at the nucleus,

$$H_{hf} = \left(\frac{8\pi}{3}\right) 2g_N \mu_B \mu_N |\Psi_s(0)|^2 (\mathbf{S} \cdot \mathbf{I}). \tag{2.10}$$

This is the famous Fermi contact interaction for s electrons. Inasmuch as only s electrons have non-vanishing amplitude at the nucleus, this interaction is often written in the form

$$H_{hf}(\text{Fermi}) = \left(\frac{8\pi}{3}\right) 2g_N \mu_B \mu_N \ \delta(\mathbf{r})(\mathbf{S} \cdot \mathbf{I}). \tag{2.11}$$

However, for other orbitals one has to use the general dipolar interaction

$$H_{hf}(\text{dipolar}) = \sum_j 2\gamma_N \mu_B \left\{ -\frac{(\mathbf{S}_j \cdot \mathbf{I})}{r_j^3} + \frac{3(\mathbf{S}_j \cdot \mathbf{r}_j)(\mathbf{r}_j \cdot \mathbf{I})}{r_j^5} \right\}. \tag{2.12}$$

In general, the orbital angular momentum $\mathbf{L}$ is quenched in a crystal field for transition-metal ions, i.e. $\langle \mathbf{L} \rangle = 0$ but $\langle \mathbf{L}^2 \rangle \neq 0$. If the paramagnetic ion has non-quenched orbital angular momentum $\mathbf{l}$ as in rare-earth ions, we have to include the term due to magnetic field produced by the orbital current, i.e.

$$H_{hf}(\text{orbital}) = 2\gamma_N \mu_B \left(\frac{1}{r^3}\right)(\mathbf{l} \cdot \mathbf{I}). \tag{2.13}$$

Thus the total hyperfine interaction can be written as

$$H_{hf} = 2\gamma_N \mu_B \left\{ \sum_j \frac{(\mathbf{l}_j - \mathbf{S}_j) \cdot \mathbf{I}}{r_j^3} + 3 \frac{(\mathbf{r}_j \cdot \mathbf{S}_j)(\mathbf{r}_j \cdot \mathbf{I})}{r_j^5} \right.$$

$$\left. + \sum_k \left(\frac{8\pi}{3}\right) \delta(\mathbf{r}_k)(\mathbf{S}_k \cdot \mathbf{I}) \right\}. \tag{2.14}$$

It is worth noting that the entire interaction can be derived from the total current density $\mathbf{j}$ (total) associated with the electron in the orbital state Ψ

with an external magnetic field described by the vector potential $\mathbf{A}$

$$\mathbf{j}(\text{total}) = \frac{ie\hbar}{2mc}(\Psi\nabla\Psi^* - \Psi^*\nabla\Psi)$$

$$-\frac{e^2}{2mc^2}|\Psi|^2\mathbf{A} + g\mu_B c \; \text{curl}(\Psi^*\mathbf{s}\Psi) \tag{2.15}$$

using the Biot–Savart law.

It may be noted in passing that the first term on the right-hand side of eqn (2.15) is a paramagnetic term (giving rise to the so called Van Vleek paramagnetism) while the second term is a diamagnetic one (giving the so called Langevin diamagnetism). The two taken together are gauge-invariant. The last term is the 'molecular current' due to the electron spin and is paramagnetic.

The hyperfine interaction of a paramagnetic ion with the surrounding ligand (anion) nuclei gives extra fine structure in electron spin resonance spectra in an external magnetic field. The strength of this extra structure depends on the amount of admixing (covalency) of the cation and anion orbitals. These experimental results make it possible to probe the covalency effect. This will be discussed later.

2.2. Phenomenological theories of relaxation and line width

In the foregoing section we discussed the status of a non-interacting spin in an external static magnetic field and the transitions induced between them in the presence of a small oscillating transverse field. However, there are several dissipative channels which lead to relaxation and linewidth. A phenomenological way of incorporating these was first proposed by Bloch (1946). The basic assumption of his theory is that there are two character-istic relaxation times τ_1 and τ_2 describing the relaxation of the longitudinal and transverse components respectively of the spin magnetization. The governing equations are

$$\frac{\mathrm{d}M_z}{\mathrm{d}t} = \frac{M_0 - M_z}{\tau_1} + \gamma(\mathbf{M} \times \mathbf{B})_z \tag{2.16}$$

and

$$\frac{\mathrm{d}M_x}{\mathrm{d}t} = \gamma(M \times \mathrm{B})_x - \frac{M_x}{\tau_2} \tag{2.17}$$

$$\frac{\mathrm{d}M_y}{\mathrm{d}t} = \gamma(M \times \mathrm{B})_y - \frac{M_y}{\tau_2} \tag{2.18}$$

where M_0 is the equilibrium magnetization and is equal to the product of the static external field and the static susceptibility. Physically τ_1 arises from the relaxation of the z component of the magnetization and therefore involves the exchange of energy with a reservoir through spin–lattice coupling. On the other hand, τ_2 describes the decay of the transverse component and hence does not involve exchange of energy with the reservoir. In essence, τ_2 originates from the spread in the local field due to the dipolar fields of the neighbouring spin moments. In the most general stochastic analysis one can say that both are due to fluctuating random magnetic fields at the site of the spin in question. Indeed, τ_1 and τ_2 can be expressed in terms of the spectral density of the random magnetic field $\mathbf{h}(t)$. Explicitly (Slichter 1963)

$$\frac{1}{\tau_1} = \gamma^2 \{ K_{xx}(\omega_0) + K_{yy}(\omega_0) \} \tag{2.19}$$

$$\frac{1}{\tau_2} = \gamma^2 \{ K_{yy}(\omega_0) + K_{zz}(\omega_0) \} \tag{2.20}$$

where we define the correlation function

$$K_{ij}(\omega) = \tfrac{1}{2} \int_{-\infty}^{+\infty} \langle h_i(t) h_j(t+\tau) \rangle exp -i\omega\tau \; d\tau \tag{2.21}$$

and ω_0 is the resonance frequency.

In the case when the correlation function has the simple form

$$\langle h_i(t) h_j(t+\tau) \rangle = \langle h_i^2 \rangle \delta_{ij} \, exp\left(\frac{-|\tau|}{\tau_0} \right) \tag{2.22}$$

τ_0 being a correlation time, we obtain

$$\frac{1}{\tau_1} = \gamma^2 (\langle h_z^2 \rangle + \langle h_y^2 \rangle) \frac{\tau_0}{1 + \omega_0^2 \tau_0^2} \tag{2.23}$$

$$\frac{1}{\tau_2} = \gamma^2 (\langle h_z^2 \rangle \tau_0 + \langle h_y^2 \rangle) \frac{\tau_0}{1 + \omega_0^2 \tau_0^2} \tag{2.24}$$

2.3. Microscopic mechanism of relaxation

2.3.1. *Spin–lattice relaxation by modulation of the dipolar magnetic field (Waller process)*

In this process the spin interacts with the quantized lattice-vibrational modes and energy is exchanged between the spin and the lattice subsystems by the emission and absorption of quanta along with the transition between two spin levels. The basic mechanism consists in the coupling of the spin moment with the local fluctuating magnetic field generated (directly or indirectly) by lattice-vibration modes involving one or two phonons.

The one-phonon Waller process emanates from the modulation of the distance-dependent (r-dependent) dipolar spin–spin interaction by the vibrational modes. It may be recalled that the magnetic field due to an elementary dipole of moment $\boldsymbol{\mu}$ at position $\mathbf{r}$ is given by

$$\mathbf{h} = \frac{3\hat{\mathbf{r}}(2 \cdot \hat{\mathbf{r}}) - \boldsymbol{\mu}}{r^3} \qquad (2.25)$$

where $\hat{\mathbf{r}}$ is the unit vector along $\mathbf{r}$. The local strain due to the lattice vibration modulates $\mathbf{r}$. Considering a single lattice-vibrational mode of frequency ω, one can write

$$\frac{1}{r_i^3} \cong r_{0i}^{-3}(1 - 3\varepsilon\cos \omega t) \qquad (2.26)$$

where r_{0i} is the equilibrium separation of the ith site.

The mean square value of the fluctuating field is thus

$$h_1^2 = (3\varepsilon)^2 2\mu^2 \sum_{\text{all sites } i} r_{0i}^{-6} \equiv (3\varepsilon)^2 h_0^2.$$

This interaction finally leads to the relaxation frequency

$$\frac{1}{\tau_1^*}(\text{one phonon}) = \frac{9h_0^2\gamma^2\hbar\omega^3}{16\pi\rho v_s^5}\coth\left(\frac{\hbar\omega}{2k_\text{B}T}\right). \qquad (2.27)$$

This is a direct process involving one quantum of a vibrational mode. Inasmuch as the density of states of phonons at the resonance frequency is small, the Waller process gives an insignificant contribution to the relaxation frequency. On the other hand, if we were to consider a two-phonon process, the joint two-phonon density of states could be considerably larger and may compensate for the smallness of the higher-order matrix element. Such a process should give a much larger relaxation frequency in the higher-temperature ranges. The relevant expression turns out to be

$$\frac{1}{\tau_1^w}(\text{two phonon}) = 6!\left(\frac{27}{32\pi^3}\right)\frac{\gamma^2\hbar^2h_0^2}{\rho^2v_s^{10}}\left(\frac{k_\text{B}T}{\hbar}\right)^7. \qquad (2.28)$$

Estimates show that this is appreciable above 50 K.

2.3.2. Spin–lattice relaxation by modulation of the ligand field via spin–orbit coupling

The Waller mechanism discussed above is several orders of magnitude too weak to account for observed relaxation frequencies. A much stronger mechanism of relaxation is the fluctuation of the electrostatic crystal field due to the motion of ligands seen by the paramagnetic ion through spin–orbit coupling. This was developed by Kronig (1939) and Van Vleck (1939, 1940) who obtained the right order of magnitude for the relaxation time. The modulation of the ligand field (lf) at the paramagnetic site can be expressed in terms of the local strain ε_s due to lattice vibration as

$$V_{lf}(\text{osc}) = V_{lf}^0 + V_{lf}^{(1)}\varepsilon_s + V_{lf}^{(2)}\varepsilon_s^2 + \dots \tag{2.29}$$

where the matrix element of the strain ε_s connecting phonon states differing by one occupation number is given by (see Chapter 8)

$$|\langle N_{qs} - 1|\varepsilon_s|N_{qs}\rangle|^2 \approx \frac{q^2\hbar N_{qs}}{2M\omega_{qs}} \quad \langle\text{annihilation}\rangle \tag{2.30}$$

$$|\langle N_{qs} + 1|\varepsilon_s|N_{qs}\rangle|^2 \approx \frac{q^2\hbar(N_{qs}+1)}{2M\omega_{qs}} \quad \langle\text{creation}\rangle \tag{2.31}$$

Here the term V_{lf}^0 is the ligand field which together with spin–orbit coupling generates spin–orbital eigenstates. The interaction given above can cause a transition between two spin–orbit states, $|1\rangle$ and $|2\rangle$ say. The term involving $V_{lf}^{(1)}$ gives the one-phonon process where the energy of the phonon involved must match the splitting ΔE_{12} of the two levels in question, i.e. E_1 and E_2. Time-dependent first-order perturbation theory gives us the relaxation frequency (see Landau and Lifshitz (1958) for a short account of time-dependent perturbation theory).

$$\frac{1}{\tau_1^d}(\text{one-phonon non-Kramers}) = \frac{3\Delta E_{12}^2 k_B T}{\pi \rho v_s^2 \hbar^4}|\langle 1|V_{lf}^{(1)}|2\rangle|^2. \tag{2.32}$$

For the case of Kramers degeneracy (spin half-integral case) the states $|1\rangle$ and $|2\rangle$ are time conjugate to one another and the matrix element vanishes identically for reasons of time-reversal symmetry. For such a situation, an external magnetic field renders the transition allowed by mixing into $|1\rangle$ and $|2\rangle$ some excited states, $|3\rangle$ say. For example, state $|1\rangle$ is modified as

$$|1\rangle + \frac{\langle 3|\mu \cdot B|1\rangle}{\Delta_3}|3\rangle \tag{2.33}$$

where Δ_3 is the energy denominator. Thus for a Kramers case we obtain

$$\frac{1}{\tau_1^d}(\text{one-phonon Kramers}) = \frac{12\,\mu_B^2 g^2 B^4 k_B T}{\pi \rho v_s^2 \hbar^4 \Delta_3^2}|\langle 3|\mu|1\rangle\langle 1|V_{lf}^{(1)}|3\rangle|^2. \tag{2.34}$$

In addition to the above one-phonon processes, there are two-phonon Raman processes which involve absorption of a phonon together with spin transition followed by emission of a phonon. It can readily be seen that this mechanism will dominate at higher temperatures. This is because of the fact that the one-phonon process involves only resonant phonons and as such only a restricted number of phonons can take part. However, the two-phonon processes involve the entire phonon spectrum and should dominate at higher temperatures. In this case we also have to distinguish between Kramers and non-Kramers cases. For non-Kramers paramagnetic ions, a straightforward second-order time-dependent perturbation theory gives

$$
\frac{1}{\tau_1} \text{(two-phonon non-Kramers)} = \frac{9(6!)}{4\pi^3 \rho^2 v_s^{10}} \left(\frac{k_B T}{\hbar}\right)^7 \sum_i \frac{1}{\Delta_i}
$$

$$
\times |\langle 1|V_{lf}^{(1)}(a)|i\rangle \langle i|V_{lf}^{(1)}(e)|2\rangle
$$

$$
+ \langle 1|V_{lf}^{(1)}(e)|i\rangle \langle i|V_{lf}^{(1)}(a)|2\rangle|^2
$$

(23.5)

where the summation $|i\rangle$ runs over intermediates states and $V_{lf}^{(1)}(a)$ and $V_{lf}^{(1)}(e)$ denote the absorption and emission of a phonon respectively.

Let us consider the situation when we have Kramers degeneracy, i.e. states $|1\rangle$ and $|2\rangle$ are time-conjugate states of half-integral spin. In this case the relevant matrix element involves intermediate states which also occur as time-conjugate pairs $|t\rangle$ and $|t^*\rangle$, say. As a result of time-reversal symmetry and parity, we have

$$
\langle 1|V_{lf}^{(1)}(a)|t\rangle \langle t|V_{lf}^{(1)}(e)|2\rangle = -\langle 1|V_{lf}^{(1)}(e)|t\rangle \langle t|V_{lf}^{(1)}(a)|2\rangle.
$$

(2.36)

Taking this into account, the relaxation frequency turns out to be

$$
\frac{1}{\tau_1} \text{(two-phonon Kramers)} = \frac{9! \, \hbar^2}{\pi^2 \rho^2 v_s^{10}} \left(\frac{k_B T}{\hbar}\right)^9
$$

$$
\times \sum_{\substack{\text{time-conjugate} \\ \text{pairs}}} \frac{\langle 1|V_{lf}^{(1)}(a)|t\rangle \langle t|V_{lf}^{(1)}(e)|2\rangle}{\Delta_t^2}^2
$$

(2.37)

where the sum spans all the time-conjugate pairs. It should be noted that in the presence of an external magnetic field B the time-conjugate degeneracy is lifted to order $(g\mu_B B/\Delta_t)$. As a consequence the relaxation frequency is proportional to $B^2 T^7$ instead of T^9.

2.3.3. Spin–lattice relaxation by the Orbach process

This is a special case of two-phonon processes in which energy is conserved at each intermediate stage and gives rise to resonance relaxation. In this case the lifetime $\hbar\Gamma_i$ of the intermediate states becomes important; Γ_i is the width of the state caused by spontaneous and induced transitions arising from the orbit–lattice interaction. The calculations are similar to those for the usual two-phonon process except that the energy denominator contains imaginary parts corresponding to the linewidth (lifetime) of the intermediate state. The relaxation frequency is given by (Orbach 1961, 1962)

$$\frac{1}{\tau_1}(\text{Orbach}) = \frac{3}{2\pi\rho\hbar v_s^5} \sum_i \frac{(\Delta_i/\hbar)^3}{|\exp(\Delta_i/k_B T) - 1|}$$

$$\times \frac{|\langle 1|V_{lf}^{(1)}(e)|i\rangle \langle i|V_{lf}^{(1)}(a)|2\rangle|^2}{|\langle 1|V_{lf}^{(1)}(e)|i\rangle|^2 + |\langle i|V_{lf}^{(1)}(a)|2\rangle|^2}. \tag{2.38}$$

For temperatures such that $k_B T \ll \Delta_i$ the relaxation frequency of the Orbach process is proportional to $\exp(-\Delta_i/k_B T)$.

Since the relaxation frequencies are additive, we can write the overall frequency as the sum of the individual contributions. Thus for a non-Kramers situation we have

$$\frac{1}{\tau_1}(\text{total non-Kramers}) = A\Delta_{12}^2 T + BT^7 + C\exp\left(\frac{-\Delta}{k_B T}\right) \tag{2.39}$$

where the various terms on the right-hand side denote the one-phonon direct process, the two-phonon Raman process, and the two-phonon Orbach (resonance) process respectively. The corresponding expression for the Kramers case in the presence of a magnetic field is given by

$$\frac{1}{\tau_1}(\text{total Kramers}) = A'B^4 T + B'T^9 + B''B^2 T^7 + C'\exp\left(-\frac{\Delta}{k_B T}\right). \tag{2.40}$$

We shall now briefly discuss some experimental confirmation of the various relaxation processes described above. For a non-Kramers system such as Tb^{3+} in yttrium ethyl sulphate, the experimentally measured relaxation frequency can be approximated by (Larson and Jeffries 1966)

$$\frac{1}{\tau_1}(\text{total non-Kramers}) = 10^3 T + (10^{-2} - 10^2)T^7 + (10^3 - 10^5)\Delta^3 \exp\left(-\frac{\Delta}{k_B T}\right) \tag{2.41}$$

where the splitting Δ is expressed in kelvins and τ_1 in seconds. Thus the experimentally fitted curve described by eq (2.41) supports the theoretical expression given in eq (2.39).

An example of the Kramers system treated by Larson and Jeffries is Nd^{3+} in yttrium ethyl sulphate where the empirically fitted curve is represented by

$$\frac{1}{\tau_1}(\text{total Kramers}) = 1\cdot 8T + 1\cdot 59 \times 10^{-4}T^9 \text{ s}^{-1} \tag{2.42}$$

for a static field B of 3390 G and a resonance frequency of 9·40 GHz. In this case the direct and Raman processes are dominant.

2.4. Relaxation due to spin–spin interaction (calculation of τ_2)

In the previous sections we have discussed the various microscopic mechanisms that relax the z component of the spin via spin–lattice interactions. They contribute to the relaxation frequency $1/\tau_1$. In this section we shall briefly discuss the relaxation of the transverse component of the spin as a result of spin–spin interaction. This corresponds to the calculation of τ_2. As noted earlier, the most general form of the spin–spin interaction is

$$H_{s-s} = \sum_{\alpha,\beta} J_{\alpha,\beta}(r_{ij}) S_{i\alpha} S_{j\beta} \tag{2.43}$$

where i, j are the site indices and α, β denote the Cartesian components of the spin. Here S_i etc. are effective spins and, in general, have contributions from the orbital motion. The interaction constant $J_{\alpha\beta}(r_{ij})$ may arise from various mechanisms. The simplest case is that of the magnetic dipolar interaction discussed earlier. However, if the effective spins have orbital contributions a Coulombic contribution from electric quadrupole interaction is possible. The other possibility is the direct or indirect exchange interaction (see Chapters 3 and 4). As an illustration of the method of calculation, we discuss the case when the interaction is predominantly magnetic dipolar in nature. The strength is typically of the order of 10^{-1} cm^{-1}, and hence there is a general broadening and no extra structure. Also for simplicity we take the case of identical spins with an isotropic g factor.

The Hamiltonian given in eq (2.43) in general does not commute with the total z component $\Sigma_i S_{iz}$. For the discussion of transverse relaxation, the Hamiltonian is first decomposed into two parts, one commuting with $\Sigma_i S_{iz}$ (the secular part) and one which does not commute. The first part is relevant for the relaxation of the transverse component. Thus the truncated Hamiltonian is

$$H_{s-s} = \sum_{i,j} (J_{\text{iso}} - \tfrac{1}{2} J_{zz})(\mathbf{S}_i \cdot \mathbf{S}_j) + \tfrac{3}{2} J_{zz} S_{iz} S_{jz} \tag{2.44}$$

where J_{iso} is the isotropic part of the interaction. The calculation of the transverse relaxation frequency $1/\tau_2$ involves the mean square deviation from the resonance frequency. Assuming symmetrical lineshape, we have

$$\langle \omega^2 \rangle = \langle \omega_0^2 \rangle + \langle \Delta\omega^2 \rangle. \tag{2.45}$$

Since the transitions connecting the spin states m and m', say, are caused by the x component of the total spin operator

$$\langle \omega^2 \rangle = \sum_{mm'} \frac{\{\omega_{mm'}{}^2 |(S_x)_{mm'}|^2\}}{\sum_{mm'} |(S_x)_{mm'}|^2}. \tag{2.46}$$

The result, as first derived by Van Vleck (1948), is

$$\hbar^2 (\Delta \omega^2) = \tfrac{1}{2} S(S+1) \sum_{j>i} (\tfrac{3}{2} J_{zz})_{ij}{}^2. \tag{2.47}$$

Explicitly, we have

$$(J_{zz})_{ij} = g^2 \mu_B{}^2 r_{ij}{}^{-3} (1 - 3 \cos^2 \theta_{ij}). \tag{2.48}$$

It is important to note that only the anisotropic part of the interaction is responsible for relaxation.

The relaxation time τ_2 is, of course, related to $\langle \Delta \omega^2 \rangle$, as

$$\tau_2 = \frac{1}{\sqrt{\langle \Delta \omega^2 \rangle}} \tag{2.49}$$

2.5. Determination of the covalency effect from the ligand hyperfine interaction

One of the direct experimental methods of measuring the covalency effects in a dilute magnetic system is through the measurement of the hyperfine splitting of the paramagnetic resonance lines. Let us consider the simple transition metal complex MI_6. The hyperfine splitting arises from the covalent transfer of an unpaired electron from the metal ion to a ligand with nuclear spin I. For simplicity, we take an s-type ligand orbital. The hyperfine Hamiltonian is written as (axis of symmetry along the z axis)

$$A' S_z I_z + B'(S_x I_x + S_y I_y) + Q\{I_z{}^2 - \tfrac{1}{2} I(I+1)\} \tag{2.50}$$

where the first two terms are due to the interactions between the transferred electron spin and the spin of the ligand nucleus. The last term is due to the nuclear quadrupole interaction. For the simple case of $Mn^{2+}F_6{}^-$ and $Ni^{2+}F_6{}^-$, where the lowest ligand orbitals are s type, the contribution to the coefficients A' and B' is of the form

$$A_s = \frac{\lambda_s{}^2 A_s{}^0}{2S} \tag{2.51}$$

where

$$A_s{}^0 = \frac{16\pi}{3} g_N \mu_B \mu_N |\psi_s(0)|^2.$$

This is the dominant contribution when allowed. On the other hand, if the lowest-lying orbitals of the ligand are of p type, the calculation is somewhat involved. As discussed in (1.12), we have the partially filled antibonding orbitals of symmetry $e_g{}^*$ and $t_{2g}{}^*$. The $e_g{}^*$ orbital involves combination of the $d_z{}^2(d_{x^2-y^2})$ metal-ion orbital with the σ-type ligand orbitals from the p_z orbital of each ligand. On the other hand, the $t_{2g}{}^*$ orbital involves metal-ion orbital of type d_{xy} etc. and π-type orbitals from the p_x and p_y orbitals of the ligand.

The Hamiltonian is of the form (ignoring the quadrupole and core-polarization interaction)

$$2A_p S_z I_z - A_p(S_x I_x + S_y I_y).\tag{2.52}$$

The above is for the pure p orbital of the ligand. If the covalency effects are taken into account the contributions to the hyperfine interaction coefficient due to the fractional occupancy of the ligand p orbital (as occurs in (1.12)) are given by

$$2A_\sigma = \frac{2\lambda_\sigma{}^2 A_p}{2S} \quad \text{and} \quad -A_\sigma = \frac{\lambda_\sigma{}^2 A_p}{2S}.\tag{2.53}$$

Similarly for p_x and p_y orbitals, we have

$$-2A_\pi = -\frac{2\lambda_\pi{}^2 A_p}{2S} \quad \text{and} \quad A_\pi = \frac{\lambda_\pi{}^2 A_p}{2S}.\tag{2.54}$$

The experimental measurement of the hyperfine splitting thus gives an ideas of the covalency effect (i.e. measure of $\lambda_\sigma{}^2$, $\lambda_\pi{}^2$ etc.). The covalency parameters for $Mn^{2+}F_6{}^-$ (in NaF) and $Ni^2F_6{}^-$ (in NaF) are given in Table 2.1.

TABLE 2.1

Ion	Host	A	B	$\lambda_s{}^2$	$\lambda_p{}^2$	Reference
		$10^{-4}\,cm^{-1}$	$10^{-4}\,cm^{-1}$	%	%	
Mn^{2+}	NaF	19·4	9·7	0·43	1·4	Hall et al. 1963a
Ni^{2+}	NaF	59·2	18·5	0·49	3·4	Hall et al. 1963b

3

MECHANISMS OF EXCHANGE COUPLING

In this chapter we shall consider the mechanisms of exchange interactions between paramagnetic ions which lead to spin-dependent coupling of their magnetic moments. It should be emphasized that magnetism is a purely quantum-mechanical phenomenon which follows from some general considerations; a classical system of interacting charged particles has no magnetization in the equilibrium state (see Mattis 1965). The basic concept of the quantum-mechanical exchange interaction was developed by Heisenberg (1928) and Dirac (1929). This formed the basis of subsequent theoretical work on ferromagnetism, ferrimagnetism, and anti-ferromagnetism (Van Vleck 1937, Néel, 1932, 1948). We shall, however, introduce the concept of exchange energy in a somewhat different manner (see Lowdin 1962).

3.1. Heisenberg exchange Hamiltonian for a two-centre two-electron system

Let us consider a system of two identical paramagnetic ions having one unpaired electron each in addition to the closed-shell core, the role of which is neglected. The atoms are assumed fixed, with interatomic spacing R_{ab}. The Hamiltonian of the system can be expressed as

$$H = H_a + H_b + H_{ab} \tag{3.1}$$

where

$$H_a = \frac{p_1^2}{2m} - \frac{Ze^2}{r_{1a}} \tag{3.2a}$$

$$H_b = \frac{p_2^2}{2m} - \frac{Ze^2}{r_{2b}}. \tag{3.2b}$$

$p_1^2/2m$ is the kinetic energy operator of electron 1 and $-Ze^2/r_{1a}$ is its potential energy operator in the force field of ion core a; similarly H_b is the Hamiltonian of electron 2 in the field of ion core b. The atomic orbitals which are solutions of the corresponding Schrödinger equations are denoted by ϕ_a and ϕ_b, i.e.

$$H_a\phi_a(\mathbf{r}_1) = E_a\phi_a(\mathbf{r}_1) \tag{3.3a}$$

$$H_b\phi_b(\mathbf{r}_2) = E_b\phi_b(\mathbf{r}_2), \tag{3.3b}$$

where E_a and E_b are the energy eigenvalues. H_{ab} is the interaction

Hamiltonian and has the form

$$H_{ab} = \frac{Z^2 e^2}{R_{ab}} - \frac{Ze^2}{r_{1b}} - \frac{Ze^2}{r_{2a}} + \frac{e^2}{r_{12}}. \qquad (3.4)$$

Here $Z^2 e^2 / R_{ab}$ is the mutual repulsion of the two ion cores which each have a charge Ze. The second and the third terms in eqn (3.4) represent the attractive potentials on electron 1 due to ion b and electron 2 due to ion a respectively; e^2 / r_{12} is the mutual Coulomb repulsion between the two electrons. The Hamiltonian given in eqn (3.1) has no explicit dependence on the spin variables of the electrons. The spin dependence enters implicitly into the problem when we take the exclusion principle into account in the formulation of the total state function of the many-electron system (e.g. the two electrons in question). First, we define the one-electron spin orbitals which are products of the space and spin wavefunctions of an electron:

$$\phi_i(\xi) \equiv \phi_i(\mathbf{r}, \sigma) = \phi_i(\mathbf{r})\chi_i(\sigma) \qquad (3.5)$$

where ξ denotes collectively the space variable $\mathbf{r}$ and the spin variable σ.

For many electrons it is convenient to work with those state functions which are eigenfunctions of the square of the total spin operator S^2 and the total Z component S^z. Since S^2 and S^z commute with the Hamiltonian, there are no non-zero matrix elements of the Hamiltonian operator between states corresponding to different values S of the total spin and its projections M_S.

For an N-electron system the state functions are linear combinations of the products of one-electron spin orbitals $\phi_i(\xi)$ that satisfy the antisymmetry requirement. This is satisfied automatically if we choose a determinantal form for these products constructed from a given set of N orthonormal spin orbitals $\phi_1, \phi_2, \ldots, \phi_N$. We can write

$$\psi = \frac{1}{\sqrt{N!}} \begin{vmatrix} \phi_1(\xi_1)\phi_2(\xi_1) \ldots \phi_N(\xi_1) \\ \phi_1(\xi_2)\phi_2(\xi_2) \ldots \phi_N(\xi_2) \\ \phi_1(\xi_N)\phi_2(\xi_N) \ldots \phi_N(\xi_N) \end{vmatrix} \qquad (3.6a)$$

$$\equiv \frac{1}{\sqrt{N!}} [\phi_1(\xi_1)\phi_2(\xi_2) \ldots \phi_N(\xi_N)] \qquad (3.6b)$$

$$= \frac{1}{\sqrt{N!}} \sum_P (-1)^P P^S \phi_1(\mathbf{r}_1)\phi_2(\mathbf{r}_2) \ldots \phi_N(\mathbf{r}_N)$$

$$\times P^\sigma \chi_1(\sigma_1)\chi_2(\sigma_2) \ldots \chi_N(\sigma_N). \qquad (3.6c)$$

Eqn (3.6b) is a compact representation of the full determinant which is expanded in eqn (3.6c), where P^S and P^σ are the permutation operators on the space and spin co-ordinates respectively, $P = P^S P^\sigma$, and $1/\sqrt{N!}$ is a normalization factor. Thus the factor $(-1)^P$ will have ± 1 values accordingly as P is an even or an odd permutation of the spin orbitals. The eigenstates of the total spin operator S^2 are suitable linear combinations of such determinants. Returning to the two-electron system, we find that the various eigenstates of the S^2 and S^Z operators are the triplets

$$^3|S=1, M_s=1\rangle_{ab} = \frac{[\phi_a \phi_b]}{(1 - S_{ab}{}^2)^{1/2}} \tag{3.7a}$$

$$^3|S=1, M_s=0\rangle_{ab} = \left\{ \frac{[\phi_a \overline{\phi}_b] + [\overline{\phi}_a \phi_b]}{\{2(1 - S_{ab}{}^2)\}^{1/2}} \right\}^{1/2} \tag{3.7b}$$

$$^3|S=1, M_s=-1\rangle_{ab} = \frac{[\overline{\phi}_a \overline{\phi}_b]}{(1 - S_{ab}{}^2)^{1/2}} \tag{3.7c}$$

and the singlets

$$^1|S=0, M_s=0\rangle_{ab} = \frac{[\phi_a \overline{\phi}_b] - [\overline{\phi}^a \phi_b]}{\{2(1 + S_{ab}{}^2)\}^{1/2}} \tag{3.8}$$

$$^1|S=0, M_s=0\rangle_{aa} = [\phi_a \overline{\phi}_a] \tag{3.9}$$

$$^1|S=0, M_s=0\rangle_{bb} = [\phi_b \overline{\phi}_b]. \tag{3.10}$$

In writing these determinantal states, the following convention has been adopted:

$$\frac{1}{N!}[\phi_1(\xi_1)\phi_2(\xi_2) \cdots \phi_N(\xi_N)] \equiv [\phi_1 \phi_2 \phi_3 \cdots \phi_N]$$

i.e. the normalization factor $(1/\sqrt{N!})$ is understood to have been absorbed in $[\ldots]$; the spin orbitals without bars denote the spin-up functions $\phi_1 \equiv \phi_1(\mathbf{r}_1)\alpha(1)$ and those with bars denote spin-down functions $\phi_3 = \phi_3(\mathbf{r}_3)\beta(3)$, α and β being the spin-up and the spin-down functions χ. Also,

$$S_{ab} = \langle \phi_a(\mathbf{r})|\phi_b(\mathbf{r})\rangle = \int \phi_a{}^*(\mathbf{r})\phi_b(\mathbf{r})\mathrm{d}^3\mathbf{r} \tag{3.11}$$

is the overlap or non-orthogonality integral for the orbital functions $\phi_a(\mathbf{r})$ and $\phi_b(\mathbf{r})$. The triplet states in eqn (3.7) and the singlet state in eqn (3.8) correspond to the states considered by Heitler and London (1927) for the hydrogen molecule $H-H$. The singlet states in eqns (3.9) and (3.10) correspond to ionic configurations such as H^+H^- and H^-H^+ in which one hydrogen has two electrons and the other is a bare proton. The ground-state singlet configuration (cf. eqn (3.8)) will interact with the excited-state configurations (cf. eqns (3.9) and (3.10)). There will be a second-order correction to the singlet states owing to this interaction. It should be noted that there are no such corrections for the triplet states within the two-orbital manifold $\phi_a(\mathbf{r})$ and $\phi_b(\mathbf{r})$. This is because excited states having two electrons with parallel spins cannot exist either in $\phi_a(\mathbf{r})$ or $\phi_b(\mathbf{r})$ owing to the exclusion principle.

Let us formally denote the energy of the triplet states by ^3E and the energy of the singlet state together with the second-order corrections due to the interaction with excited states by ^1E. If we were to express this in a compact form, we could use the formula

$$^{(2S+1)}E = K - \{S(S+1) - 1\}J \qquad (3.12)$$

where

$$K \equiv [^1E + {}^3E]/2 \qquad (3.13)$$

$$J \equiv [^1E - {}^3E]/2 \qquad (3.14)$$

The relation in eqn (3.12) can be recast as

$$^{(2S+1)}E = K - \tfrac{1}{2}(1 + 4\mathbf{s}_1 \cdot \mathbf{s}_2)J \qquad (3.15)$$

Here $\mathbf{s}_1$ and $\mathbf{s}_2$ are the vector spin operators of the individual electrons. Their components are given in terms of the wellknown spin matrices, namely

$$s^x = \tfrac{1}{2}\begin{pmatrix} 0 & 1 \\ 1 & 0 \end{pmatrix}, \qquad s^y = \tfrac{1}{2}\begin{pmatrix} 0 & -i \\ i & 0 \end{pmatrix}, \qquad s^z = \tfrac{1}{2}\begin{pmatrix} 1 & 0 \\ 0 & -1 \end{pmatrix}. \qquad (3.16)$$

These operators are defined in the two-dimensional representation in which s^z is diagonal. The basis functions are the eigenstates of $s^z(j)$ given by

$$\alpha(j) \equiv \begin{pmatrix} 1 \\ 0 \end{pmatrix} \qquad \text{and} \qquad \beta(j) \equiv \begin{pmatrix} 0 \\ 1 \end{pmatrix}. \qquad (3.17)$$

Thus

$$s^z\alpha(j) = \tfrac{1}{2}\alpha(j)$$
$$s^z\beta(j) = -\tfrac{1}{2}\beta(j) \qquad (3.18)$$

i.e. the eigenvalues are $+\tfrac{1}{2}$ and $-\tfrac{1}{2}$ respectively (in units of $\hbar$). The functions $\alpha(j)$ and $\beta(j)$ constitute a complete set in the two-dimensional spin space of an electron. It is expedient to note some other relations also. Thus

$$s^x\alpha(j) = \tfrac{1}{2}\beta(j), \qquad s^x\beta(j) = \tfrac{1}{2}\alpha(j)$$
$$s^y\alpha(j) = \tfrac{i}{2}\beta(j), \qquad s^y\beta(j) = -\tfrac{i}{2}\alpha(j). \qquad (3.19)$$

It can easily be shown that the eigenvalues of the operator $s^2 \equiv (s^x)^2 + (s^y)^2 + (s^z)^2$ are given by

$$s^2 \alpha(j) = \tfrac{3}{4}\alpha(j)$$
$$s2\beta(j) = \tfrac{3}{4}\beta(j) \qquad (3.20)$$

From eqn (3.16) the following commutation relations follow immediately:

$$\mathbf{s} \times \mathbf{s} = i\mathbf{s}, \qquad (s^x)^2 = (s^y)^2 = s^z)^2 = \tfrac{1}{4}$$

$$s^x s^y + s^y s^x = 0, \qquad s^y s^z + s^z s^y = 0, \qquad s^z s^x + s^x s^z = 0$$

$$2s^y s^z = i s^x, \qquad 2s^z s^x = i s^y, \qquad 2s^x s^y = i s^z.$$

On the basis of the vector model (Dirac 1929), the resultant spin of the two-electron system $\mathbf{S} = \mathbf{s}_1 + \mathbf{s}_2$. The resultant spin can thus have the values $S = 0$ (singlet state) and $S = 1$ (triplet state).

Making use of the relation

$$S^2 = s_1{}^2 + s_2{}^2 + 2\mathbf{s}_1 \cdot \mathbf{s}_2 = \tfrac{3}{2} + 2\mathbf{s}_1 \cdot \mathbf{s}_2 \qquad (3.21)$$

we can say that the operator

$$\tfrac{1}{2}(1 + 4\mathbf{s}_1 \cdot \mathbf{s}_2) \qquad (3.22)$$

will have the eigenvalues $S(S+1) - 1)$, i.e. 1 for the triplet state and -1 for the singlet state. This shows the equivalence of eqns (3.12) and (3.15).

Let us now turn to the definition of the exchange energy, i.e.

$$J = \tfrac{1}{2}({}^1E - {}^3E).$$

This shows that, if J is positive, the triplet state lies lowest and parallel spin alignment (ferromagnetism) is energetically favoured. On the other hand, when J is negative the singlet state is more stable favouring antiferromagnetic ordering. So far, we have considered a formal treatment. We shall obtain a more explicit form by evaluating the singlet and triplet energies ${}^1E$ and ${}^3E$ as described above. In calculating the energy of the singlet ground state ${}^1E$, we include the second-order corrections to the energy of singly occupied state ${}^1|S = 0, M_s = 0\rangle_{ab}$ from its interaction with the doubly occupied singlet configurations given in eqns (3.9) and (3.10).

This gives us

$$J = \frac{1}{1 - S_{ab}{}^4}\left\{ \left(\langle ab\left|\frac{e^2}{r_{12}}\right|ba\rangle + S_{ab}\left\langle a\left|\frac{-Ze^2}{r_{2a}}\right|b\right\rangle + S_{ab}\left\langle b\left|\frac{-Ze^2}{r_{1b}}\right|a\right\rangle\right) \right.$$

$$\left. - S_{ab}{}^2\left\{\left\langle ab\left|\frac{e^2}{r_{12}}\right|ab\right\rangle + \left\langle b\left|\frac{-Ze^2}{r_{1a}}\right|b\right\rangle + \left\langle a\left|\frac{-Ze^2}{r_{2b}}\right|a\right\rangle\right\} \right\} \qquad (3.23)$$

$$- \frac{1}{1 + S_{ab}{}^2}\left\{ \frac{|\langle a| - Ze^2/r_{1a}|b\rangle|^2}{\Delta E(b \to a)} + \frac{|\langle b| - Ze^2/r_{2b}|a\rangle|^2}{\Delta E(a \to b)} \right\}.$$

In writing this expression, we have omitted the constant inter-ion core repulsion term $(Z^2 e^2/R_{ab})$. It is customary to treat this as a parameter. The explicit forms of the quantities occurring in eqn (3.23) are as follows:

$$\langle a|V(\mathbf{r})|b\rangle \equiv \int \phi_a{}^*(\mathbf{r})V(\mathbf{r})\phi_b(\mathbf{r})\mathrm{d}^3\mathbf{r}$$

the matrix element of the one-electron operator $V(\mathbf{r})$ connecting the orbitals ϕ_a and ϕ_b, and

$$\left\langle ab \left| \frac{e^2}{r_{12}} \right| cd \right\rangle \equiv \int \phi_a{}^*(\mathbf{r}_1)\phi_b{}^*(\mathbf{r}_2)\left(\frac{e^2}{r_{12}}\right)\phi_c(\mathbf{r}_1)\phi_d(\mathbf{r}_2)\mathrm{d}^3\mathbf{r}_1\mathrm{d}^3\mathbf{r}_2.$$

As remarked earlier, the last two terms in eqn. (3.23) arise from the interaction of the ground singlet with the two excited singlets representing the ionic configurations. The energy corrections appear in the second order; $\Delta E(a{\to}b)$ is the energy denominator involved. In point of fact it represents the repulsive energy when two electrons are in the same orbital state.

The expression (3.23) is a more exact representation of the exchange energy than that considered by Heisenberg (1928). If we neglect higher powers of the overlap integral S_{ab}, say $S_{ab}{}^2$ and $S_{ab}{}^4$, we obtain a somewhat simplified form of the Heisenberg exchange energy generalized so as to include the electron transfer effects

$$J_\mathrm{H} = \left\langle ab \left| \frac{e^2}{r_{12}} \right| ba \right\rangle - 2(S_{ab} + \Gamma_{ab})\langle b|V|a\rangle \tag{3.24}$$

where we have introduced the notation

$$\Gamma_{ab} = \frac{\langle a|V|b\rangle}{\Delta E(a{\to}b)}$$

and

$$V = \frac{Ze^2}{r_{1b}}. \tag{3.25}$$

The spin-dependent part of the energy (cf. eqn (3.15)) can thus be expressed as

$$H(\text{Heisenberg}) = -2J_\mathrm{H}\mathbf{s}_1 \cdot \mathbf{s}_2 \tag{3.26}$$

with J_H given by eqn (3.24). The exchange integral $\langle ab|e^2/r_{12}|ba\rangle$ is always positive definite, being the self-energy of the complex overlap charge $e\phi_a{}^*(\mathbf{r}_1)\phi_b(\mathbf{r}_1)$. If this term dominates the second term of eqn (3.24), J_H would be positive and the ferromagnetic (triplet) state would be favoured. On the other hand, if the second term involving the overlap integral S_{ab} and the transfer effect Γ_{ab} dominates, J_H would be negative and the antiferromagnetic (singlet) state is favoured. Thus, depending on the sign of J_H, antiferromagnetic or ferromagnetic coupling of the two spins will prevail. These are some simple inferences from a generalized Heisenberg formulation.

3.2. Exchange Hamiltonian for N localized spins

Let us now consider the formulation of the exchange Hamiltonian for a system consisting of N magnetic ions having one localized unpaired electron in addition to the core electrons. As before, we shall assume that the core electrons are not involved in the interaction processes. The Hamiltonian for such a system is given by

$$H = \sum_i \frac{p_i^2}{2m} + \sum_{n,i} V(\mathbf{r}_i - \mathbf{R}_n) + \sum_{i<j} \frac{e^2}{r_{ij}} \tag{3.27}$$

where $p_i^2/2m$ is the kinetic energy operator, $V(\mathbf{r}_i - \mathbf{R}_n)$ is the potential energy operator of the ith electron in the field of the nth ion core, and e^2/r_{ij} is the two-body Coulomb interaction between electrons i and j.

The many-body Hamiltonian given in eqn (3.27) is far too complicated to be treated exactly and a systematic perturbation scheme is needed. Here, we follow a simple approach where the unperturbed Hamiltonian is taken for N non-interacting atoms each having one extra core electron in a non-degenerate orbital. The effect of electron–electron interactions and the interaction of an electron (personalized to a particular atom) with the core potential of other ion cores will be treated as perturbations within the manifold of the one-electron orbital. A detailed discussion of this point is given by Stevens (1976).

Accordingly, the derivation is based on the idealized model. The basic assumption is that the distinct singly occupied orbitals ϕ_1, ϕ_2, ..., ϕ_N, localized at sites 1, 2, ..., N respectively, are orthogonal to one another. It will be convenient for later discussion to derive the results following the method of second quantization (see Landau and Lifshitz 1958). This will also provide a suitable introduction to this elegant technique which is found to be extremely useful in many-body problems.

We noted earlier that the N-particle wavefunction for a system of electrons (which are fermions and therefore obey Fermi–Dirac statistics) must be antisymmetric, i.e. an antisymmetrized product function (determinantal function). The number of electrons residing in a spin-orbital state $\phi_j(\xi)$ can be either zero or unity. The essence of the second-quantization representation is to introduce the concept of the occupation number for each state.

Thus, in terms of occupation numbers the state function of a many-particle system can be denoted by the ket

$$|n_1, n_2, \ldots, n_j, \ldots\rangle \tag{3.28}$$

where n_j denotes the occupation number for the one-electron state $\phi_j(\xi)$. In this representation a set of single-particle basis states is chosen which is complete and orthogonal. Of course, all of these may not be occupied. The occupation number operator for the single-particle state $\phi_i(\zeta)$ is defined as

$$C_i^+ C_i \equiv N_i \tag{3.29}$$

whose eigenvalues with respect to the state (say eqn (3.28)) gives the occupation number n_i for $\phi_i(\xi)$. Here C_i is the annihilation operator and destroys a particle in the single-particle state $\phi_i(\xi)$, and C_i^+ is its Hermitian conjugate and creates a particle in this state. These creation and annihilation operators are defined by the following relations;

$$C_r^+ |n_1, n_2, \ldots, n_r, \ldots\rangle = (1 - n_r)^{1/2}(-1)^{n_1 + n_2 + \cdots + n_{r-1}} \times |n_1, n_2, \ldots, (n_r + 1)\rangle \tag{3.30}$$

and

$$C_r |n_1, n_2, \ldots, n_r, \ldots\rangle = n_r^{1/2}(-1)^{n_1 + n_2 + \cdots + n_{r-1}} + |n_1, n_2, \ldots, (n_r - 1)\rangle \tag{3.31}$$

It follows from these relations that

$$C_r^+ C_r |n_1, n_2, \ldots, n_r, \ldots\rangle = n_r |n_1, n_2, \ldots, n_r, \ldots\rangle. \tag{3.32}$$

Thus the eigenvalue of the operator $C_r^+ C_r (\equiv N_r)$ is n_r which takes values 0 or 1. The phase factor $(-1)^{n_1 + n_2 \cdots + n_{r+1}}$ displays the antisymmetry requirement.

Similarly, we can show that

$$C_r C_r^+ |n_1, n_2, \ldots, n_r, \ldots\rangle = (1 - n_r)|n_1, n_2, \ldots, (n_r - 1)\rangle. \tag{3.33}$$

Thus the eigenvalue of $C_r C_r^+$ is $1 - n_r$. From the above, we obtain the following anticommutation relations:

$$\{C_r, C_s^+\} \equiv C_r C_s^+ + C_s^+ C_r = \delta_{rs} \qquad \text{(Kronecker delta)}$$

$$\{C_r^+, C_s^+\} = \{C_r, C_s\} = 0. \tag{3.34}$$

These reflect the antisymmetry requirement.

These fermion operators are related to the spin matrices of spin-$\frac{1}{2}$ particles discussed earlier. The occupancy of a spin-orbital $\phi_i(\xi)$ is given by the number operator $C_i^+ C_i$. If we explicitly display the spin variable, the occupation of the ith orbital is described by $\Sigma_\sigma C_{i\sigma}^+ C_{i\sigma}$, where the summation over σ implies summation over spin-up ($\uparrow$ or $+$) and spin-down ($\downarrow$ or $-$) values.

The important relations are

$$C_{i\uparrow}{}^{+}C_{i\uparrow}+C_{i\downarrow}{}^{+}C_{i\downarrow}\equiv 1\equiv N_{i\uparrow}+N_{i\downarrow} \qquad \text{(for singly occupied orbitals)}$$

$$C_{i\uparrow}{}^{+}C_{i\uparrow}-C_{i\downarrow}{}^{+}C_{i\downarrow}=2s_{i}{}^{z}$$

$$C_{i\uparrow}{}^{+}C_{i\downarrow}=s_{i}{}^{+}\equiv s_{i}{}^{x}+is_{i}{}^{y} \qquad (3.35)$$

$$C_{i\downarrow}{}^{+}C_{i\uparrow}=s_{i}{}^{-}\equiv s_{i}{}^{x}-is_{i}{}^{y}.$$

In terms of the fermion creation and annihilation operators, the Hamiltonian given in eqn (3.27) can be re-expressed as (Landau and Lifshitz 1958)

$$H=\sum_{lm\sigma} V_{lm}C_{l\sigma}{}^{+}C_{m\sigma}+\tfrac{1}{2}\sum_{\substack{jlmn\\\sigma\sigma'}} U_{mn}{}^{jl}C_{l\sigma'}{}^{+}C_{j\sigma}{}^{+}C_{m\sigma}C_{n\sigma'} \qquad (3.36)$$

where V_{lm} is the matrix element of the one-body Hamiltonian connecting the orbital states ϕ_{l} and ϕ_{m}, or more specifically

$$V_{lm}=\langle\phi_{l}|\frac{p^{2}}{2m}+V(r)|\phi_{m}\rangle \qquad (3.37)$$

and

$$U_{mn}{}^{jl}=\langle\phi_{j}(\mathbf{r}_{1})\phi_{l}(\mathbf{r}_{2})\Big|\frac{e^{2}}{r_{12}}\Big|\phi_{m}(\mathbf{r}_{1})\phi_{n}(\mathbf{r}_{2})\rangle. \qquad (3.38)$$

It is instructive to separate the Hamiltonian in eqn (3.36) into the diagonal and off-diagonal terms

$$H=H_{0}+H_{\text{ex}}+H_{\text{corr}}+H_{\text{tr}} \qquad (3.39)$$

where

$$H_{0}=\sum_{l\sigma}\varepsilon_{1}C_{l\sigma}{}^{+}C_{l\sigma}+\tfrac{1}{2}\sum_{l,m,\sigma,\sigma',} K_{lm}C_{l\sigma}{}^{+}C_{l\sigma}C_{m\sigma'}{}^{+}C_{m\sigma'}. \qquad (3.40)$$

Here ε_{1} is the one-electron orbital energy and K_{lm} is the two-body Coulomb integral defined by

$$K_{lm}\equiv\langle\phi_{l}(\mathbf{r}_{1})\phi_{m}(\mathbf{r}_{2})\Big|\frac{e^{2}}{r_{12}}\Big|\phi_{1}(\mathbf{r}_{1})\phi_{m}(\mathbf{r}_{2})\rangle.$$

H_{ex} is the spin-dependent exchange term of the Dirac model, namely

$$H_{\text{ex}}=\tfrac{1}{2}\sum_{\substack{l\neq m\\\sigma\sigma'}} J_{lm}C_{la'}{}^{+}C_{m\sigma}{}^{+}C_{l\sigma}C_{m\sigma'} \qquad (3.41)$$

with

$$J_{lm} = \langle \phi_l(\mathbf{r}_1)\phi_m(\mathbf{r}_2) \left| \frac{e^2}{r_{12}} \right| \phi_m(\mathbf{r}_1)\phi_l(\mathbf{r}_2) \rangle.$$

This so-called potential exchange can be expressed in terms of the spin operators by summing over the spin variables and σ and using the relations (3.35). This is given below

$$\sum_{\sigma\sigma'} C_{l\sigma'}{}^+ C_{m\sigma}{}^+ C_{l\sigma} C_{m\sigma'} = C_{l\uparrow}{}^+ C_{m\uparrow}{}^+ C_{l\uparrow} C_{m\uparrow}$$

$$+ C_{l\downarrow}{}^+ C_{m\downarrow}{}^+ C_{l\downarrow} C_{m\downarrow}$$

$$+ C_{l\uparrow}{}^+ C_{m\downarrow}{}^+ C_{l\downarrow} C_{m\uparrow}$$

$$+ C_{l\downarrow}{}^+ C_{m\uparrow}{}^+ C_{l\uparrow} C_{m\downarrow}$$

which on making use of eqn (3.35) becomes

$$-(\tfrac{1}{2} + 2\mathbf{s}_l \cdot \mathbf{s}_m) \tag{3.42}$$

It must be re-emphasized that the above relation holds strictly for singly occupied orbital states. Thus H_{ex} can be written as

$$H_{\text{ex}} = -\tfrac{1}{4} \sum_{l \neq m} J_{lm} - \sum_{l \neq m} J_{lm}\mathbf{s}_l \cdot \mathbf{s}_m. \tag{3.43}$$

So far, we have considered terms of eqn (3.39) which fall within the premises of Dirac's formulation in which one-electron transfer processes were not included. Although most of these excitations can be shown to vanish (Brillouin theorem), the spin-independent electron transfer between singly occupied orbitals will remain even when Hartree–Fock orbitals are chosen. As a consequence, we must take into account the other two terms of eqn (3.39), namely,

$$H_{\text{corr}} = \sum_{m\sigma} U_{mm} C_{m\sigma}{}^+ C_{m\sigma} C_{m-\sigma}{}^+ C_{m-\sigma} \tag{3.44}$$

where U_{mm} is the two-body Coulomb repulsion between two electrons with antiparallel spins residing in the same orbital ϕ_m. As the singly occupied orbitals on different atoms are taken to be equivalent, we can write $U_{mm} = U$. Finally, we have

$$H_{\text{tr}} = \sum_{\substack{l \neq m \\ \sigma}} V_{lm} C_{l\sigma}{}^+ C_{m\sigma} \tag{3.45}$$

which involves the transfer of an electron from the atom m (in state ϕ_m) to atom l (in state ϕ_l).

We shall now apply a canonical transformation in order to eliminate the off-diagonal transfer terms in eqn (3.45) in the first order. This is given by

$$H_T = e^{-iS} H e^{iS}$$

$$= H + i[H, S] + \frac{i^2}{2!}[[H, S], S] + \dots \tag{3.46}$$

$$\equiv H_d + H_{tr} + i[H_0, S] + i[H_{tr}, S] + \frac{i^2}{2}[[H_d + H_{tr}, S], S] + \dots$$

where

$$H_d = \sum_{l\sigma} E_l C_{l\sigma}{}^+ C_{l\sigma} + U \sum_{m,\sigma} C_{m\sigma}{}^+ C_{m\sigma} C_{m,-\sigma}{}^+ C_{m,-\sigma} \tag{3.47}$$

with E_l representing the Hartree–Fock spin-independent single-particle energy (i.e.

$$\varepsilon_1 + \tfrac{1}{2} \sum_{m\sigma} (K_{lm}\langle n_{m\sigma}\rangle - \tfrac{1}{2} J_{lm}\langle n_{m\sigma}\rangle);$$

S is the generator of the canonical transformation and is determined from the condition

$$H_{tr} + i[H_d, S] = 0. \tag{3.48}$$

We choose the following form of the generator S (which has to be Hermitian)

$$S = \sum_{lm} A_{lm} C_{l\sigma}{}^+ C_{m\sigma} C_{l,-\sigma}{}^+ C_{l,-\sigma} + \text{h.c.} \tag{3.49}$$

where h.c denotes the Hermitian conjugate and the A_{lm} are coefficients to be determined with the help of relation (3.48). After some calculations and making use of the fermion commutation relations, we obtain

$$A_{lm} = \frac{iV_{lm}}{E_l + U - E_m}. \tag{3.50}$$

As we have taken all the magnetic atoms to be equivalent the condition $E_m = E_l$ holds. With this simplification in mind the spin-dependent interaction term, to second order in the perturbation obtained from the fourth and fifth terms of eqn. (3.46), turns out to be

$$H_{int} = \tfrac{1}{2}[H_{tr}, S] = \sum_{\substack{l \neq m \\ \sigma}} \frac{V_{lm}{}^2}{U} C_{l\sigma}{}^+ C_{m,-\sigma}{}^+ C_{l,-\sigma} C_{m\sigma}. \tag{3.51}$$

On carrying out the summation over the spin variables and making use of eqn (3.35), H_{int} becomes

$$H_{int} = -\sum_{\substack{lm \\ l \neq m}} \frac{|V_{lm}|^2}{U} \tfrac{1}{2}(1 - 4\, \mathbf{s}_l \cdot \mathbf{s}_m) \qquad (3.52a)$$

$$= \text{constant} + 2\sum_{l \neq m} \frac{|V_{lm}|^2}{U} \mathbf{s}_l \cdot \mathbf{s}_m \qquad (3.52b)$$

the so-called kinetic exchage term. In this formulation, it is implicit that all unoccupied states are energetically far removed for the singly occupied states.

Thus combining eqns (3.43) and (3.52), the generalized effective Heisenberg–Dirac exchange Hamiltonian can be written as

$$H_{H-D} = C - \sum_{l \neq m} \left(J_{lm} - \frac{2|V_{lm}|^2}{U} \right) \mathbf{s}_l \cdot \mathbf{s}_m. \qquad (3.53)$$

The kinetic exchange term (second term of eqn (3.53)) always stabilizes the antiferromagnetic state. This can be physically seen by noting that the hopping is a one-body process and is allowed when the spins at neighbouring sites are antiparallel. This hopping is forbidden when the spins are parallel. This is reflected by the presence of the projection operator $\tfrac{1}{2}(1 - 4\, \mathbf{s}_l \cdot \mathbf{s}_m)$ in eqn (3.52a) which annihilates the triplet state for which $\mathbf{s}_l \cdot \mathbf{s}_m = \tfrac{1}{4}$. On the other hand, as we have seen earlier the potential exchange between spins of two different atoms is positive definite and hence this interaction favours ferromagnetic coupling. The overall interaction depends on the difference between these two contributions. This simplified result has been obtained because the orbital functions have been taken to be orthogonal (or are understood to have been orthogonalized, i.e. the overlap parameter S_{ab} is zero). In this context, it may be mentioned that serious objections were raised by Inglis (1934) and Slater (1930) owing to the suspected occurrence of divergence in the overlap and energy matrices when non-orthogonal orbitals are used and the number of electrons becomes infinitely large. Some recent careful examinations of the problem by Mizuno and Izuyama (1959), Arai (1962), and Herring (1962) have dispelled these doubts, to a certain degree, and have shown that the non-orthogonality catastrophe is not as serious as thought previously. This assurance is indeed gratifying.

There are important additional mechanisms when magnetic systems contain other background electrons which can undergo exchange polarization. Examples are conduction electrons in magnetic metals and alloys or semiconductors and intervening diamagnetic ions in magnetic insulators. We consider their effects next.

3.3. Indirect exchange mechanisms

So far we have discussed exchange processes that involve the localized electrons which are responsible for the magnetic moments of the atoms. However, the magnetic system may contain other electrons, for example conduction electrons or the electrons of the diamagnetic atoms of the system. These will lead to additional exchange processes via the polarization of the conduction electrons or of the electrons of the diamagnetic atoms. We shall first discuss the indirect exchange mechanism via s–d or s–f exchange.

For studying this type of indirect exchange coupling, we shall work within the Hamiltonian

$$H = H_s + H_d + H_{ex}(s\text{--}d) \tag{3.54}$$

where we have not written the direct exchange effects between the localized d (or f) electrons and the effects arising from d–d transfer and correlation. These have been discussed in the previous sections. Here

$$H_s = \sum_{k,\sigma} E_k C_{k\sigma}{}^+ C_{k\sigma} \tag{3.35}$$

is the Hamiltonian of the conduction electrons; $C_{k\sigma}{}^+$, $C_{k\sigma}$ are the electron creation and annihilation operators for the Bloch states $|k\sigma\rangle$, where k is the electron wave vector and σ the spin index. E_k is the single-particle unperturbed energy of an electron in this conduction state. Next,

$$H_d = \sum_{l\sigma} E_l C_{l\sigma}{}^+ C_{l\sigma} \tag{3.56}$$

where E_l is the one-electron energy of a non-degenerate d (or f) orbital ϕ_l at the site R_l; $C_{l\sigma}{}^+$, $C_{l\sigma}$ are the corresponding electron creation and, annihilation operators.

The s–d exchange Hamiltonian is expressed as (see Vonsovskii and Izyumov 1963)

$$H_{ex}(s\text{--}d) = -\frac{1}{N} \sum_{k,k',l} J(|k-k'|)\exp\{i(k-k')\cdot R_l\}$$
$$\times \{(C_{k'}{}_\uparrow{}^+ C_k{}_\uparrow - C_{k'}{}_\downarrow{}^+ C_k{}_\downarrow)S_l{}^Z + C_{k'}{}_\uparrow{}^+ C_k{}_\downarrow \; S_l{}^- + C_{k'}{}_\downarrow{}^+ C_k{}_\uparrow S_l{}^+\} \tag{3.57}$$

where we have explicitly shown the summation over spin variables and used the relation (3.35) between spin operators and fermion operators for the localized electrons. Here

$$J(|k-k'|) = N\langle \phi_l(r_1)\phi_l(r_2-R_l)|\exp\{-i(k-k')\cdot R_l\} \times \frac{e^2}{r_{12}}|\phi_k(r_2)\phi_l(r_1-R_l)\rangle \tag{3.58}$$

where

$$|\mathbf{k}\rangle \equiv \phi_\mathbf{k}(\mathbf{r}) = \frac{1}{\sqrt{\Omega_v}} \exp\{i\mathbf{k}\cdot\mathbf{r}\} U_\mathbf{k}(\mathbf{r}) \tag{3.59}$$

where $U_\mathbf{k}(\mathbf{r})$ is the periodic part of the Bloch function and Ω_v is the volume. Thus $H_{ex}(s-d)$ represents the Hamiltonian for the exchange interaction between conduction electrons and localized d (or f) electrons. In the above we have implicitly assumed that the exchange integral depends only on $|\mathbf{k}-\mathbf{k}'|$. It should be noted that this is true only for spherically symmetric orbitals. A more rigorous treatment calls for the expansion of $J(\mathbf{k}, \mathbf{k}')$ in terms of spherical harmonics and for retaining only the dominant terms corresponding to the particular partial wave scattering. It is expedient to absorb the diagonal part of the $s-d$ exchange Hamiltonian in the free-electron energy term, i.e. we redefine

$$H_s = \sum_{\mathbf{k},\sigma} (E_k - SJ(0)) C_{\mathbf{k}\sigma}{}^+ C_{\mathbf{k}\sigma} \equiv \sum_{\mathbf{k},\sigma} \varepsilon_{\mathbf{k}\sigma} C_{\mathbf{k}\sigma}{}^+ C_{\mathbf{k}\sigma} \tag{3.60}$$

where $S = 1/N \sum_l \langle S_l^z \rangle$ which is proportional to the net magnetization of the localized spins.

The above amounts to extracting the mean field from the $s-d$ exchange term. This gives rise to an equal and opposite energy shift of the spin-up and spin-down conduction electron states.

Let us now consider the effect of the off-diagonal term of the $s-d$ exchange Hamiltonian $H_{ex}(s-d)$. The wavefunction of the conduction electrons will be modified owing to this perturbation. Up to first order in the interaction, we obtain

$$\psi_{\mathbf{k}\sigma} = \phi_{\mathbf{k}\sigma} + \sum_{\mathbf{k}',\sigma'} \frac{\langle \mathbf{k}'|H_{ex}(s-d)|\mathbf{k}]}{\varepsilon_{\mathbf{k}\sigma} - \varepsilon_{\mathbf{k}'}} \phi_{\mathbf{k}',\sigma'}. \tag{3.61}$$

Substituting from eqn (3.58), we obtain

$$\psi_{\mathbf{k}(\pm)} = \phi_{\mathbf{k}(\pm)} - \frac{1}{N} \sum_{\mathbf{k}',l} J(\mathbf{k}-\mathbf{k}') \exp\{i(\mathbf{k}-\mathbf{k}')\cdot \mathbf{R}_l\}$$
$$\times \left\{ \frac{S^\pm \phi_{\mathbf{k}'(\mp)}}{\varepsilon_{\mathbf{k}(\pm)} - \varepsilon_{\mathbf{k}'(\mp)}} \pm \frac{S_l{}^z \phi_{\mathbf{k}'(\pm)}}{\varepsilon_{\mathbf{k}(\pm)} - \varepsilon_{\mathbf{k}'(\pm)}} \right\}. \tag{3.62}$$

The prime over the sign of summation excludes $\mathbf{k} = \mathbf{k}'$. The effect of exchange polarization on the conduction electron with spin up $(+)$ relative to that with spin down $(-)$ is clear from eqn (3.62). In taking the matrix element in eqns (3.61) and (3.62), we have factored out the part which is dependent on the conduction electrons leaving the impurity spin operators. The modification of the conduction electron state as given in eqn (3.62) consists of two parts. The spin-flip part involves the change in the impurity spin together with the reversal of the conduction electron spin. In the second term in braces, the impurity and conduction electrons do not change spin.

The densities of the up and down spins can be easily derived:

$$\rho_\pm(\mathbf{r}) = \sum_{\mathbf{k}}^{k_m(\pm)} \psi_{\mathbf{k}(\pm)}^* \psi_{\mathbf{k}(\pm)} = \left(\frac{1}{\Omega_v} \sum_{\mathbf{k}}^{km(\pm)}\right) \mp \frac{1}{N\Omega_v} \sum_{\mathbf{k},\mathbf{k}'} \frac{J(\mathbf{k}-\mathbf{k}')}{\varepsilon_{\mathbf{k}(\pm)} - \varepsilon_{\mathbf{k}'(\pm)}}$$

$$\times \sum_l [\exp\{i(\mathbf{k}-\mathbf{k}') \cdot (\mathbf{r}-\mathbf{R}_l)\} + \text{h·c}] \langle S_l^z \rangle \qquad (3.63)$$

where $k_m(\pm)$ is the maximum value of the electron wave vector. Now

$$\frac{1}{\Omega_v} \sum_{\mathbf{k}}^{k_m(\pm)} = \frac{n(\pm)}{\Omega_v} \qquad (3.64)$$

where

$$n(\pm) = \frac{n_c}{2} \pm \left(\frac{3n_c}{4E_F}\right) \frac{1}{N} J(0) \sum_l \langle S_l^z \rangle$$

n_c is the total number of conduction electrons, and E_F is the unperturbed Fermi energy. Thus $3n_c/4E_F$ is the density of free electron states at the Fermi surface and $\pm 1/N\, J(0) \sum_l \langle S_l^z \rangle$ denotes the energy shift of the spin-up and spind-down electrons. The final expression for the spin density then turns out to be

$$\rho_\pm(\mathbf{r}) = \frac{n_c}{2\Omega_v} \pm \frac{3n_c}{4E_F} \frac{J(0)}{N\Omega_v} \sum_l \langle S_l^z \rangle$$

$$+ \frac{1}{N\Omega_v} \sum_{\mathbf{q}} \sum_{\mathbf{k}} \frac{J(\mathbf{q})}{\varepsilon_{\mathbf{k}-\mathbf{q}(\pm)} - \varepsilon_{\mathbf{k}(\pm)}} \sum_l [\exp\{i\mathbf{q} \cdot (\mathbf{r}-\mathbf{R}_l)\} + \text{h·c}] \langle S_l^z \rangle \qquad (3.65)$$

where we have used $\mathbf{k}-\mathbf{k}' = \mathbf{q}$. For the conduction electrons we choose the usual parabolic dispersion relation

$$\varepsilon_{\mathbf{k}(\pm)} = \frac{\hbar^2 k^2}{2m^*} \mp SJ(0)$$

where m^* is the effective mass. In evaluating the summation over $\mathbf{k}$ in eqn (3.65), we can ignore $\pm SJ(0)$ in choosing the upper limit of the wave vector as they would contribute in the second order of $J(q)/E_F$.

Accordingly,

$$\sum_{\mathbf{k}}^{k_F} (\varepsilon_{\mathbf{k}-\mathbf{q}} - \varepsilon_{\mathbf{k}})^{-1} = \left(\frac{3}{16} \frac{n_c}{E_F}\right) f(q) \qquad (3.66)$$

where

$$f(\mathbf{q}) = 1 + \left(\frac{4k_F^2 - q^2}{4k_F q}\right) \ln\left|\frac{2k_F + q}{2k_F - q}\right| \tag{3.67}$$

the well-known Lindhard function, where the maximum wave vector has been taken to be the Fermi wave vector. Next, we are required to perform the summation over $\mathbf{q}$. For this purpose it is assumed that $J(\mathbf{q})$ is a very slowly varying function of $\mathbf{q}$, particularly in the region near the Fermi surface which gives the maximum contribution. A typical summation (integration) gives

$$\frac{1}{N} \sum_{\mathbf{q}} f(\mathbf{q}) \exp\{i\mathbf{q} \cdot \mathbf{R}\} = -12\pi \frac{n_c}{N} F(2k_F R) \tag{3.68}$$

where

$$F(x) = \frac{x \cos x - \sin x}{x^4} \tag{3.69}$$

the Ruderman–Kittel function (1954). Making use of these relations and approximating $J(q) = J_0$

$$\rho_{\pm(r)} = \frac{n_c}{2} \mp \frac{9\pi}{2} \left(\frac{n_c}{\Omega_v}\right) \frac{J_0}{E_F} \frac{n_c}{\Omega_v} \sum_l F(2k_F(|\mathbf{r} - \mathbf{R}_l|) \langle S_l^z \rangle \tag{3.70}$$

which gives the net polarization

$$\rho_{+(r)} - \rho_{-(r)} = \frac{-9\pi\, n_c^2 J_0}{E_F\, N\Omega_v} \sum_l \langle S_l^z \rangle \frac{\cos(2k_F|\mathbf{r} - \mathbf{R}_l|)}{(k_F|\mathbf{r} - \mathbf{R}_l|)^3}. \tag{3.71}$$

Let us consider the physical interpretation of the above expressions. The first term of eqn (3.70) gives the spin density of conduction electrons in the absence of s–d exchange. The second term gives the spin polarization effect induced by $H_{ex}(s$–$d)$. The behaviour of the inhomogeneous polarization has the the spin density function is very transparent. The polarization has the maximum value at the magnetic ion and falls off in an oscillatory manner as $1/R^3$.

We now consider the indirect exchange coupling between localized spins induced by the above polarization effects. This appears in the second order of perturbation:

$$H_{eff}^{ex} = \sum_{\substack{l \neq m\, \mathbf{k}, \mathbf{k}' \\ \sigma\ \ \sigma'}} \frac{\langle \mathbf{k}\sigma|H_{ex}(s-d)|\mathbf{k}'\sigma'\rangle \langle \mathbf{k}'\sigma'|H_{ex}(s-d)|\mathbf{k}\sigma\rangle}{\varepsilon_{\mathbf{k}\sigma} - \varepsilon_{\mathbf{k}'\sigma'}}. \tag{3.72}$$

On writing the full form of $H_{ex}(s$–$d)$ and taking the matrix element of the fermion operators with respect to the Bloch states, we obtain

$$H_{\text{eff}}^{\text{ex}} = \frac{1}{N^2} \sum_{l \neq m} \sum_{\mathbf{k},\mathbf{k}'} \frac{J^2(\mathbf{k}-\mathbf{k}')}{\varepsilon_{\mathbf{k}} - \varepsilon_{\mathbf{k}'}} \exp\{i\mathbf{k}-\mathbf{k}') \cdot \mathbf{R}_{lm}\}$$

$$\times \left[\{ n_{\mathbf{k}(+)}(1 - n_{\mathbf{k}'(+)}) + n_{\mathbf{k}(-)}(1 - n_{\mathbf{k}'(-1)}) \} S_l^z S_m^z \right. \tag{3.73}$$

$$\left. + n_{\mathbf{k}(-)}(1 - n_{\mathbf{k}'(+)}) \, S_l^+ S_m^- + n_{\mathbf{k}(+)}(1 - n_{\mathbf{k}'(-)}) S_l^- S_m^+ \right]$$

with

$$\mathbf{R}_{lm} = \mathbf{R}_l - \mathbf{R}_m$$

where $n_{\mathbf{k}(\pm)}$ is the fermion occupation number for the state $|\mathbf{k}\pm>$. The energy denominator occurring in eqn (3.73) is taken to be the unperturbed energy. Also, we use the approximation $n_{\mathbf{k}(+)} = n_{\mathbf{k}(-)} = n_{\mathbf{k}}$ in the spirit of second-order perturbation. Thus the above equation reduces at the absolute zero of temperature to

$$H_{\text{eff}}^{\text{ex}} = -\frac{3}{8} \frac{n_c J_0^2}{N^2 E_F} \sum_{\mathbf{q}} \sum_{\substack{lm \\ l \neq m}} f(q) \exp(i\mathbf{q} \cdot \mathbf{R}_{lm})(\mathbf{S}_l \cdot \mathbf{S}_m) \tag{3.74}$$

where, as before, we have neglected the $\mathbf{q}$ dependence of $J(q)$, i.e. $J(\mathbf{q}) \equiv J_0$. Carrying out the $\mathbf{q}$ integration, i.e. using eqn (3.68), the final result becomes

$$H_{\text{eff}}^{\text{ex}} = \frac{9\pi}{2} \frac{J_0^2}{E_F} \left(\frac{n_e}{N}\right)^2 \sum_{\substack{lm \\ l \neq m}} F(2k_F R_{lm}) \mathbf{S}_l \cdot \mathbf{S}_m. \tag{3.75}$$

This type of exchange coupling is known as the RKKY mechanism (Ruderman and Kittel 1954, Kasuya 1956, and Yosida, 1957). The initial suggestions of the importance of s–d exchange for spin coupling in magnetic metals and alloys were made by Vonsovskii (1946) and Zener (1951). The strength of the coupling falls off as R_{lm}^{-3}, where R_{lm} is the distance between the magnetic atoms. However, the sign is determined by the oscillating function $F(x)$. This is capable of giving either ferromagnetic or antiferromagnetic ordering between the atoms involved depending on their separation. Furthermore, unlike the Heisenberg-type exchange interaction discussed in the previous section, the indirect coupling (cf. eqn (3.75)) has a long-range character.

The RKKY type of indirect coupling in magnetic semiconductors has been studied by several authors. It is found that the coupling strength becomes temperature dependent and decays exponentially with distance for intrinsic semiconductors (see Darby (1969) for a review). The transition from oscillatory behaviour for a metal to an exponential decay for a semiconductor is a smooth function of the degeneracy parameter $E_F/k_B T$, where k_B is the Boltzmann constant and T is the temperature.

Some very interesting evidence for and a consequence of this long-range oscillatory exchange is the occurrence of the spin-glass phase in dilute magnetic alloys such as Cu Mn, with upto 1 at % of a transition metal (Mn) in a noble metal (Cu). Here the Mn atoms bearing localized magnetic moment are randomly dispersed through the host matrix Cu. The conduction electrons of the host metal mediate the indirect RKKY interaction between the local moments. The random siting of the magnetic atoms, however, cause exchange interaction to change sign randomly. The competition of ferro- and antiferromagnetic coupling leads to a mixed ordered state at sufficiently low temperatures where the impurity spins freeze in definite directions that vary randomly from site to site and thus there is no overall magnetization. We shall not, however, pursue this topic any further (for recent developments see Hooper and de Graaf (1973).

If the localized states lie in the conduction band continuum, there will be a resonant mixing of the localized and Bloch states which can be expressed as

$$H_{mix}(s-d) = \sum_{kl\sigma} \exp(i\mathbf{k} \cdot \mathbf{R}_l) V_{sd} C_{k\sigma}{}^+ C_{l\sigma} + \text{h.c.} \qquad (3.76)$$

where V_{sd} is the matrix element which connects the Bloch state ϕ_k and the localized state ϕ_l at site R_l. That this type of mixing can lead to spin–spin coupling has been studied by several authors (Alexander and Anderson 1964, Kim and Nagaoka 1963, Kumar and Sinha 1966). The coupling between localized spins via this mechanism appears in the fourth-order processes involving $H_{mix}(s-d)$, i.e. those which involve eight fermion operators, four for conduction electrons and four for localized states. After summing over the conduction electron states, one obtains the effective interaction between localized spins as

$$H_{eff}{}^{mix} = \frac{9\pi}{2} \left(\frac{n_c}{N}\right)^2 \frac{|V_{sd}|^4}{E_F U^2 S^4} \sum_{l \neq m} F(2k_F R_{lm}) \mathbf{S}_1 \cdot \mathbf{S}_m \qquad (3.77)$$

It can be seen that this expression also has the same spatial dependence as the Ruderman–Kittel function. The similarity between the two, as far as the oscillatory behaviour is concerned, exists only for large distances and does not hold for small R_{lm}. This mechanism is expected to be important only in dilute alloys. The oscillating nature of magnetic ordering has indeed been observed in Heusler alloys (see Kumar and Sinha 1966).

4

EXCHANGE INTERACTIONS IN MAGNETIC INSULATORS

In this chapter we consider the origin and nature of exchange interactions in magnetic compounds which, in contrast to metals and alloys, behave like insulators. In such compounds there are, in addition to the paramagnetic ions, diamagnetic ions which constitute the main matrix of the crystalline lattice. The sites occupied by the paramagnetic ions are characterized by their special co-ordination depending on whether they are tetrahedral, octahedral, cubic, or any other co-ordination of the diamagnetic (usually negative) ions. The diamagnetic matrix plays a very special role. First, it determines the electronic state of the paramagnetic ions, in particular the nature of the valence shell which contains the unpaired electrons (see Chapter 1). Secondly, the diamagnetic ions have an indirect influence in bringing about the eventual coupling between the spins of the paramagnetic ions through one-body covalent admixture or two-body exchange polarization and correlation effects.

In Chapter 1 we summarized some essential features of the state of paramagnetic ions in the presence of ligand fields. The pattern of magnetic ordering in these compounds (e.g. halides and chalcogenides) as revealed by neutron diffraction studies (see Izyumov and Ozerov 1970) indicates that the strongly coupled paramagnetic ions are separated from each other by large intervening diamagnetic anions (0^{2-}, F^-, S^{2-}, etc.). Thus the large magnitude of the interaction in such coupled systems cannot be attributed to the direct exchange interaction. These considerations suggest the importance of indirect exchange mechanisms that involve spin–dependent excited configurations of the intermediate anions or of the unit (cation–anion–cation) as a whole. This type of spin coupling was first considered by Kramers (1934). Following him, several apparently distinct mechanisms have been suggested by many workers. Quite often the emphasis on a particular mechanism depends on the representation which is chosen in the mathematical formulation of the problem. In what follows, we shall try to give a unified treatment wherein the various mechanisms appear naturally instead of being invoked on intuitive grounds. We shall see that, broadly speaking, they fall in the following categories (Sinha 1973).

(a) Direct potential exchange involving the orthogonal orbitals of the paramagnetic ions. This compling is always ferromagnetic.

(b) Kinetic exchange arising from the virtual transfer of electrons between singly occupied orbitals of the paramagnetic ions in conjunction with correlation effects. This coupling is second order and is always anti-ferromagnetic.

(c) Indirect exchange arising through spin polarization of the intervening diamagnetic ions. This coupling can be either antiferromagnetic or ferromagnetic.

(d) Correlation superexchange in which two anion electrons each make virtual transitions to the neighbouring paramagnetic ions. This coupling is always antiferromagnetic. In addition, if there are low-lying excited orbitals, the two electrons, one coming from each paramagnetic ion, can make virtual transitions to the excited states. The coupling induced by this process will be antiferromagnetic if the excited orbital is non-degenerate and ferromagnetic otherwise.

A few words about the nature of the one-electron orbitals in question is in order here. It is generally accepted that the magnetic electrons are fairly localized, apart from some covalent admixture with the orbitals of the diamagnetic ligand atoms. Accordingly, the basis orbitals will be assumed to be localized and orthogonal Hartree–Fock orbitals of the entire crystal. Such orbitals need not necessarily be of the Bloch type (see Gondaira and Tanabe 1966, Stevens 1976). Further, we shall distinguish between the core orbitals and the valence orbitals. The electrons in the former will be assumed to be confined to their respective atoms and will not be considered in the formulation.

The zeroth-order ground-state configuration of the system will be assumed to comprise singly occupied orbitals of the paramagnetic ions and doubly occupied orbitals of the valence shell of the diamagnetic ions (outermost s and p orbitals). In addition, there will be completely empty orbitals belonging to a particular atom or a group of atoms. This description is in keeping with the situation where, in the excited state, it is difficult to label the electronic states as specifying the cation or the anion.

With this description, we set out to formulate the exchange interaction between electrons of the singly occupied orbitals of the different paramagnetic ions.

4.1. Hamiltonian of the system

Let us consider a crystalline solid consisting of paramagnetic and diamagnetic ions. In the first quantization, the Hamiltonian of the system is given by

$$H = f(\mathbf{r}_i) + g(r_{ij}) \tag{4.1}$$

where $f(\mathbf{r}_i)$ is the one-particle operator comprising the kinetic energy $p_i^2/2m$

and the one-body potential energy $V(\mathbf{r}_i)$ due to all the ion cores and $g(r_{ij})$ represents the two-body interelectronic interaction. In the spirit of the discussion about the expected nature of the zeroth-order ground state, we introduce the following notation. The singly occupied orbitals are denoted by ϕ_m, the doubly occupied ones by ϕ_l, and the completely empty ones by ϕ_λ; ϕ_g stands for any one of these orbitals. These orbitals are derived by a variational procedure in which the energy E_0 of the ground-state configuration is minimized, or more explicitly

$$\delta E_0 = 0 \tag{4.2}$$

along with the subsidiary (orthonormalization) condition

$$\langle \phi_g | \phi_{g'} \rangle = \delta_{gg'}. \tag{4.3}$$

In should be noted that the ϕ_g's constitute a complete orthonormal set of one-particle eigenstates of the Hartree–Fock Hamiltonian which is to be determined self-consistently. The energy function for a given set of orbital occupation numbers ($n = 0$, 1, or 2) is given by (see Gondaira and Tanabe 1966)

$$E(n) = \sum_g n_g F_{gg} + \tfrac{1}{2} \sum_{gg'} n_g n_{g'} (K_{gg'} - J_{gg'}) \tag{4.4}$$

where

$$F_{gg} = \langle \phi_g | f(1) | \phi_g \rangle$$
$$K_{gg'} = \langle \phi_g \phi_{g'} | g(12) | \phi_g \phi_{g'} \rangle \tag{4.5}$$
$$J_{gg'} = \langle \phi_g \phi_{g'} | g(12) | \phi_{g'} \phi_g \rangle$$

Now for the ground state, we set $n_m = 1$ for singly occupied states and $n_l = 2$ for doubly occupied states. Thus the zeroth-order ground state will involve a set of singly occupied orbitals ϕ_m and doubly occupied orbitals ϕ_l. The Hartree–Fock equation for doubly occupied orbitals which is derived from eqns (4.2)–(4.4) has the form

$$h_{\text{H–F}} \phi_l = \varepsilon_l \phi_l + \sum_m \phi_m \frac{\lambda_{ml}}{2} \tag{4.6}$$

where λ_{ml} are Lagrange multipliers which ensure that there is orthogonality between the singly and the doubly occupied orbitals. The operator $h_{\text{H–F}}$ is defined by

$$h_{\text{H–F}}(1) = f(1) + \sum_g n_g \{ \langle \phi_g(2) | g(12) | \phi_g(2) \rangle - \tfrac{1}{2} \langle \phi_g(2) | g(12) | P(12) \phi_g(2) \rangle \} \tag{4.7}$$

with the summation taken over orbitals which are occupied in the ground state. The first and second terms in the braces are the usual Coulomb and exchange operators defined by

$$\langle\phi_g(2)|g(12)|\phi_g(2)\rangle\psi(1)=\int d^3r_2\phi_g{}^*(2)g(12)\psi(1)\phi_g(2) \qquad (4.8a)$$

and

$$\langle\phi_g(2)|g(12)|P(12)\phi_g(2)\rangle\psi(1)=\int d^3r_2\phi_g{}^*(2)g(12)\phi_g(1)\psi(2). \qquad (4.8b)$$

Likewise, the Hartree–Fock equation for the singly occupied orbitals has the form

$$\{h_{\mathrm{H-F}}(1)-\tfrac{1}{2}\langle\phi_m(2)|g(12)|\phi_m(2)\rangle\}\phi_m(1)$$

$$=\varepsilon_m\phi_m(1)+\sum_{m'}\phi_m(1)\mu_{m'm}+\sum_l\phi_l(1)\lambda_{ml} \qquad (4.9)$$

where $\mu_{m'm}$ are the Lagrange multipliers and satisfy the relations $\dot{\mu}_{m'm}=\mu_{mm'}$. The Lagrange multipliers can be evaluated with the help of the coupled eqns (4.6) and (4.9) and using the appropriate orthogonality conditions (cf. eqn. (4.3)).

After some algebra, we obtain

$$\lambda_{ml}=-\langle\phi_m\phi_l|g(12)|\phi_m\phi_l\rangle \qquad (4.10)$$

$$\mu_{mm'}=\langle\phi_m|h_{\mathrm{H-F}}|\phi_{m'}\rangle-\tfrac{1}{2}\langle\phi_m\phi_{m'}|g(12)|\phi_m\phi_{m'}\rangle. \qquad (4.11)$$

In order that $\mu_{mm'}=\mu_{m'm}$, the Hartree–Fock orbitals should satisfy the equality

$$\langle\phi_m\phi_{m'}|g(12)|\phi_{m'}\phi_{m'}\rangle=\langle\phi_{m'}\phi_m|g(12)|\phi_m\phi_m\rangle. \qquad (4.12)$$

It should be noted that the above symmetrization of $\mu_{mm'}$ is always possible.

Thus with the help of the foregoing procedure, we obtain a set of singly occupied and doubly occupied Hartree–Fock orbitals which are localized in character. As remarked earlier, there will be a set of completely empty orbitals which has to be included if we want to improve the functions further by perturbation methods. There are additional one-electron spin-independent excitations which do not vanish. These involve transfer effects between singly occupied orbitals; other spin-independent one-electron excitations are forbidden by the Brillouin theorem. The explicit expression for the surviving terms can be written as

$$t_{m'm}=\langle\phi_{m'}|h_{\mathrm{H-F}}|\phi_m\rangle+\tfrac{1}{2}\langle\phi_{m'}\phi_{m'}|g(12)|\phi_{m'}\phi_m\rangle-\tfrac{1}{2}\langle\phi_{m'}\phi_m|g(12)|\phi_m\phi_m\rangle$$

$$=\langle\phi_m|h_{\mathrm{H-F}}|\phi_{m'}\rangle=t_{mm'}. \qquad (4.13)$$

Now that we have formulated a satisfactory picture of the starting orbital functions, we are in a position to write down the complete Hamiltonian inclusive of one-electron and two-electron excitations (perturbation terms). The above orbitals constitute the basis set of orthogonal functions with respect to which the fermion creation and annihilation operators are defined. Thus in the second quantization representation

$$H = H_0 + H_{\text{dir}} + H_{\text{tr}} + H_{\text{pol}} + H_{\text{corr}}. \tag{4.14}$$

Here

$$H_0 = W_0 + \sum_{m\sigma} \varepsilon_m C_{m\sigma}{}^+ C_{m\sigma} + \sum_{l\sigma} \varepsilon_l C_{l\sigma}{}^+ C_{l\sigma}$$

$$+ \sum_{\lambda\sigma} \varepsilon_\lambda C_{\lambda\sigma}{}^+ C_{\lambda\sigma} + \sum_{m\sigma} U C_{m\sigma}{}^+ C_{m\sigma} C_{m,-\sigma}{}^+ C_{m,-\sigma} \tag{4.15}$$

where W_0 is a constant energy term; ε_m, ε_l, and ε_λ represent the one-electron energies of the singly occupied, doubly occupied and empty Hartree–Fock orbitals respectively; $C_g{}^+$ and C_g are the creation and annihilation operators. The last term is the intra-orbital Coulomb repulsion which occurs when two electrons happen to be in the same orbital state with opposite spins. Further,

$$H_{\text{dir}} = \tfrac{1}{2} \sum_{\substack{m_1 m_2 \\ \sigma_1 \sigma_2}} J_{m_1 m_2}{}^{m_2 m_1} C_{m_1 \sigma_1}{}^+ C_{m_2 \sigma_2}{}^+ C_{m_1 \sigma_2} C_{m_2 \sigma_1} \tag{4.16}$$

is the direct exchange interaction involving singly occupied orbitals. This is the usual Heisenberg direct exchange term for orthogonal orbitals which' was discussed in the previous chapter. Next,

$$H_{\text{tr}} = \sum_{m_1, m_2, \sigma} t_{m_1 m_2} C_{m_1 \sigma}{}^+ C_{m_2 \sigma} \tag{4.17}$$

represents the single-electron spin-independent transfer process. Also,

$$H_{\text{pol}} = \sum J_{lm_1}{}^{m_1 \lambda} C_{m_1 \sigma_1}{}^+ C_{\lambda \sigma_2}{}^+ C_{m_1 \sigma_2} C_{l\sigma_1} + \text{h.c.} \tag{4.18}$$

where

$$J_{lm_1}{}^{m_1 \lambda} = \langle \phi_{m_1} \phi_\lambda | g(12) | \phi_l \phi_{m_1} \rangle \tag{4.19}$$

represents the exchange polarization terms and involves one-orbital transition $(l \rightarrow \lambda)$ along with spin exchange. Finally, we have the two-electron excitation terms given by

$$H_{\text{corr}} = \sum G_{l_1 l_2}{}^{m_1 m_2} C_{m_1 \sigma_1}{}^+ C_{m_2 \sigma_2}{}^+ C_{l_2 \sigma_2} C_{l_1 \sigma_1} + \text{h.c.}$$

$$+ \sum G_{m_1 m_2}{}^{\mu_1 \mu_2} C_{\mu_1 \sigma_1}{}^+ C_{\mu_2 \sigma_2}{}^+ C_{m_2 \sigma_2} C_{m_1 \sigma_1} + \text{h.c.} \tag{4.20}$$

where

$$G_{m_1m_2}{}^{g_1g_2} = \langle \phi_{g_1}\phi_{g_2}|g(12)|\phi_{m_1}\phi_{m_2}\rangle \tag{4.21}$$

4.2. Derivation of the effective exchange Hamiltonian

We shall now consider the derivation of the effective exchange Hamiltonian for two unpaired electrons on two different magnetic atoms, say m_1 and m_2, arising from the various terms occurring in eqn (4.14); H_{dir} is already in the exchange Hamiltonian form. On carrying out the summation over the spin indices σ_1 nd σ_2 and noting the relations (3.35), we obtain

$$\sum_{\sigma_1\sigma_2} C_{m_1\sigma_1}{}^+ C_{m_2\sigma_2}{}^+ C_{m_1\sigma_2} C_{m_2\sigma_1} = -\tfrac{1}{2}(1+4\mathbf{s}_{m_1}\cdot\mathbf{s}_{m_2}).$$

Thus eqn (4.16) reduces to

$$H_{dir} = \text{constant} - \sum_{m_1<m_2} 2J_{m_1m_2}{}^{m_2m_1}\mathbf{s}_{m_1}\cdot\mathbf{s}_{m_2}. \tag{4.22}$$

The other terms in eqn (4.14), namely $H_{tr}+H_{pol}+J_{corr}$, bring about an effective spin coupling in the second order. This can be achieved by a straightforward perturbation treatment. Alternatively, one can eliminate these terms in the first order by means of a canonical transformation.

The transformed Hamiltonian is given by

$$H_T = e^{-iS}He^{iS} = H + i[H, S] + \frac{i^2}{2}\Big[[H, S], S\Big] + \dots. \tag{4.23}$$

In the present case, the generator S is determined from the condition

$$H_{tr}+H_{pol}+H_{corr}+i[H_0, S]=0 \tag{4.24}$$

and the effective intereaction is derived from

$$H_{eff}{}^{ex} = \frac{i}{2}[H_{tr}+H_{pol}+H_{corr}, S]. \tag{4.25}$$

The above will comprise several terms. Some correspond to effective exchange coupling while the rest give scattering terms. Their contribution to exchange will arise in still higher order perturbations. We shall select only those exchange terms which appear in the lowest order, i.e. the second order. These are enumerated below.

Excitations involving single-electron transfer between singly occupied orbitals give

$$H_{eff}{}^{ex}(tr) = -\sum_{\substack{m_1m_2\\\sigma}} \frac{|t_{m_1m_2}|^2}{\Delta E(m_1\to m_2)} C_{m_1\sigma}{}^+ C_{m_2,-\sigma}{}^+ C_{m_1,-\sigma} C_{m_2\sigma} \tag{4.26}$$

which on carrying out spin summation and noting the relation given by eqn (3.35) becomes

$$H_{\text{eff}}^{\text{ex}}(tr) = -\sum_{m_1 m_2} \frac{|t_{m_1 m_2}|^2}{U} \frac{1}{2}(1 - 4s_{m_1} \cdot s_{m_2})$$

$$= \text{constant} - \sum_{m_1 m_2} 2\left(-\frac{|t_{m_1 m_2}|^2}{U}\right) s_{m_1} \cdot s_{m_2}.$$

(4.27)

From the form of the spin operators, it can be seen that this will always stabilize the singlet (antiferromagnetic) state relative to the triplet state. Here $\Delta E(m_1 \rightarrow m_2)$ is the energy involved in the transfer of an electron from the orbital ϕ_{m_1} to the orbital ϕ_{m_2}. In the present case it is nearly equal to U, the Coulomb repulsion energy when two electrons (with antiparallel spins) occupy the same orbital. Such interaction terms for magnetic compounds were first formulated elegantly by Anderson (1959) (see also Kondo 1957).

The spin-polarization contribution involves a virtual excitation of an electron from a singly occupied orbital (say ϕ_{m_1}) to an empty orbital (ϕ_λ) along with the excitation of an electron from the doubly occupied orbital (say ϕ_l) (cf. eqn (4.18)) to ϕ_{m_1}. The effective interaction turns out to be

$$H_{\text{eff}}^{\text{ex}}(\text{pol}) = \sum_{\substack{l, \lambda m_1 m_2 \\ \sigma_1 \sigma_2}} \frac{J_{l m_1}{}^{m_1 \lambda}(J_{l m_2}{}^{m_2 \lambda})^*}{\Delta E(l \rightarrow \lambda)} C_{m_1 \sigma_1}{}^+ C_{m_2 \sigma_2}{}^+ C_{m_1 \sigma_2} C_{m_2 \sigma_1}$$

which on spin summation becomes

$$= -\sum_{\substack{m_1 m_2 \\ l \lambda}} \frac{J_{l m_1}{}^{m_1 \lambda}(J_{l m_2}{}^{m_2 \lambda})^*}{\Delta E(l \rightarrow \lambda)} \frac{1}{2}(1 + 4s_{m_1} \cdot s_{m_2})$$

$$= \text{constant} - 2 \sum_{m_1 m_2} J_{\text{eff}}(\text{pol}) s_{m_1} \cdot s_{m_2}.$$

(4.28)

Here $\Delta E(l \rightarrow \lambda) \approx (E_\lambda - E_l)$, i.e. the energy difference corresponding to the orbitals ϕ_λ and ϕ_l; $\Delta E(l \rightarrow \lambda)$ is positive here. However, the sign of $J_{\text{eff}}(\text{pol})$ is determined by the product of hybrid integrals $J_{l m_1}{}^{m_1 \lambda}$ and $(J_{l m_2}{}^{\lambda m_2})^*$. It is not possible to predict the sign without making a careful analysis of the relative symmetry of the orbital involved. For example, for collinear systems, such as metal–ligand–metal (M_1–L–M_2), the symmetry of the orbitals can be defined with respect to reflection in a plane which is the perpendicular bisector of the molecular axis. Let R be the reflection operator, and

$$R\phi_l = \pm \phi_l \binom{\text{even}}{\text{odd}}$$

and

$$R\phi_\lambda = \pm\phi_\lambda\binom{\text{even}}{\text{odd}}.$$

Then a careful examination shows that transitions between orbitals ϕ_l and ϕ_λ having the same symmetry stabilizes the triplet (ferromagnetic) state. On the other hand, if they have opposite symmetry the spin-polarization mechanism will stabilize the singlet (antiferromagnetic) state. It is necessary, therefore, to make a detailed analysis of the symmetry, spatial disposition, and relative energies of the orbitals involved. It may be noted that the spin-polarization mechanism is analogous to the RKKY mechanism of exchange coupling in dilute alloys and rare-earth metals discussed in the previous chapter. In magnetic insulators the electrons of the intervening diamagnetic ligand ions (e.g. O^{2-}, S^{2-}, etc.) play the same role as the conduction electrons in metals. The empty states ϕ_λ correspond to the states above the Fermi level in metals. The exchange polarization mechanism was first discussed qualitatively by Slater (1953). Mathematical formulations were given independently by Koide, Sinha and Tanabe (1959) (see also Sinha 1961) and Anderson (1959) (for application to some specific systems, see Halpern (1966)).

Finally, there are contributions which arise from two-electron excitation (cf. eqn (4.20)). The effective interation turns out to be

$$H_{\text{eff}}^{\text{ex}}(\text{corr}) = \left\{ -\sum \frac{G_{m_1 m_2}{}^{ll} G_{ll}{}^{m_1 m_2}}{\Delta E(m_1 m_2 \leftarrow ll)} - \sum \frac{G_{m_1 m_2}{}^{\mu\mu} G_{\mu\mu}{}^{m_1 m_2}}{\Delta E(\mu\mu \leftarrow m_1 m_2)} \right\}$$

$$\times C_{m_{1\sigma}}{}^+ C_{m_{2,-\sigma}}{}^+ C_{m_{1,-\sigma}} C_{m_{2\sigma}}$$

(4.29)

which on spin summation via eqn (3.35) gives

$$H_{\text{eff}}^{\text{ex}}(\text{corr}) = \text{constant} - 2\sum_{m_1 m_2} \left\{ -\sum_l \frac{|G_{ll}{}^{m_1 m_2}|^2}{\Delta E(m_1 m_2 \leftarrow ll)} \right.$$

$$\left. -\sum_\mu \frac{|G_{m_1 m_2}{}^{\mu\mu}|^2}{\Delta E(\mu\mu \leftarrow m_1 m_2)} \right\} \times \mathbf{s}_{m_1} \cdot \mathbf{s}_{m_2}.$$

(4.30)

This mechanism also stabilizes the antiferromagnetic state. The first term of eqn (4.30) represents the process in which two electrons from the doubly filled orbital (say ϕ_l) make a virtual transition to the adjoining singly occupied orbitals, one each to ϕ_{m_1} and ϕ_{m_2} (see Nesbet 1958). The second term denotes two-electron virtual transitions, one each from ϕ_{m_1} and ϕ_{m_2}, to a non-degenerate empty orbital ϕ_μ (Sinha 1961).

Taking all the processes noted above, the effective exchange Hamiltonian can be written as

$$H_{\text{eff}}^{\text{ex}}(\text{total}) = -2\sum_{m_1 < m_2} J_{m_1 m_2}(\text{total})(\mathbf{s}_{m_1} \cdot \mathbf{s}_{m_2}) \qquad (4.31)$$

where $J_{m_1 m_2}(\text{total})$ is the algebraic sum of the coefficients occurring in eqns (4.22), (4.27), (4.28), and (4.30). The overall sign of $J_{m_1 m_2}(\text{total})$ will depend on the magnitudes of the contributions coming from various sources, e.g. $J(\text{dir})$, $J(\text{tr})$, $J(\text{pol})$, and $J(\text{corr})$. In the next section we consider some quantitative calculations for these terms for some physical systems.

4.3. Applications to the 'three-centre and four-electron' problem

So far we have presented a formal treatment of the exchange mechanisms which are thought to be important in magnetic insulators. It is not possible to give a detailed calculation for the entire crystal. At best, one can exemplify the mechanism for some simple typical units of the crystal which represent the physical situation. The most commonly discussed unit is the 'three-centre and four-electron system'.

This system is represented by M_1–X–M_2, where the M's represent the paramagnetic metal ions and X the diamagnetic ligand ion. Such magnetically correlated collinear units occur in rocksalt- and perovskite-type magnetic compounds (e.g. MnO, NiO, LaFeO$_3$ CaMnO$_3$, KNiF$_3$, etc.).

In the examples noted above the paramagnetic ions (e.g. Ni^{2+} etc.) have the configuration of the argon shell plus $d\varepsilon^n d\gamma^m$ with $n+m$ less than 10; in particular $d\varepsilon^6 d\gamma^2$ for Ni^{2+}. These are surrounded octahedrally by six ligand ions X (e.g. F$^-$, O^{2-}). The ligand ions have the configuration $1s^2 2s^2 2p^6$. We choose the central ion of the unit to be the ligand ion with two metal ions on each side as shown in Fig. 4.1. Further, we have chosen those atomic orbitals which exhibit maximum overlap, i.e. the $p_z(\equiv p_\sigma)$ orbital of the anion and the $d_{2z^2-x^2-y^2}(\equiv d_\sigma)$ of the paramagnetic ions. Here the Z axis is along the molecular axis. The phases of the orbitals are chosen such that $S_1 = -S_2$, where $S_1 = \langle d\sigma_1/p_\sigma\rangle$ and $S_2 = \langle d\sigma_2/p_\sigma\rangle$. To start with, there are

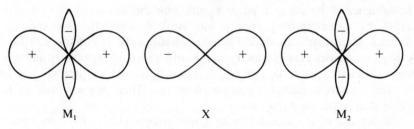

M_1 X M_2

FIG. 4.1. Angular disposition of orbtials of a typical metal–ligand–metal (M_1–X–M_2) unit.

two electrons in p and one each in the d_1 and d_2 orbitals. In order to include the covalency effects, we start with bonding and antibonding orbitals. The appropriate orbitals for the present three-centre unit are chosen with respect to the symmetry plane intersecting the molecular axis normally at the centre. The orbitals are

$$p = \frac{p_\sigma + \gamma(d\sigma_1 - d\sigma_2)}{(1 + 2\gamma S_1 - 2\gamma S_2 + 2\gamma^2)^{1/2}} \tag{4.32}$$

$$\phi_1 = \frac{d\sigma_1 - (\gamma + S_1)p_\sigma}{(1 + \gamma^2 - S_1{}^2)^{1/2}} \tag{4.33}$$

$$\phi_2 = \frac{d\sigma_2 + (\gamma - S_2)p_\sigma}{(1 + \gamma^2 - S_2{}^2)^{1/2}} \tag{4.34}$$

where γ is the covalency parameter (see Chapters 1 and 2). We note that under the reflection R in the symmetry plane $d\sigma_1 \xleftarrow{R} d\sigma_2$, $p_\sigma \xrightarrow{R} -p_\sigma$. Hence p is an odd function and $\phi_1 \xleftrightarrow{R} \phi_2$. Furthermore, ϕ_1 and ϕ_2 are nearly orthogonal to p (i.e. on neglecting third-order terms in S and γ), and they are nearly orthogonal to each other as

$$\langle \phi_1 | \phi_2 \rangle \infty \langle d\sigma_1 | d\sigma_2 \rangle + S_1{}^2 - \gamma^2 \tag{4.35}$$

where $S_1{}^2$ and γ^2 are comparable and almost cancel each other and $\langle d\sigma_1 | d\sigma_2 \rangle$ is negligible.

The wavefunction given by eqns (4.32) and (4.34) contains the appropriate admixture of the metal-ion and the ligand orbitals, and therefore, as far as the occupied orbitals are concerned, electron transfer effects are included. Within the manifold of orbital states p, ϕ_1 and ϕ_2, it is not possible to realize the polarization of anion electrons in the presence of the paramagnetic ions. It is expected that the charge density of the two anion electrons will be modified in such a way that they interact differently with the two magnetic ions (exchange and correlation polarization effects). The modification of the p orbital function due to the above interactions under the influence of the adjacent paramagnetic ions can be described, to a large extent, by superimposing appropriate available orbitals. Two types of available excited orbitals should be considered for the symmetric unit M_1–X–M_2, i.e. one with even symmetry and the other with odd symmetry under R. We shall denote them by ϕ_{ev} and ϕ_{odd}. It should be noted that there will be a set of such orbitals in increasing order of energy. These are assumed to be orthogonal to the set ϕ_1, ϕ_2, and p.

Making use of the wavefunctions given in eqns (4.32)–(4.34), we obtain the transfer integral

$$t_{m_1 m_2} = \langle \phi_1 | V | \phi_2 \rangle$$
$$= \{ \langle d\sigma_1 | V | d\sigma_2 \rangle + 2(\gamma + S_1) \langle d\sigma_1 | V | p_\sigma \rangle$$
$$+ (\gamma + S_1)^2 \langle p_\sigma | V | p_\sigma \rangle \}(1 + \gamma^2 - S_1^2)^{-1}. \qquad (4.36)$$

Owing to the fact that the direct transfer term $\langle d\sigma_1 | V | d\sigma_2 \rangle$ is of the order of $-S^2(E_d - E_p)$ and the last two terms give $(\gamma + S)^2(E_d - E_p)$, the above can be approximately written as (see Anderson 1963)

$$t_{m_1 m_2} \approx \{ (\gamma + S_1)^2 - S_1^2 \}(E_d - E_p) \qquad (4.37)$$

where $E_d - E_p$ is the energy difference between d and p orbitals. Thus the contribution to the exchange integral due to the kinetic transfer process becomes

$$\frac{2|t_{m_1 m_2}|^2}{U} \approx \frac{2\{(\gamma + S_1)^2 - S_1^2\}^2 (E_d - E_p)^2}{U}. \qquad (4.38)$$

For magnetic systems which involve two Ni^{2+} ions separated by an F^- ion, both experimental and theoretical estimates (Owen and Thornley 1966) show that $\gamma \sim 0.12$ and $S_1 \sim 0.07$; also $U = 10$ eV. Further, taking $E_d - E_p \sim 8$ eV, we obtain

$$\frac{2|t_{m_1 m_2}|^2}{U} \sim 1.5 \times 10^{-2} \text{ eV}$$

$$\sim 140 \text{ K in temperature units.}$$

The direct exchange integral involving ϕ_1 and ϕ_2 turns out to be

$$\langle \phi_1(1)\phi_2(2) \left| \frac{e^2}{r_{12}} \right| \phi_2(1)\phi_1(2) \rangle$$

$$\approx 2(\gamma + S_1)^2 \langle d\sigma_1(1) p_\sigma(2) \left| \frac{e^2}{r_{12}} \right| p_\sigma(1) d\sigma_1(2) \rangle \qquad (4.39)$$

$$\approx 2(\gamma + S_1)^2 J_{d\sigma p_\sigma}$$

where we have included only the dominant terms. The estimate of $J_{d\sigma p_\sigma}$ shows that it is of the order of 0.2 eV. Thus the direct exchange term is about 1.44×10^{-2} eV, i.e. 170 K which is of the same order of magnitude as the kinetic exchange term but of opposite sign. This kind of cancellation of the two effects was also noted by Anderson (1964).

Next, we consider the correlation exchange interaction as discussed by Nesbet (1958) (cf. eqn (4.30)). The relevant two-electron excitation integral within the manifold of states given by eqns (4.32)–(4.34) is

$$G_{ll}{}^{m_1 m_2} \equiv \langle \phi_1(1)\phi_2(2) \left| \frac{e^2}{r_{12}} \right| p(1)p(2) \rangle$$

$$\cong \langle d\sigma_1(1)d\sigma_2(2) \left| \frac{e^2}{r_{12}} \right| p_\sigma(1)p_\sigma(2) \rangle$$

$$+ 2\lambda\gamma \{ \langle d\sigma_1(1)p_\sigma(2) \left| \frac{e^2}{r_{12}} \right| p_\sigma(1)d\sigma_1(2) \rangle$$

$$+ \langle d\sigma_1(1)p_\sigma(2) \left| \frac{e^2}{r_{12}} \right| d\sigma_1(1)p_\sigma(2) \rangle \}$$

$$- \gamma^2 \langle d\sigma_1(1)d\sigma_2(2) \left| \frac{e^2}{r_{12}} \right| d\sigma_1(1)d\sigma_2(2) \rangle$$

$$- \lambda^2 \langle p_\sigma(1)p_\sigma(2) \left| \frac{e^2}{r_{12}} \right| p_\sigma(1)p_\sigma(2) \rangle$$

(4.40)

with $\lambda = \gamma + S$. The integrals involved in these calculations have been computed by Rimmer (1969) for $KNiF_3$. Making use of these values, we obtain $G_{ll}{}^{m_1 m_2} \sim 0.46$ eV.

Now the energy denominator involved in the two-electron excitation process has been estimated to be 23 eV (Anderson 1959). Hence we obtain

$$\frac{|G_{ll}{}^{m_1 m_2}|^2}{\Delta E} = 9.2 \times 10^{-3} \text{eV}$$

$$\sim 110 \text{ K}.$$

The contribution from the second term of eqn (4.30) is rather small:

$$\frac{|G_{ll}{}^{m_1 m_2}|^2}{\Delta E} = 9.25 \times 10^{-3} \text{eV}$$

$$\sim 1.5 \text{ K}.$$

Let us now consider the exchange polarization term (cf. eqn (4.29)). As remarked earlier, the relative symmetry of the orbitals involved is important. We shall illustrate the calculation by choosing some typical empty orbitals.

The excited orbitals belonging to the central ion, i.e. $F^{-\delta}$ in the present case, are far removed from the ground state and can be ignored. The 4s and 4p orbitals of the metal ions are a few electronvolts higher than the 3d orbitals. For convenience, we choose the 4s type orbitals. The appropriate combinations involving these empty orbitals are (denoting 4s by the symbol

χ) (Koide *et al.* 1959, see also Sinha 1961)

$$\phi_{ev} = \frac{\chi_1 + \chi_2}{\sqrt{2}}$$

$$\phi_{odd} = \frac{\chi_1 - \chi_2 - 2S_0 p}{\{2(1 - 2S_0)^2\}^{1/2}}$$

where $S_0 = \langle \chi_1 | p \rangle = -\langle \chi_2 | p \rangle$. The relevant exchange integrals are $J_{p\phi}{}^{\phi_1 \phi_{ev}}$ and $J_{p\phi_1}{}^{\phi_1 \phi_{odd}}$ or, more explicitly.

$$J_{p\phi_1}{}^{\phi_1 \phi_{ev}} \approx \frac{\gamma + S}{\sqrt{2}} \langle d\sigma_1(1)\chi_1(2) \left| \frac{e^2}{r_{12}} \right| d\sigma_1(1)d\sigma_2(2) \rangle$$

$$\approx \frac{0.19}{2} \times 0.07 \approx \frac{0.0133}{\sqrt{2}} \text{ a.u.}$$

(1 a.u. = 27·2 eV). Similarly,

$$J_{p\phi_1}{}^{\phi_1 \phi}{}_{odd} \approx \frac{(\gamma + S)}{\sqrt{2}} \langle d\sigma_1(1)\chi_1(2) \left| \frac{e^2}{r_{12}} \right| d\sigma_1(1)d\sigma_1(2) \rangle$$

$$- \frac{2S_0}{\sqrt{2}} \langle d\sigma_1(1)p_\sigma(2) \left| \frac{e^2}{r_{12}} \right| p_\sigma(1)d\sigma_1(2) \rangle.$$

Estimates show that $S_0 \sim 0.3$ and $\langle d\sigma_1(1)p_\sigma(2)e^2/r_{12}p_\sigma(1)d\sigma_1(2) \rangle \sim 0.007$ a.u.

Thus

$$J_{p\phi_1}{}^{\phi_1 \phi_{odd}} \sim \frac{0.009}{\sqrt{2}} \text{ a.u.}$$

If we assume that the excited even and odd orbitals have about the same energy, the corresponding denominator for this process is of the order of 10 eV. The contribution from the exchange polarization term is

$$\frac{1}{\Delta E(pol)} \left(|J_{p\phi_1}{}^{\phi_1 \phi_{ev}}|^2 - |J_{p\phi_1}{}^{\phi_1 \phi_{odd}}|^2 \right)$$

$$\sim 3.6 \times 10^{-3} \text{ eV}$$

$$\sim 43 \text{ K}.$$

Thus, in the present case, it favours antiferromagnetic coupling but is weaker than the other processes. Although we have illustrated the calculation for the spin-polarization mechanism making use of a limited set of excited orbitals, a realistic computation must include a complete set. This is not practicable at the moment in view of the lack of knowledge of the wavefunctions (particularly the empty ones).

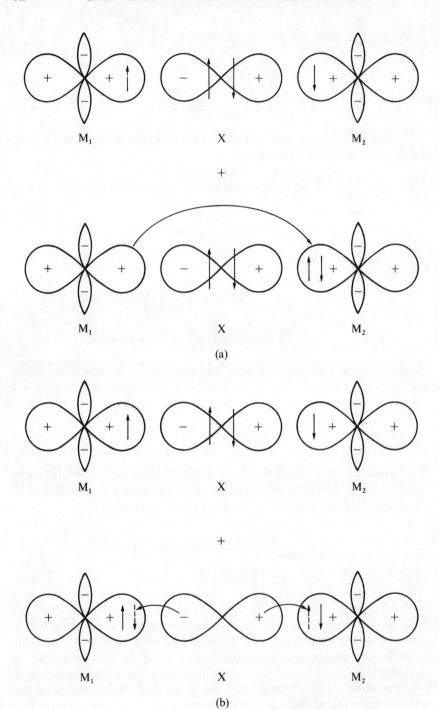

(a)

(b)

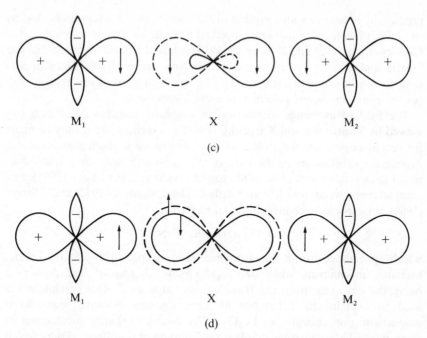

FIG. 4.2. Schematic representation of (a) the kinetic exchange interaction involving one-electron transfer, (b) the correlation exchange interaction involving two-electron transfer, (c) the polarization exchange involving angular polarization of the ligand electrons, and (d) the polarization exchange involving 'in–out' polarization of the ligand electrons.

Including the computed values for the various mechanisms noted above, we can write down the total effective exchange integral for the unit under consideration as

$$J_{12}(\text{total}) = (J_{(\text{dir})} + J_{(\text{kin})} + J_{(\text{pol})} + J_{(\text{corr})})$$

$$\approx (170\ \text{K} - 140\ \text{K} - 43\ \text{K} - 110\ \text{K})$$

$$\approx -123\ \text{K}.$$

Thus the exchange constant $J_{12}(\text{total})$ is negative and favours antiferromagnetic coupling. The experimental value for $KNiF_3$ is -45 K (Anderson 1963). In view of the order-of-magnitude estimate the agreement seems reasonable. The main point to note is that we know the principal causes of the exchange interaction in magnetic solids. A precise calculation depends, of course, on the knowledge of the wavefunctions and covalency parameters in various solids.

To sum up, any theoretical computation of the effective exchange interaction must take account of the four important processes illustrated above (also see Fig. 4.2). At present, there does not seem to be a clear-cut rule to predict the nature of spin coupling in various magnetic compounds. Anderson (1963) has listed a few semiempirical rules in his review article (e.g. the Goodenough (1963) and Kanamori (1959) rules). It should be noted that the kinetic and correlation exchange mechanisms are probably more important in transition-metal compounds. The spin-polarization mechanism may play a more significant role in rare-earth compounds.

The field of exchange interaction in magnetic insulators has been reviewed by Vonsovskii and Karpenko (1968) to which reference may be made for recent papers on the subject. For a discussion of exchange involving degenerate orbitals, as in the case of the rare-earth and some transition-metal ions, reference may be made to the review article of Levy (1975). For completeness, we should like to mention Dzialoshinskii (1958) and Moriya (1960) anisotropic–exchange–interaction terms

$$\mathbf{D} \cdot (\mathbf{S}_1 \times \mathbf{S}_2) + \mathbf{S}_1 \cdot \mathbf{\Gamma} \cdot \mathbf{S}_2$$

which appear because of the combined effect of spin–orbit and the kinetic exchange mechanism, where $D \sim J_{kin}(\Delta g/g)$, $\Gamma \sim J_{kin}(\Delta g/g)^2$, and $\Delta g = g - 2$ being the deviation from the free electron value $g = 2$. This mechanism is used to explain the behaviour of some systems showing 'weak ferrimagnetism' (for example $\alpha - Fe_2O_3$). The double exchange mechanism in some mixed-valence oxides involves the hopping of quasifree carriers which is possible only between pairs of ions having parallel spins and leads to ferromagnetism (see Anderson 1963).

5

SPIN WAVES IN MAGNETICALLY ORDERED INSULATORS

In the previous chapters we have discussed the various mechanisms of exchange interactions in magnetic solids. The effective exchange interaction may have a positive or a negative sign depending on the relative strengths of the various competing processes. This eventually determines the type of magnetic ordering in the solid. Thus, at the absolute zero of temperature, we can picture the spins of the paramagnetic ions aligned (apart from the possible zero-point fluctuations) in a definite pattern (ferromagnetic, ferrimagnetic or antiferromagnetic). This state is considered to be the magnetic ground state of the solid.

We shall now consider the nature of the elementary excitations over this ground state at a non-zero temperature or with the application of a small perturbation on the system. Any local deviation from perfect alignment of the spin system will not in general remain confined in the region, but, owing to exchange coupling, will propagate like a wave. These low-lying excitations are called spin waves and were first introduced by Bloch (1930). The spin wave can be thought of as one spin reversal spread coherently over the entire crystal. When spin waves are quantized, we refer to the state of excitation in terms of a certain number of magnons in the particular mode. They behave like field quanta and obey Bose statistics. It should be noted that the concept of magnons as non-interacting quasiparticles is valid in very-low temperature regions, i.e. far below the characteristic temperature beyond which long-range magnetic order breaks down. At elevated temperatures certain kinematic and dynamic interactions have to be considered.

5.1. Spin waves in ferromagnets

Let us consider a simple ferromagnet which can be described by the exchange Hamiltonian for an arbitrary spin S as

$$H_F = \text{constant} - \sum_{l<m} 2J(R_{lm})\mathbf{S}_l \cdot \mathbf{S}_m - g\mu_B B \times \sum_l S_l^Z$$
$$+ \sum_{l,m} D_{lm}\left[\mathbf{S}_l \cdot \mathbf{S}_m - \frac{3(\mathbf{S}_l \cdot \mathbf{R}_{lm})(\mathbf{S}_m \cdot \mathbf{R}_{lm})}{R_{lm}^2}\right] + H_{an}$$

(5.1)

where the first term is the isotropic exchange Hamiltonian and for a ferromagnetic ordering $J(R_{lm})$ is positive. The second term is the Zeeman energy of the spin system in the external magnetic field **B** which is directed along the z direction. The third term is the Hamiltonian for the magnetic dipole–dipole interaction. For the classical magnetic interaction

$$D_{lm} = g^2 \mu_B^2 / R_{lm}^3 \tag{5.2}$$

where μ_B is the Bohr magneton and g is the spectroscopic splitting factor. It should be noted that D_{lm} will have a complicated form for pseudo-dipolar coupling or anisotropic exchange interaction (Van Vleck 1937); H_{an} is the anisotropic energy term. The presence of the dipolar term complicates matters considerably. It is found that neither $\Sigma_l S_l^z$ nor $(\Sigma_l S_l)^2$ commutes with the second part of the dipolar interaction term. Hence these are no longer constants of motion.

The spin-deviation formulation in the second-quantized representation was first given by Holstein and Primakoff (HP) (1940). They noted the similarity between spin-lowering (S_l^-) and spin-raising (S_l^+) operators and the creation and annihilation operators for a harmonic oscillator. It is well known that the energy levels of a spin in an effective magnetic field constitute an equally spaced sequence. This is reminiscent of the sequence of the energy levels of a harmonic oscillator. The only difference is that, whereas in the case of harmonic oscillators the sequence is infinite, here it has to be truncated at the multiplicity value $2S + 1$ for a spin S (kinematic constraint). This can be reconciled by the following artifice. Although we are dealing with matrices of infinite dimensions, all matrix elements corresponding to spin deviations larger than $2S$ can be taken to be zero. In effect we are projecting out the physical subspace of dimensions of the spin multiplicity $2S + 1$.

Now the operator S_l^- (S_l^+) create (destroy) spin deviations on a specific site. Furthermore, the product of operators such as $S_l^+ S_m^-$ exchange spin deviations between two sites. HP introduced the spin deviation number operator by the definition

$$n_l = a_l^+ a_l = S - S_l^z. \tag{5.3}$$

In terms of these deviations the well-known relations involving the algebra of angular momentum operators, namely

$$S_l^\pm |S, S_l^z\rangle = \{S(S+1) - S_l^z(S_l^z \pm 1)\}^{1/2} |S, S_l^z \pm 1\rangle \tag{5.4}$$

can be written as

$$S_l^+ |n_l\rangle = (2S)^{1/2} \left\{ 1 - \frac{n_1 - 1}{2S} \right\}^{1/2} \sqrt{n_l} |n_l - 1\rangle \tag{5.5}$$

and

$$S_l^- |n_l\rangle = (2S)^{1/2} \sqrt{(n_l + 1)} \left(1 - \frac{n_1}{2S} \right)^{1/2} |n_l + 1\rangle. \tag{5.6}$$

This suggests the relationship between S_l^+, S_l^-, and a_l, a_l^+, namely

$$S_l^- = (2S)^{1/2} a_l^+ \left(1 - \frac{a_l^+ a_l}{2S}\right)^{1/2} \qquad (5.7)$$

$$S_l^+ = (2S)^{1/2} \left(1 - \frac{a_l^+ a_l}{2S}\right)^{1/2} a_l \qquad (5.8)$$

where a_l^+ and a_l can be interpreted as spin-deviation creation and anni-hilation operators obeying Bose commutation relations (cf. eqn (5.12)). A few words about the HP radical, i.e.

$$T_l(S) \equiv \left(1 - \frac{a_l^+ a_l}{2S}\right)^{1/2} \qquad (5.9)$$

will be in order. For any given value of S (integral or half-integral), it is always possible to construct a polynomial of order $2S$ which will have the same structure as the HP radical in the physical domain, i.e. $0 \leq a^+ a \leq 2S$. Outside this physical domain, of course, the correspondence is lost. For large values of S, however, it is not easy to construct the above polynomial. On the other hand, for small values of $n_l/2S$ the Taylor expansion, namely

$$T_l(S) = 1 - \frac{1}{2}\left(\frac{n_l}{2S}\right) + \frac{1}{8}\left(\frac{n_l}{2S}\right)^2 + \dots \qquad (5.10)$$

$$\approx 1$$

becomes asymptotically exact for $n_l/2S \to 0$. Accordingly, for small fractional spin deviation $(n_l/2S) \ll 1$, we can truncate the above expansion at an appropriate stage. This is evidently valid in the low-temperature region. On substituting the relations (5.7) and (5.8) into the commutation relation

$$S_l^+ S_m^- - S_l^- S_m^+ = 2S_l^z \delta_{lm} \qquad (5.11)$$

we obtain

$$a\, a_m^+ - a_m^+ a_l \equiv [a_l, a_m^+] = \delta_{lm} \qquad (5.12)$$

all other commutators being zero.

The commutation relations given by eqn (5.12) are reminiscent of bosons. The complete Hamiltonian (cf. eqn (5.1)) can now be written in a diagonal form in spin-wave variables after a series of canonical transformations. It will be illuminating, however, to determine first the nature of the elementary spectrum for a truncated Hamiltonian, i.e. a Hamiltonian containing only the isotropic exchange and Zeeman terms. Thus we take

$$H_F(\text{tr}) = \text{constant} - 2 \sum_{l<m} J(R_{lm})\{S_l^Z S_m^Z + \tfrac{1}{2}(S_l^+ S_m^- + S_l^- S_m^+)\} \qquad (5.13)$$

$$- g\mu_B B \sum_l S_l^Z$$

On making use of the relations (5.7) and (5.8), we obtain, in the site representation,

$$H_F(\text{tr}) = \text{constant} - 2 \sum_{l<m} J(R_{lm})[2Sa_l^+ T_l T_m a_m - Sa_l^+ a_l \qquad (5.14)$$

$$- Sa_m^+ a_m + a_l^+ a_l a_m^+ a_m] + g\mu_B B \sum_l a_l^+ a_l.$$

As we shall confine ourselves to very-low-temperature regions, we take $n_l/4S \ll 1$ and hence we can take $T \approx 1$ in eqn (5.14). Also, we neglect terms other than those that are bilinear in the spin-deviation creation and annihilation operators. In order to diagonalize the remaining terms in eqn (5.14), we perform the following spin-wave transformations

$$a_1 = \frac{1}{\sqrt{N}} \sum_\lambda \exp(-i\lambda \cdot \mathbf{R}_l) a_\lambda \qquad (5.15)$$

$$a_l^+ = \frac{1}{\sqrt{N}} \sum_\lambda \exp(i\lambda \cdot \mathbf{R}_l) a_\lambda^+ \qquad (5.16)$$

and the inverse transformations

$$a_\lambda = \frac{1}{\sqrt{N}} \sum_l \exp(i\lambda \cdot \mathbf{R}_l) a_l \qquad (5.17)$$

$$a_\lambda^+ = \frac{1}{\sqrt{N}} \sum_l \exp(-i\lambda \cdot \mathbf{R}_l) a_l^+ \qquad (5.18)$$

where λ is identified as a propagation vector. The possible values of λ are obtained by imposing the usual periodic boundary conditions. Thus, we have the lattice summation

$$\sum_l \exp(i\lambda \cdot \mathbf{R}_l) = N\delta(\lambda) \qquad (5.19)$$

where

$$\delta(\lambda) = 0 \qquad \text{for } \lambda \neq \mathbf{K}$$

$$= 1 \qquad \text{for } \lambda = \mathbf{K}$$

Here $\mathbf{K}$ is a reciprocal lattice vector. We shall, however, restrict ourselves to the condition $\mathbf{K}=0$ and adopt the reduced zone scheme so that the vector λ is confined to the first Brillouin zone. Substituting the relations (5.15) and (5.16) into eqns (5.12) and noting (5.19), we obtain the commutation relations

$$[a_\lambda, a_{\lambda'}{}^+]=\delta_{\lambda\lambda'}$$
$$[a_\lambda, a_{\lambda'}]=[a_\lambda{}^+, a_{\lambda'}{}^+]=0. \tag{5.20}$$

In terms of these spin-wave operators, the Hamiltonian given in eqn (5.14) becomes

$$H_F(\text{tr})=\text{constant}+\sum_\lambda \hbar\omega_\lambda(a_\lambda{}^+ a_\lambda +\tfrac{1}{2})$$
$$=\text{constant}+\sum_\lambda \hbar\omega_\lambda(n_\lambda +\tfrac{1}{2}) \tag{5.21}$$

where

$$\hbar\omega_\lambda=2JS\ Z(1-\gamma_\lambda)+g\mu_B B \tag{5.22}$$

with

$$\gamma_\lambda=\frac{1}{Z}\sum_h \exp(\mathrm{i}\ \lambda\cdot\mathbf{R}_h) \tag{5.23}$$

where $\mathbf{R}_h$ is the position vector of the nearest-neighbour paramagnetic atom and Z is the co-ordination number. This Hamiltonian has the well-known harmonic oscillator form. Here $a_\lambda{}^+ a_\lambda$ is the number operator n_λ, $a_\lambda{}^+$ creates a spin-wave quantum and a_λ annihilates a spin-wave quantum. These quanta are referred to as magnons. As can be seen from eqn (5.20), magnons obey Bose statistics. The dispersion relation, i.e. the dependence of the magnon frequency ω_λ on λ takes a simple form in the long-wavelength limit $\lambda\cdot\mathbf{P}_h\ll 1$. Thus eqn (5.22) becomes

$$\hbar\omega_\lambda=JS\sum_h \lambda^2 R_h{}^2\ \cos^2\ \theta_{\lambda,h}+g\mu_B B \tag{5.24}$$

where $\theta_{\lambda,h}$ is the angle between the vectors λ and $\mathbf{R}_h$. The mean value of $\cos^2\theta_{\lambda,h}$ is $\tfrac{1}{3}$ and the mean value of $ZR_h{}^2$ is $6a^2$ for cubic systems, where a is the lattice constant. Accordingly, we can write

$$\hbar\omega_\lambda=2JS\lambda^2 a^2 +g\mu_B B \tag{5.25}$$

which has a parabolic dependence with respect to the wave vector. The eigenfunctions of the magnon Hamiltonian (cf. eqn (5.21)) in the occupation number representation have the well-known form

$$|\ldots n_\lambda \ldots\rangle=\prod_\lambda \frac{1}{\sqrt{n_\lambda!}}(a_\lambda{}^+)^{n_\lambda}|\ldots 0 \ldots\rangle \tag{5.26}$$

where $|\ldots 0 \ldots \rangle$ is the spin-wave vacuum, i.e. $a_\lambda| \ldots 0 \ldots \rangle = 0$. In the present case, the vacuum corresponds to complete ferromagnetic alignment. These functions constitute a complete orthonormal set. It is convenient to note the action of magnon creation and annihilation operators on these states, i.e.

$$a_\lambda{}^+|\ldots n_\lambda \ldots \rangle = (1+n_\lambda)^{1/2}| \ldots (n_\lambda+1) \ldots\rangle$$
$$a_\lambda|\ldots n_\lambda \ldots \rangle = (n_\lambda)^{1/2}| \ldots (n_\lambda-1) \ldots \rangle.$$

$$(5.27)$$

So far we have ignored the dipolar interaction and quadrilinear terms in magnon operators. Using the previous spin-deviation and spin-wave transformations on the complete Hamiltonian, we obtain

$$H_\mathrm{F} = \mathrm{constant} + \sum_\lambda E_\lambda a_\lambda{}^+ a_\lambda + \sum_\lambda \tfrac{1}{2}(B_\lambda a_\lambda a_{-\lambda} + B_\lambda{}^* a_\lambda{}^+ a_{-\lambda}{}^+)^\bullet$$
$$- \sum_{\lambda,\mu}(G_{\lambda,\mu} a_\lambda{}^+ a_{\mu-\lambda}{}^+ a_\mu + G_{\lambda,\mu}{}^* a_\lambda a_{\mu,-\lambda} a_\mu{}^+)$$

$$(5.28)$$

$$+\text{fourth and higher-order terms}$$

where

$$E_\lambda = \hbar\omega_\lambda + A_\lambda$$
$$A_\lambda = -\sum_h \frac{2g^2 \mu_\mathrm{B}{}^2 S}{R_h{}^3}(1-3\,\cos^2\theta_\lambda)\{2+\exp(i\lambda\cdot\mathbf{R}_h)\}$$
$$B_\lambda = -\sum_h \frac{6g^2 \mu_\mathrm{B}{}^2 S}{R_h{}^3}\sin^2\theta_h \exp(2i\phi_h) \exp(i\lambda\cdot\mathbf{R}_h)$$
$$G_{\lambda,\mu} = \sum_h \frac{6g^2 \mu_\mathrm{B}{}^2 \sqrt{(2S)}}{\sqrt{N}} \frac{\cos\theta_h \sin\theta_h \exp(i\phi_h)}{R_h{}^3} \exp\{i(\mu-\lambda)\cdot\mathbf{R}_h\}$$

$$(5.29)$$

and θ_h and ϕ_h are the polar angles of the vector $\mathbf{R}_h$. The above Hamiltonian contains magnon interaction terms of third and higher order. These will contribute to the magnon–magnon interactions which will be considered later. HP diagonalized terms involving two magnon operators (i.e. including those terms which involve $a_\lambda{}^+ a_\lambda{}^+$ and $a_\lambda a_{-\lambda}$ etc.) by making use of the Weyl–Bogoliubov transformation

$$a_\lambda = u_\lambda C_\lambda + v_\lambda{}^* C_{-\lambda}{}^+$$
$$a_\lambda{}^+ = u_\lambda{}^* C_\lambda{}^+ + v_\lambda C_{-\lambda}{}^+$$

$$(5.30)$$

with

$$|u_\lambda|^2 - |v_\lambda|^2 = 1.$$

In order that the bilinear Hamiltonian $H_F(2)$ given by

$$H_F^{(2)} = \sum_\lambda E_\lambda a_\lambda^+ a_\lambda + \tfrac{1}{2}\sum_\lambda (B_\lambda a_\lambda a_{-\lambda} + B_\lambda^* a_\lambda^+ a_{-\lambda}^+) \qquad (5.31)$$

be diagonal in the new operators, we must have

$$u_\lambda = \left\{ \frac{1}{2} \frac{E_\lambda + (E_\lambda^2 - |B_\lambda|^2)^{1/2}}{(E_\lambda^2 - |B_\lambda|^2)^{1/2}} \left(\frac{B_\lambda}{|B_\lambda|} \right) \right\}^{1/2} \qquad (5.32a)$$

$$v_\lambda = -\left\{ \frac{1}{2} \frac{E_\lambda - (E_\lambda^2 - |B_\lambda|^2)^{1/2}}{(E_\lambda^2 - |B_\lambda|^2)^{1/2}} \left(\frac{B_\lambda}{|B_\lambda|} \right) \right\}^{1/2}. \qquad (5.32b)$$

Thus we obtain

$$H_F^{(2)} \text{ (diagonal)} = \sum_\lambda (E_\lambda^2 - |B_\lambda|^2)^{1/2} C_\lambda^+ C_\lambda. \qquad (5.33)$$

It can be shown, however, that the ratio $|B_\lambda|/E_\lambda \sim D/J \ll 1$, where D is the coefficient of the dipolar term. Thus we introduce an error of the order $(D/J)^2$ if we write

$$H_F^{(2)} = \sum_\lambda E_\lambda a_\lambda^+ a_\lambda. \qquad (5.34)$$

This is equivalent to putting $u_\lambda = 1$ and $v_\lambda = 0$.

5.1.1. Specific heat and magnetization in the spin-wave approximation

We shall now compute the specific heat and magnetization of a ferromagnet within the spin-wave approximation. To do this we neglect all magnon–magnon interactions, which is justifiable in the very-low-temperature regions. We have seen that magnons behave like Bose particles. Thus the internal energy of a system of magnons in thermal equilibrium at temperature T is given by (neglecting zero-point energy)

$$U_F = \sum_\lambda \hbar\omega_\lambda \langle a_\lambda^+ a_\lambda \rangle = \sum_\lambda \hbar\omega_\lambda \langle n_\lambda \rangle$$

$$\sum_\lambda \frac{\hbar\omega_\lambda}{\exp(\hbar\omega_\lambda/K_B T) - 1}. \qquad (5.35)$$

The Zeeman and the dipolar contributions to the internal energy are relatively small compared with the exchange term. Accordingly, we take $\hbar\omega_\lambda = 2JS\lambda^2 a^2$ in the long-wavelength limit. At low temperatures, the main contribution to U_F comes from this domain. Using the relation

$$\sum_\lambda = \frac{Na^3}{8\pi^3} \int d\lambda^3 \qquad (5.36)$$

we obtain

$$U_F = \frac{Na^3}{8\pi^3} 4\pi \int_0^{\lambda_{max}} \frac{2JS\lambda^2 a^2 \lambda^2 d\lambda}{\exp(2JS\lambda^2 a^2 / k_B T) - 1} \qquad (5.37)$$

where a^3 is the volume of the unit cell and N is the number of such cells in a cubic crystal. Introducing the dimensionless variable $\xi = 2JS\lambda^2 a^2 / k_B T$ and noting that $\xi_{max} \gg 1$, we can let the upper limit tend to infinity. Thus, expanding the denominator in a power series, we can write (see Van Kranendonk and Van Vleck 1958)

$$\begin{aligned} U_F &= \frac{N(2JS)}{4\pi^2} \left(\frac{k_B T}{2JS}\right)^{5/2} \int_0^\infty \frac{\xi^{3/2}}{e^\xi - 1} d\xi \\ &= \frac{N(2JS)}{4\pi^2} \left(\frac{k_B T}{2JS}\right)^{5/2} \Gamma\left(\frac{5}{2}\right) \zeta\left(\frac{5}{2}; 1\right) \end{aligned} \qquad (5.38)$$

where $\Gamma(x)$ and $\zeta(x; 1)$ are, respectively, the gamma and the Riemann zeta functions. The heat capacity C_m of the magnon system in a zero external field easily follows from the relation

$$C_m = \frac{dU_F}{dT} = \nu N k_B \left(\frac{k_B T}{2JS}\right)^{3/2} \qquad (5.39)$$

where $\nu \approx 0.113$, $0.113/2$ and $0.113/4$ for the simple cubic (s.c), body-centred cubic (b.c.c.), and face-centred cubic (f.c.c.) lattices respectively. Thus the heat capacity for a ferromagnet in the low-temperature region arising mainly from magnons is proportional to $T^{3/2}$. This may be contrasted with the T^3 law for phonons, the difference being attributable to different dispersion relations.

The magnetization $M(T)$ as a function of temperature can be computed by noting that each spin-wave mode leads to one spin reversal (distributed coherently throughout the entire lattice). Thus the spontaneous magnetization at temperature T is given by

$$M_s(T) = g\mu_B (NS - \sum_\lambda a_\lambda^+ a_\lambda) \qquad (5.40)$$

where $M_s(0) = g\mu_B NS$ is the saturation magnetization.

The reduction in magnetization due to thermal spin-wave excitation is (for a b.c.c. lattice, say)

$$\begin{aligned} \Delta M(T) &= M_s(0) - M_s(T) \\ &= g\mu_B \sum \langle n_\lambda \rangle \\ &= 0.1173 \frac{g\mu_B}{2a^3} \left(\frac{k_B T}{2JS}\right)^{3/2}. \end{aligned} \qquad (5.41)$$

This is the famous $T^{3/2}$ law of Bloch giving the deviation from the maximum value at $T=0$. If we were to include higher-order terms in the expansion of $1 - \gamma_\lambda$, we would obtain for a simple-cubic lattice (as obtained by Oguchi 1960),

$$
\begin{aligned}
\frac{M_s(T)}{Ng\mu_B} = S &- \zeta(\tfrac{3}{2}; 1)\left(\frac{k_B T}{8\pi JS}\right)^{3/2} - \tfrac{3}{4}\zeta(\tfrac{5}{2}; 1)\left(\frac{k_B T}{8\pi JS}\right)^{5/2} \\
&- \frac{33\pi^2}{32}\zeta(\tfrac{7}{2}; 1)\left(\frac{k_B T}{8\pi JS}\right)^{7/2} + \dots
\end{aligned}
\tag{5.42}
$$

with $\zeta(\tfrac{3}{2}; 1) = 2\cdot612$, $\zeta(\tfrac{5}{2}; 1) = 1\cdot314$, and $\zeta(\tfrac{7}{2}; 1) = 1\cdot127$.

The inclusion of magnon–magnon interaction terms gives rise to some additional quartic terms in the low-temperature expansion of the magnetization (Dyson 1956, Oguchi 1960).

5.2. Spin waves in antiferromagnets

In this section we consider the energy spectrum and properties of elementary excitations in antiferromagnetic systems. In contrast to a ferromagnet, where the ground state is exactly known (complete spin alignment), the problem of the exact ground state of a three-dimensional antiferromagnet has remained unsolved (see Van Kranendonk and Van Vleck 1958). In fact, not only is the completely antiparallel alignment of spins not the ground state, it is not even an eigenstate of the total spin Hamiltonian. Furthermore, there is an additional complication owing to the orientational degeneracy. This can be removed for a ferromagnet by an external magnetic field, but for an antiferromagnet, however, it can only be removed by assuming the presence of an alternating anistoropy field B_{an} that fixes the spin alignment with respect to the crystal axes.

The simplest model of a three-dimensional antiferromagnet consists of two interpenetrating cubic sublattices which together form a b.c.c. lattice. The nearest neighbours belong to the two different sublattices. Further, the effective exchange is only between the nearest neighbours and has a negative sign. Thus, in the Néel state the spins of one sublattice (A) point up $(+z)$ and those of the other (B) point down $(-z)$. Also, the alternating anisotropy field B_{an} for the sublattice A is along the $+z$ direction and that for the sublattice B is along the $-z$ direction. It has been shown by several workers that this arrangement of the spins of the sublattices (i.e. Néel state) represents the antiferromagnetic ground state fairly closely (Anderson 1952, Kubo 1953). The deviation ($\sim 7\%$) from the maximum sublattice magnetization can be accounted for by the zero-point fluctuations of the z component of the spin.

The Hamiltonian for such a system can be written as

$$H_{AF} = H_{ex} + H_Z + H_{an}$$

$$= 2J\sum_{lm}\mathbf{S}_l \cdot \mathbf{S}_m - Bg\mu_B\sum_l S_l^z - B_{an}g\mu_B\left(\sum_l S_l^z - \sum_m S_m^z\right) \tag{5.43}$$

where l spans sublattice A and m spans sublattice B; B_{an} is the alternating anisotropy field and J is the magnitude of the exchange integral. The magnitude of the spin at each sublattice is the same, i.e. $S_A = S_B = S$. As in the case of a ferromagnet, the spin deviation operators for the two sublattices can be defined in a slightly different manner. For the sake of simplicity, however, we shall retain terms linear in spin-deviation operators. We also introduce the spin-wave transformations. Thus, for the sublattice A, we have

$$S_l^+ \approx (2S)^{1/2}a_l = \left(\frac{2S}{N}\right)^{1/2}\sum_{\lambda}\exp(-i\lambda \cdot \mathbf{R}_l)a_\lambda$$

$$S_l^- \approx (2S)^{1/2}a_l^+ = \left(\frac{2S}{N}\right)^{1/2}\sum_{\lambda}\exp(i\lambda \cdot \mathbf{R}_l)a_\lambda^+ \tag{5.44}$$

$$S - S_l^z = a_l^+ a_l = \frac{1}{N}\sum_{\lambda,\lambda'}\exp\{i(\lambda - \lambda') \cdot \mathbf{R}_l\}a_\lambda^+ a_{\lambda'}$$

and for the sublattice B

$$S_m^+ \approx (2S)^{1/2}d_m^+ = \left(\frac{2S}{N}\right)^{1/2}\sum_{\lambda}\exp(i\lambda \cdot \mathbf{R}_m)d_\lambda^+$$

$$S_m^- \approx (2S)^{1/2}d_m = \left(\frac{2S}{N}\right)^{1/2}\sum_{\lambda}\exp(-i\lambda \cdot \mathbf{R}_m)d_\lambda \tag{5.45}$$

$$S + S_m^z = d_m^+ d_m = \frac{1}{N}\sum_{\lambda,\lambda'}\exp\{i(\lambda - \lambda') \cdot \mathbf{R}_m\}d_\lambda^+ d_\lambda.$$

Here a_λ, a_λ^+ and d_λ, d_λ^+ are the spin-wave annihilation and creation operators for the two sublattices in question. The propagation vectors λ span the N points of the first Brillouin zone of the reciprocal space. This corresponds to N spins of each sublattice. The transformed Hamiltonian is

$$H_{AF} = \text{constant} + 2JS\sum_{\lambda}\gamma_\lambda(a_\lambda^+ a_\lambda + d_\lambda^+ d_\lambda + a_\lambda d_\lambda + a_\lambda^+ d_\lambda^+)$$

$$+ g\mu_B\sum_{\lambda}(B + B_{an})a_\lambda^+ a_\lambda + (B_{an} - B)d_\lambda^+ d_\lambda \tag{5.46}$$

$$\gamma_\lambda = \frac{1}{z}\sum_h\exp(i\lambda \cdot \mathbf{R}_h).$$

The above Hamiltonian is not diagonal. To cast it in a diagonal form we make use of the Weyl–Bogoliubov canonical transformation

$$a_\lambda = \alpha_\lambda \cosh \theta_\lambda + \beta_\lambda^+ \sinh \theta_\lambda$$
$$d_\lambda = \alpha_\lambda^+ \sinh \theta_\lambda + \beta_\lambda \cosh \theta_\lambda$$

(5.48)

together with their Hermitian conjugates. In order that the Hamiltonian be diagonal, the coefficients must satisfy the relations

$$\tanh 2\theta_\lambda = -\omega_e\, Y_\lambda / \omega_e + \omega_A$$

where

$$\omega_e = 2zSJ/\hbar$$
$$\omega_A = g\mu_B B_{an}/\hbar.$$

(5.49)

Thus the Hamiltonian becomes

$$H_{AF}(\text{magnon}) = \sum_\lambda \hbar\omega_\lambda^{(+)}(\alpha_\lambda^+ \alpha_\lambda + \tfrac{1}{2})$$
$$+ \sum_\lambda \hbar\omega_\lambda^{(-)}(\beta_\lambda^+ \beta_\lambda + \tfrac{1}{2})$$

(5.50)

where

$$\omega_\lambda^{(\pm)} = \{(\omega_e + \omega_A)^2 - \omega_e^2\, Y_\lambda^2\}^{1/2} \pm \omega_H$$
$$\omega_H = g\mu_B B/\hbar.$$

(5.51)

We see that there are two magnon branches; α_λ^+, α_λ and β_λ^+, β_λ are the corresponding Bose creation and annihilation operators for the two magnon branches α and β. The two branches are degenerate in the absence of the Zeeman term. It should be noted that the anisotropy has been incorporated in the energy. It may be readily seen from eqn (5.51) that the lowest excitation energy goes negative for $\omega_H^2 > \omega_A^2 + 2\omega_e\omega_A$, implying instability. This is the spin-flop transition induced by a magnetic field. For $\omega_e \gg \omega_A$, the condition may be rewritten as

$$B > B_{critical} = \sqrt{\frac{4zJB_{an}}{g\mu_B}}$$

Let us consider the dispersion relation. In the long-wavelength approximation ($\lambda \cdot \mathbf{R}_\lambda \ll 1$) and neglecting the anisotropy energy, the dispersion relation is considerably simplified. We obtain for cubic systems

$$\hbar\omega_\lambda^{(\pm)} = 2(2z)^{1/2} SJ\lambda a \pm g\mu_B B.$$

(5.52)

Thus, unlike the ferromagnetic case, we obtain a linear dispersion relation. In this respect, magnons in antiferromagnets behave like Debye phonons.

5.2.1. *Specific heat and sublattice magnetization in antiferromagnets*

We have seen that in the absence of an external magnetic field the two magnon branches are degenerate, i.e.

$$\hbar\omega_\lambda^{(\pm)} = 2(2z)^{1/2} SJ\lambda a = \hbar\omega_\lambda. \tag{5.53}$$

Taking the two-fold degeneracy into account, the internal magnon energy for antiferromagnets can be written as

$$U_{AF} = \frac{2Na^3}{8\pi^3} 4\pi \int_0^{\lambda_{max}} \frac{\hbar\omega_\lambda \lambda^2 d\lambda}{\exp(\hbar\omega_\lambda/k_B T) - 1}. \tag{5.54}$$

As before we can introduce a dimensionless variable $\xi = \hbar\omega_\lambda/k_B T$; also the upper limit can be taken as infinity for temperatures small compared with the Néel temperature. Thus

$$U_{AF} = \frac{2N(k_B T)^4}{2\pi^2 \{2SJ(2z)^{1/2}\}^3} \int_0^\infty \xi^3 (e^{-\xi} + e^{-2\xi} + \dots) d\xi \tag{5.55}$$

and the magnon heat capacity is given by

$$C_m = \frac{\partial U_{AF}}{\partial T} = \frac{4! N k_B}{2\pi^2} \left(\frac{k_B T}{2(2z)^{1/2} JS} \right)^3 \zeta(4; 1) \tag{5.56}$$

For a s.c. lattice, Kouvel and Brooks (1954) obtained

$$C_m = 13 \cdot 7 k_B \left(\frac{k_B T}{12 JS} \right)^3. \tag{5.57}$$

Thus the predicted magnon part of the heat capacity is proportional to T^3 which is similar to the Debye phonon heat capacity. This is in very good agreement with the experimental results of Borovik–Romanov and Kalinkina (1961) on $MnCO_3$.

The sublattice magnetization is given by

$$M(T) = g\mu_B \sum_l (S - a_l^+ a_l) \tag{5.58}$$

$$= g\mu_B (NS - \sum_\lambda \sin^2 h\theta_\lambda - \sum_\lambda \langle \alpha_\lambda^+ \alpha_\lambda \rangle \cosh 2\theta_\lambda),$$

where we have made use of the spin-wave canonical transformation. The second term of eqn (5.58) gives the zero-point contribution to the sublattice spin deviation. It can be shown, on neglecting the Zeeman and anisotropy terms, that

$$\Delta M_{zeropoint} = g\mu_B \sum_\lambda \sin^2 h\theta_\lambda = \tfrac{1}{2} g\mu_B \sum_\lambda \{(1 - \Upsilon_\lambda^2)^{-1/2} - 1\}. \tag{5.59}$$

For a s.c. lattice this turns out to be $0.078g\mu_BN$. It should be noted that this is in contrast to the case of ferromagnets where we have zero-point energy but no zero-point spin deviation. For antiferromagnets zero-point magnetization of a sublattice has indeed been observed experimentally by Loopstra Van Lear, and Breel (1968) who measured the magnetic moment on the Mn^{2+} ion in K_2MnF_4 at 4·2 K by neutron diffraction. The observed magnetic moment was found to be 4·54 μ_B instead of $5\mu_B$ for the Mn^{2+} ion. This system (i.e. K_2MnF_4) is essentially a two-dimensional antiferromagnetic. According to the theory (Anderson 1952) for a two-dimensional antiferromagnet eqn (5.59) gives $\langle S^Z \rangle = S - 0.197$. This corresponds to a zero-point reduction of the magnetic moment for ion by 2×0.197 μ_B for K_2MnF_4. The observed reduction is very close to the theoretical prediction. The third term of eqn (5.58) gives the temperature-dependent part. More explicitly, we obtain

$$\Delta M(T) = g\mu_B \sum_\lambda \frac{1}{\exp(\hbar\omega_\lambda/k_BT)^{-1}} (1-\gamma_\lambda^2)^{-1/2}. \tag{5.60}$$

In the low-temperature region (long-wavelength approximation) this becomes

$$M(T) = Ng\mu_B \frac{T^2}{48S^2J^2/k_B^2} \zeta(2; 1) \tag{5.61}$$

which shows that the sublattice magnetization decreases quadratically with temperature in the low-temperature region.

5.3. Spin waves in ferrimagnets

Most of the ferromagnetic insulators are, in fact, ferrimagnetic systems (non-compensated antiferromagnets, i.e. $S_A \neq S_B$). In fact these systems contain many interpenetrating magnetic sublattices. For simplicity, however, it will be illuminating to consider a two-sublattice ferrimagnetic with the following specifications. The two otherwise equivalent cubic sublattices, which interpenetrate to form a b.c.c. lattice of paramagnetic ions, have opposite and unequal spins and unequal g factors. Thus the calculations of the previous section can be easily extended to such a system. The Hamiltonian of a ferrimagnet defined above can be written as

$$H_{ferri} = 2J_{AB} \sum_{l,m} \mathbf{S}_l \cdot \mathbf{S}_m$$

$$-(B+B_{aA})g_A\mu_B \sum_l S_l^Z - (B-B_{aB})g_B\mu_B \sum_m S_m^Z. \tag{5.62}$$

Here also the sublattices are designated by A and B and accordingly we have introduced the subscripts A and B to the various quantities (e.g. B_{aA}

and B_{aB} for the two anisotropy fields). J_{AB} is the magnitude of the effective nearest-neighbour exchange integral and S_A and S_B represent the magnitude of the spins at individual sites on the two sublattices.

The spin-deviation transformations are similar to the antiferromagnetic case except that we have to introduce S_A at the appropriate places in eqns (5.45) and (5.46). In particular, the spin deviations are now defined by

$$n_l = a_l^+ a_l = S_A - S_l^Z$$

$$n_m = d_m^+ d_m = S_B + S_m^Z \tag{5.63}$$

Apart from these differences, the spin-wave Fourier transformation and the canonical transformation remain the same. The transformation parameters are now determined from the relation

$$\tanh 2\theta_\lambda = \frac{-2J_{AB}(S_A S_B)^{1/2} z \, Y_\lambda}{J_{AB}z(S_A + S_B) + \frac{1}{2}\{(B + B_{aA})g_A\mu_B - (B - B_{aB})g_B\mu_B\}}. \tag{5.64}$$

The diagonalized magnon part has the form

$$H_{\text{ferri}}(\text{magnon}) = \text{constant} + \sum_\lambda \hbar\omega_\lambda^{(+)}(\alpha_\lambda^+ \alpha_\lambda + \tfrac{1}{2})$$

$$+ \sum_\lambda \hbar\omega_\lambda^{(-)}(\beta_\lambda^+ \beta_\lambda + \tfrac{1}{2}) \tag{5.65}$$

where the energies of the two magnon branches are obtained as (neglecting the anisotropy energy)

$$\hbar\omega_\lambda^{(\pm)} = [\{J_{AB}(S_A + S_B)z + \tfrac{1}{2}(g_A - g_B)\mu_B B\}^2 - 4J_{AB}S_A S_B z^2 \, Y_\lambda^2]^{1/2}$$

$$\pm [J_{AB}|S_B - S_A| + \tfrac{1}{2}(g_A + g_B)\mu_B B] \tag{5.66}$$

where the plus sign denotes the α branch and the minus sign the β branch. We obtain a simpler form for these two branches in the long-wavelength region. Assuming $g_A = g_B = g$, we obtain

$$\hbar\omega_\lambda^{(+)} = \frac{J_{AB}S_A S_B a^2 \lambda^2}{|S_A - S_B|} + g\mu_B B \tag{5.67}$$

$$\hbar\omega_\lambda^{(-)} = 2zJ_{AB}|S_A - S_B| + \frac{4J_{AB}S_A S_B a^2 \lambda^2}{|S_A - S_B|} - g\mu_B B \tag{5.68}$$

The above form has been obtained by assuming that the exchange term, namely $zJ|S_A - S_B|$, is much larger than the Zeeman term. It should be remembered that we cannot, therefore, put $S_A = S_B$ in the approximate forms given by eqns (5.67) and (5.68) to recover the antiferromagnetic results.

Unlike the antiferromagnetic case, the dispersion relation is quadratic. However, we obtain two branches, one lower and the other higher. By analogy with phonons they are referred to as the 'acoustic' and 'optical' branches of spin waves.

5.3.1. Specific heat and magnetization in ferrimagnets

The specific heat and magnetization of the bulk specimen is easily calculated following the procedure given earlier. We obtain for a s.c. lattice considering the acoustic branch only (i.e. low-temperature approximation)

$$C_m = 0.113 \, Nk_B \left(\frac{|S_A - S_B|}{4J_{AB}S_A S_B} \right)^{3/2} (k_B T)^{3/2} \tag{5.69}$$

and

$$M(T) = M(O) \left\{ 1 - \frac{0.1173}{|S_A - S_B|} \left(\frac{k_B T |S_A - S_B|}{4J_{AB}S_A S_B} \right)^{3/2} \right\}. \tag{5.70}$$

These results are similar to the ferromagnetic case for spins providing the effective exchange integral is now multiplied by the factor $2(S_A S_B / S|S_A - S_B|)$. However, the nature of magnetic ordering in a ferrimagnet is akin to that for an antiferromagnet. It is desirable to discuss the sublattice magnetization for a ferrimagnetic also. Here too we expect a zero-point spin deviation for each magnetic sublattice. A straightforward calculation gives (neglecting anisotropy and Zeeman terms)

$$\Delta M_A \text{ (zero point)} = \Delta M_B \text{ (zero point)}$$

$$= g\mu_B \sum_\lambda \sinh^2 \theta_\lambda \tag{5.71}$$

$$= g\mu_B \frac{1}{2} \sum_\lambda \{ (1 - C^2 \, Y_\lambda^2)^{-1/2} - 1 \}$$

where

$$C = \frac{(S_A S_B)^{1/2}}{(S_A + S_B)/2} \ll 1.$$

For the limiting case $S_A = S_B$ the antiferromagnetic result is obtained.

When one takes into account the complicated magnetic structure of the actual ferrimagnetic systems one obtains several spin-wave branches. For example, in the spinel-type structure (e.g. magnetite (Fe_3O_4) or $MnFe_2O_4$), there are six interpenetrating f.c.c. magnetic sublattices. It has been found that the spin-wave spectra indeed have six branches (see Glasser and Milford 1963). There are branches which show a quadratic dispersion relation in the long-wavelength limit with some deviations for higher values of the wave vectors. The lowest branch is, of course, the acoustic branch discussed above. A few branches are more or less flat. The dispersion relation for the lowest spin-wave branches in magnetite and yttrium iron garnet (Douglass 1960, see also Harris 1963) are given by

$$\hbar\omega_\lambda = \frac{11}{16} \frac{J_{AB}(S_{B1}+S_{B2})}{|S_{B1}+S_{B2}-S_A|} a^2\lambda^2 \tag{5.72}$$

and

$$\hbar\omega_\lambda = \frac{5}{16}(5J_{ad}-8J_{aa}-3J_{dd})a^2\lambda^2 \tag{5.73}$$

respectively, where J_{aa}, J_{ad}, and J_{dd} are the exchange integrals involving ions at octahedral (a) and tetrahedral (d) sites; B_1 and B_2 refer to various sublattices.

5.4. Experimental studies of temperature-dependent magnetization

In this section we shall give a brief survey of the experimental studies of the thermodynamic properties of magnetic insulators in relation to the spin theory developed in the preceding sections.

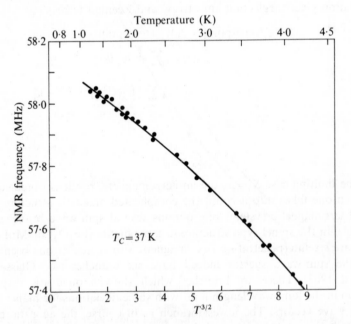

FIG. 5.1.   The temperature dependence of magnetization as revealed by the n.m.r. frequency of ^{53}Cr nuclei in CrBr$_3$ up to 0·11 T_c (after Gossard et al. 1961).

The best examples of ferromagnetic insulators are europium chalco-genides (e.g. EuO and EuS) and $CrBr_3$. Experimental measurements of the specific heat and magnetization of these systems as a function of tempera-ture support the theoretical predictions based on spin-wave theory (see Keffer 1966). Perhaps the most sensitive technique is to measure the nuclear

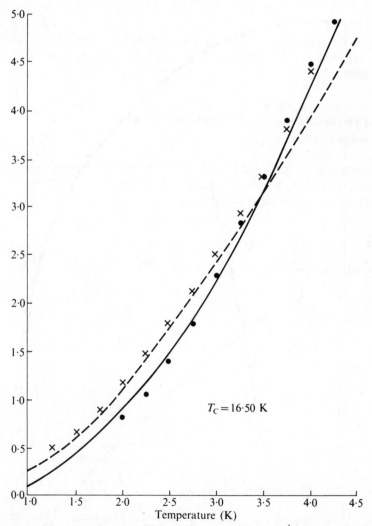

FIG. 5.2. A comparison of experimental values of the temperature dependence of magneti-zation $\Delta M = M(0) - M(T)$ in EuS with the calculated values of Charap and Boyd (1964): solid curve, calculated values of ΔM; points, experimental values of ΔM; broken curve, calculated values of C/R; crosses, experimental values of C/R. For details of units see references above.

magnetic resonance (n.m.r.) frequency as a function of temperature. This gives a direct measure of the magnetization (local induction) seen by the resonating nucleus. The measurements of Gossard *et al.* (1961) on ^{53}Cr in

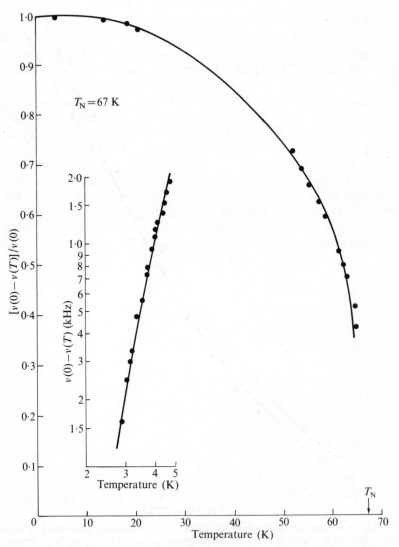

FIG. 5.3. A comparison of the calculated sublattice magnetization (Low 1963) in MnF_2 with the n.m.r. of ^{19}F (Jaccarino and Shulman 1957, Heller and Benedek 1962).

$CrBr_3$ show that the dependence of magnetization is given by

$$M(T) = M(O) \, (1 - A_1 T^{3/2} - A_2 T^{5/2}) \tag{5.74}$$

where

$$A_1 = (2 \cdot 54 \pm 0 \cdot 7) \times 10^{-3}$$

$$A_2 = (3 \cdot 0 \pm 1 \cdot 0) \times 10^{-5}.$$

They did not find any improvement in the fit when they included the $T^{7/2}$ term or the Dyson correction having a T^4 dependence. However, they covered only a limited range of temperature up to $0 \cdot 1 \, T_c$. The results are shown in Fig. 5.1. For higher-temperature regions (up to $0 \cdot 6 \, T_c$, say) renormalization effects due to magnon–magnon interactions become important. Calculations by Low (1963) and by Charap and Boyd (1964) on EuO and EuS taking magnon–magnon interactions into account in a self-consistent way are in reasonable agreement with the experimental results. A comparison of the calculated and experimental magnetization curves for EuS is shown in Fig. 5.2.

One of the best confirmations of the spin-wave-theoretical prediction for antiferromagnetic insulators is provided by n.m.r. measurements on ^{19}F in MnF_2 (Jaccarino and Shulman 1957, Heller and Benedek 1962). The calculations of the sublattice magnetization by Low (1963) are in good agreement with the experimental data up to 63 K (see Fig. 5.3.).

6

CRITICAL PHENOMENA IN MAGNETIC SYSTEMS

In this chapter we shall discuss the critical behaviour of magnetic systems. After a brief review of Landau's mean field theory of second-order phase transitions (Landau and Lifshitz 1969), we shall consider recent developments involving renormalization group theory (for a detailed review and original references see Wilson and Kogut 1974, Ma 1976, Fisher 1974).

6.1. Landau's theory of phase transition

It is expedient to discuss the mean field theory of Landau for a specific situation, for example the case of a ferromagnet. The order parameter in this case is the spontaneous magnetization $M_z(\mathbf{x})$ where z is the easy axis of magnetization. Near the transition temperature T_c (the Curie temperature in this case) the magnetization is small. Hence, one can resort to the expansion of the free energy in terms of the small parameter M_z. This involves the implicit assumption of the analyticity of the free energy in the order parameter. However, it should be noted that the free energy is, in general, not an analytic function of other thermodynamic variables such as temperature. In fact, this non-analyticity is the mathematical manifestation of the phase transition. Thus the choice of the order parameter as an expansion parameter for free energy was the first successful search for analyticity (Wilson and Kogut 1974).

At this stage, we must emphasize the idea of the order parameter which plays a crucial role in all second-order phase transitions. This is an extensive parameter and is a measure of order in the system. It vanishes in the high-temperature paramagnetic phase above T_c, but has a non-vanishing value below T_c. It transforms as an irreducible representation of the symmetry group of the higher-symmetry phase (the paramagnetic phase in the present case). In general, an order parameter could be a scalar, a vector, or a tensor quantity. For instance, for a ferromagnet with n equivalent easy axes of magnetization, the order parameter is the spontaneous magnetization M and has n components. For an antiferromagnet the corresponding quantity is the staggered magnetization.

The free-energy functional for a d-dimensional ferromagnet can be written in the Landau–Ginzburg form as

$$F = \int d^d x f(\mathbf{x})$$

with the free-energy density $f(x)$ given by

$$f(x) = \{\nabla M(\mathbf{x})\}^2 + rM^2(\mathbf{x}) + 4uM^4(\mathbf{x}) - \mathbf{B} \cdot \mathbf{M}(\mathbf{x}) + f_0(T) \qquad (6.1)$$

where r and u are constants depending on temperature and $\mathbf{B}$ is the external magnetic field.

Next, we discuss the correlation between local magnetization densities. It is convenient to fix the direction of magnetization at the origin by applying an infinitely large magnetic field and then to study the magnetization as a function of distance from the origin. Thus

$$B(\mathbf{x}) = B_0 \delta(\mathbf{x}) \qquad (6.2)$$

where B_0 is a constant.

The variation of the free-energy functional with respect to magnetization gives the following Euler–Lagrange equation

$$-\nabla^2 M(\mathbf{x}) + rM(\mathbf{x}) = B_0 \delta(\mathbf{x}). \qquad (6.3)$$

The acceptable solution is

$$M(\mathbf{x}) \sim \frac{B_0 \exp(-\sqrt{r}\mathbf{x})}{|\mathbf{x}|^{d-2}} \qquad (6.4)$$

Thus the correlation length ξ is

$$\xi = 1/\sqrt{r}. \qquad (6.5)$$

If we require the correlation length to diverge at the critical point $T = T_c$, we have $r \to 0$ as $T \to T_c$. Assuming r to be an analytic function of T, we have

$$r = r'(T_c)(T - T_c) \qquad \text{for } T \to T_c^+. \qquad (6.6)$$

Thus, we note that at the critical point the coefficient of the bilinear term in (6.3) must change sign. In order to obtain the spontaneous magnetization, we set $\mathbf{B} = 0$ and assume that there is no spatial fluctuation of magnetization, i.e.

$$\text{grad } M = 0. \qquad (6.7)$$

Minimization of F with respect to M now gives

$$M(\mathbf{x}) \equiv M = (-r/2u)^{1/2} \qquad (6.8)$$

Physically, we require M to be non-vanishing only for $T < T_c$. This demands that $r'(T_c)$ be positive. Thus we obtain

$$M(x) \equiv M \propto (T_c - T)^{1/2} \qquad \text{for } T < T_c \qquad (6.9)$$

$$= 0 \qquad \text{for } T > T_c. \qquad (6.10)$$

Recalling the definition of critical exponents (cf. §1.1(d)), we obtain the critical index $\beta = \frac{1}{2}$. Similarly the correlation length varies as $(T-T_c)-\frac{1}{2}$ giving $\nu = \frac{1}{2}$.

To obtain the index δ we have to minimize the free energy at $T = T_c$, i.e. $r = 0$, in the presence of the magnetic field. Assuming no spatial variation, we obtain

$$M = (B/4u)^{1/3} \qquad \text{giving } \delta = 3. \tag{6.11}$$

Let us now consider the specific heat C_B. This is given by

$$C_B = -T\frac{\partial^2 F}{\partial T^2}\bigg|_{B=0} \tag{6.12}$$

For $T > T_c$, we have

$$F = \int d^dx\, f_0(T) \tag{6.13}$$

and for $T < T_c$

$$F = \int d^dx\{f_0(T) - r^2/4u\} \tag{6.14}$$

Thus there is a discontinuity in the specific heat at $T = T_c$.

6.2. Effect of fluctuations and the Landau mean field theory

At this stage a few remarks about the nature of the approximations involved in Landau's mean field theory will be in order. The structure of the free-energy functional shows that it is a hydrodynamic theory in which the order parameter (magnetization) has been averaged over distances of the order of lattice spacing a. In other words, the free-energy function can describe only long-wavelength fluctuations of the order parameter. Thus the Landau theory neglects fluctuations in the intermediate-wavelength (Λ) range, i.e. $\zeta \gg \Lambda \gg a$. These points will be amplified within the framework of renormalization group theory as proposed by Wilson (1971).

The role of dimensionality in relation to fluctuation can, however, be seen from the following simple arguments. The energy content of any fluctuation of wavelength Λ scales as Λ^4. The energy is spread over a region of the order of Λ^d. The energy density then scales as Λ^{4-d}. Accordingly, for large Λ the energy density decreases for $d > 4$. Hence mean field theory is expected to hold for dimensionality $d > 4$. For real systems $d < 4$ and the effect of fluctuations cannot be ignored. The above discussion assumes that the interactions are short range.

In fact, general statistical mechanical inequalities (see Ruelle 1969) can be invoked to show that for space dimensionality $d \le 2$, isotropic Heisenberg systems can show no spontaneous long-range order at non-zero temperature. This is again due to critical fluctuation. We should note that this is not quite the same as the zero-point quantum mechanical fluctuations discussed in Chapter 5 (cf. eqns (5.59) and (5.71)). Of course, these quantum fluctuations too diverge for low dimensionalities precluding spontaneous order. The so-called low dimensional magnets, for example the quadratic layered compounds such as K_2CuF_4, Rb_2CuCl_4, are all highly anisotropic (see Navarro and Jorgh 1976).

Yet another way of looking at the failure of the Landau theory near the critical point is to note that the coefficient $r(T)$ vanishes at $T = T_c$. Thus even large fluctuations cost relatively small energy which arises from the quartic term. In other words, the fluctuations are not suppressed by the statistical-mechanical probability factor. It is, however, possible to define a critical region around T_c beyond which the Landau theory will be valid. The size of the critical region can be estimated by equating the quadratic and the quartic terms in the energy functional.

6.3. Renormalization group theory of critical phenomena

In this section we shall describe in a simplified manner the essential ideas underlying Wilson's renormalization group theoretical approach to critical phenomena (Wilson 1973). This can best be viewed as a refinement of Landau's hydrodynamic theory in that the fluctuation of wavelengths intermediate between the lattice constant and the correlation length are taken into account. It should be recalled that Landau defined the free-energy functional in terms of an order parameter (magnetization in the case considered here) M which is only a coarse-grained average of atomic moments over several lattice spacings (cf. eq (6.1)). An implicit assumption in this formulation is that the expansion coefficients r and u do not depend on the averaging length L, say. This is precisely the point of departure. Explicit dependence on the length L can be examined by choosing two averaging lengths L and $L + \delta L$ and eliminating all fluctuations of wavelengths lying between L and $L + \delta L$. This involves taking a partial trace in the partition function over the degrees of freedom to be eliminated. Mathematically, one can write

$$M(x) = M_H(x) + mM_{fl}(x) \tag{6.15}$$

where $M_H(x)$ is a slowly varying hydrodynamic part having fluctuation wavelengths greater than Λ; M_{fl} represents the short-wavelength fluctuations containing wavelengths in the range $\delta\Lambda$. It should be noted that

$$\int |M_{fl}|^2 dx = 1. \tag{6.16}$$

We shall now choose δL in such a way that it contains only one degree of freedom. From the uncertainty principle, one can readily see that $\delta L \sim \delta\Lambda \sim$

L^{d+1}/Ω_v. With this condition the partial trace operation just involves integrating over m. Thus we obtain

$$\exp\{-F_{L+\delta L}\} = \int_{-\infty}^{\infty} dm \exp\{-F_L\} \tag{6.17}$$

where the free energy F_L is evaluated with $M(x)$ given by (6.15). Retaining terms quadratic in small m occurring in the exponent and performing the resulting Gaussian integrals, we obtain

$$F_{\delta L+L}(M_H) = F_L(M_H) + \tfrac{1}{2}\ln\left\{\frac{1}{L^2} + r(L, T) + 6u(L, T) M_H^2\right\}. \tag{6.18}$$

Noting that for $L = \xi$ we must have

$$\frac{1}{L^2} = r(L, T)$$

and assuming that $r(L, T)$ is a slowly varying function of L, it is possible to expand the logarithm for small M_H, i.e. close to the critical temperature. Equating terms of the same order, we obtain

$$r(L+\delta L, T) = r(L, T)$$

$$+ \frac{1}{\Omega_v}\{3L^2u(L, T) - 3L^4u(L, T)r(L, T) + \ldots\} \tag{6.19}$$

and

$$u(L+\delta L, T) = u(L, T) - \frac{1}{\Omega_v} 9L^4u^2(L, T) + \ldots \tag{6.20}$$

Let us recall that $\delta L = L^{d+1}/\Omega_v$. Thus the difference equation can be converted into a differential equation for the L dependence of the expansion parameters r and u, i.e.

$$\frac{dr}{dL} = 3L^{-d}u - 3L^{3-d}ur \tag{6.21}$$

$$\frac{du}{dL} = -9L^{3-d}u^2. \tag{6.22}$$

These equations can readily be solved giving

$$r(L, T) \sim L^{-\varepsilon/3}(T - T_c) \qquad (\varepsilon = 4 - d) \tag{6.23}$$

$$u(L, T) \sim L^{-\varepsilon}. \tag{6.24}$$

We shall now extrapolate these solutions to the case $L \sim \xi$ and use Landau's results, namely eqns (6.5), (6.6), and (6.8). Thus we obtain

$$\xi \sim \xi^{+\varepsilon/6}(T-T_c)^{-1/2} \tag{6.25}$$

giving

$$v = (2-\varepsilon/3)^{-1}. \tag{6.26}$$

Similarly,

$$M \sim \xi^{+\varepsilon/3}(T-T_c)^{1/2}$$

giving

$$\beta = \frac{1}{2} - \frac{\varepsilon}{6}\frac{1}{1-\varepsilon/6}. \tag{6.27}$$

Hence for the case $d=3$, we obtain

$$\beta = 0.3 \qquad \text{and} \qquad v = 0.6.$$

These are significantly different from the mean field values of Landau, i.e. $\beta = 0.5$ and $v = 0.5$. The values obtained from Wilson's theory, within the crude approximation, are very close to the typical experimental values $\beta = 0.31–0.36$ and $v = 0.6–0.7$ found in several three-dimensional magnetic systems.

For $d > 4$, the L dependence vanishes and hence Landau's mean field theory holds.

In the foregoing discussion, we have given the spirit of Wilson's renormalization group theory. However, the theory *per se* is a mathematically rigorous formalism which originated in field theory. For completeness, we shall state the definition of the operations involved in this group.

The renormalization procedure is best viewed as a refinement of Kadanoff's (1966) intuitive supposition of irrelevance of scale of length at the critical point. This implies that near the critical point the order–order correlation length diverges making lengths such as the range of interaction irrelevant. Mathematically, this means that the description (the effective interaction Hamiltonian) of the system should remain unchanged if we choose some averaged cell variables instead of site variables provided that the variables are properly scaled.

As an example, let us consider the spin–spin correlation length of an Ising system at the critical point (in an Ising system the spin at each site has two values, ± 1). The fact that the correlation length is infinite dictates the form of the spin–spin correlation as

$$\langle m(0)m(r) \rangle = \frac{c}{r^{d-2+\eta}} \tag{6.28}$$

for r very much greater than all microscopic length scales. Here d is the dimensionality and η is a critical exponent which measures deviations from mean field behaviour of the Ornstein–Zernike (1914) type. It is readily seen that the form of eqn (6.28) is invariant under the following scale transformations:

$$\mathbf{r} = b\mathbf{R} \tag{6.29}$$

$$M(R) = m(R)b^{1/2(d+2-\eta)} \tag{6.30}$$

where $M(R)$ is a cell variable, i.e.

$$M = \sum_{\text{cell}} m(r) \tag{6.31}$$

and b is the linear cell dimension in the units of the original lattice constant. The rescaled correlation function reads

$$\langle m(0)\, m(R) \rangle = \frac{c}{R^{d-2+\eta}}. \tag{6.32}$$

which has the same form as (6.28). This form of invariance should imply invariance of the effective interaction Hamiltonian at the critical point. This is suggestive of a transformation group with respect to which the system must remain invariant if it is at the critical point. We shall see presently that this amounts to identifying criticality with the fixed point of certain group of transformations. One reduction of the group is the following.

Consider a d-dimensional lattice with N degrees of freedom $m_1 \ldots m_N$ in a box of linear dimension L. Let the interaction Hamiltonian be

$$H_0(N) = H_0(m_1 \ldots m_N) = \beta H \tag{6.33}$$

where H is the usual Hamiltonian function. The renormalization group involves the performance of the following operations on the Hamiltonian.

Extension. The linear dimensions are extended by a factor b so that the resultant system contains $b^d N$ degrees of freedom, i.e.

$$H_0(b^d N) = H_0(m_1 \ldots m_{b^d N}) \tag{6.34}$$

Elimination. We define the cell variables

$$M_i = \sum_{\text{cell}} m(r) \tag{6.35}$$

where the cell dimension is b times the original lattice constant. The cell variable is essentially an average magnetization. The remaining $b^d - 1$ degrees of freedom within the cell describe fluctuations. The process of elimination of these fluctuation variables involves taking a partial trace, i.e.

$$\exp(-\tilde{H}(N)) \equiv \exp(-\tilde{H}(M_1 \ldots M_N))$$

$$= \mathrm{Tr}' \exp(-H_0(M_1 \ldots M_N, m_1' \ldots m_{(b^d-1)N})) \quad (6.36)$$

where the prime on the trace denotes the partial trace with respect to the fluctuation variables m_i'.

Scale transformation. This operation involves rescaling the length and the cell magnetization according to eqns (6.29) and (6.30). This leads to the Hamiltonian

$$H_1(N) = H_1(m_1 \ldots m_N).$$

Symbolically,

$$H_0(N) \to H_N(N). \quad (6.37)$$

Repeated applications of these operations may lead to a fixed-point Hamiltonian H^*, i.e.

$$H_0 \to H_1 \to \ldots H_1 \to \ldots H^* \to H^*. \quad (6.38)$$

The fixed-point Hamiltonian H^* obviously describes the critical point since this implies $\xi = \xi/b$, where ξ is some correlation length. Since $b \neq 1$, this can only be possible if ξ is zero or infinity. The first possibility is ruled out on physical grounds. Thus, we conclude that the fixed-point Hamiltonian does describe criticality.

The question naturally arises as to how fixed point Hamiltonian depends on the starting Hamiltonian. It turns out that the space of possible Hamiltonians can be divided into domains each having its own fixed point. The domain is called the domain of attraction of the fixed point. Inasmuch as the critical behaviour depends on the fixed point, one can assert that there is universality within the domain of a particular fixed point. This will imply, in particular, that the critical exponents depend only on the symmetry of the Hamiltonian, the number of components of the order parameter, and the spatial dimensionality d. Thus other microscopic details, such as lattice constant, co-ordination number, strength of interaction, etc., are irrelevant so long as the interactions are short range.

Thus almost any system can be mapped on to some magnetic system, anisotropic in general, for studying the phase diagram and the transitions. A binary liquid mixture ($n=1$) is similar to an Ising system (i.e. $J_{xx}=J_{yy}=0$, $J_{zz}\neq0$, and $s=\frac{1}{2}$) while normal to superfluid transition of ^{4}He ($n=2$, for complex order parameter) is similar to the X–Y system ($J_{zz}=0$, $J_{xx}=J_{yy}\neq0$, $s=\frac{1}{2}$). This has been part of the motivation for including this chapter in this monograph.

7

MAGNON − MAGNON INTERACTIONS

In Chapter 5 we discussed the nature of the elementary excitations (spin waves) in ferromagnetic, ferrimagnetic, and antiferromagnetic systems. The Hamiltonian was truncated at a stage where only bilinear terms involving spin-deviation operators were retained. Appropriate transformations were introduced to diagonalize the Hamiltonian. Although the above procedure is valid at very low temperatures, the interaction processes become important at slightly elevated temperatures. The nature of the spin-wave interactions can be seen from the following general considerations. As an example we discuss the case of a ferromagnet. A spin-wave state containing a single magnon of wave vector λ is described by

$$|1_\lambda\rangle = (2S)^{-1/2} S_\lambda^- |0\rangle$$
$$\equiv (2SN)^{-1/2} \sum_l \exp(i\lambda \cdot \mathbf{R}_l) S_l^- |0\rangle \tag{7.1}$$

where $|0\rangle$ is the completely aligned (vacuum) state with spins pointing along the $+z$ axis. It is clear that these states constitute a complete set of orthonormal functions and are also eigenstates of the bilinear part of the HP Hamiltonian. The remaining terms of the Hamiltonian will have off-diagonal matrix elements connecting different spin-wave states. These represent dynamic interactions between spin waves. There is yet another interaction, i.e. the kinematic interaction, as first pointed out by Dyson (1956). This comes about on generalizing the spin-wave states (cf. eqn (7.10)) so as to contain more than one spin wave. Such a state is given by

$$|n\rangle = \prod_\lambda (2S)^{-n_\lambda/2} (n_\lambda!)^{-1/2} (S_\lambda^-)^{n_\lambda} |0\rangle \tag{7.2}$$

where n_λ represents the number of spin waves in the mode λ. These states cease to be orthonormal to each other for $(1/N)\Sigma n_\lambda > 2S$ and hence will lead to a kinematic interaction. This can be physically interpreted as the requirement that we cannot have more than $2S$ spin deviations at a site or equivalently that the total number of independent physical states should not exceed $(2S+1)^N$. The above kinematic interaction was eliminated by HP by choosing a rigorously orthonormal set of many spin-wave states, i.e.

$$|\ldots n_\lambda \ldots\rangle = \prod_\lambda \frac{1}{(n_\lambda!)^{1/2}} (a_\lambda^+)^{n_\lambda} |0\rangle. \tag{7.3}$$

This choice, however, overemphasizes the dynamic interactions which do not tend to zero even in the long-wavelength approximation. Nevertheless, as shown by Oguchi (1960), a careful analysis of the off-diagonal terms leads to a cancellation and eventually one is left with a residual weak spin-wave interaction between renormalized spin-wave modes. These considerations thus show that the spin-wave interactions in the low-frequency region are effectively weak and therefore the low-temperature behaviour can still be described by the linear spin-wave theory augmented by non-linear intereaction terms as weak perturbations.

We shall now discuss various spin-wave interaction processes along with their possible physical origin (see Keffer 1966 for details). We can have two types of interaction terms, namely those that conserve quasi-momentum and those that do not. The processes that do not conserve momentum involve the scattering of magnons from inhomogeneities and imperfections that destroy the translation symmetry of the magnetic crystal. The most important process in this category is the interaction involving the uniform-mode magnons ($\lambda = 0$) that are excited in ferromagnetic resonance experiments where the sample dimension is small compared with the wavelength of the exciting electromagnetic radiation. Energy conservation, however, requires that there be magnon modes degenerate with the uniform precession mode. The existence of these modes was first demonstrated by Anderson and Suhl (1955). They arise from the modification of the magnon dispersion relation by the magnetic dipole–dipole interaction which leads to an additional term in the Hamiltonian representing the interaction of the bulk magnetization with the microscopic demagnetization fields. Both surface and volume demagnetization fields are important and their microscopic origin lies in the dipole–dipole interaction. The demagnetization part of the Hamiltonian renormalizes the frequency of both the uniform and magnon modes of the non-zero wave vectors. In the latter case, however, the energy shift depends on the direction of the wave vector with respect to the applied magnetic field **B**. Thus, for λ parallel to **B** there is no demagnetization field, while for λ normal to the field the demagnetization field has a maximum value. This directional dependence causes a spread in the magnon dispersion relation, thereby giving rise to spin-wave modes ($\lambda \neq 0$) degenerate with the uniform-mode magnons ($\lambda = 0$).

7.1. Magnon–magnon interactions

(a) *Two-magnon interactions.* The interaction Hamiltonian for a ferromagnet has the form

$$H_{mm}^{(2)} = \sum_\lambda \{F(\lambda)a_\lambda^+ a_0 + F^*(\lambda)a_0^+ a_\lambda\} \tag{7.4}$$

which involves the destruction (creation) of a uniform-mode magnon with the creation (destruction) of another magnon with $\lambda \neq 0$. The factors responsible for the existence of such terms in real crystals are surface pits, voids, and other irregularities. The explicit form of the coefficient $F(\lambda)$ for scattering from a hemispherical surface pit of radius R is given by (see Sparks 1964)

$$F(\lambda) = \frac{8\pi^2 R^3 \, g\mu_B M}{V} (3 \cos^2\theta_\lambda - 1) \times \frac{\sin \lambda R - \lambda R \cos \lambda R}{\lambda^2 R^2} \tag{7.5}$$

where M is the bulk magnetization and V the volume of the sample. It should be noted that such two-magnon terms involving $\lambda \neq 0$ can always be diagonalized leading to a re-definition of the spin-wave spectra. This, however, does not contradict the above treatment of two-magnon scattering processes in that the uniform mode is not an exact eigenstate of the total Hamiltonian, and when it is excited selectively by external sources it will evolve into other magnon modes through the above interaction processes. In quantum-mechanical language, the external field 'prepares' the system in a definite state, namely the uniform mode which is not an exact eigenstate of the Hamiltonian, and hence the decay occurs.

(b) *Three-magnon interaction processes.* The general form of such processes which conserve quasi-momentum is given by

$$H_{\text{mm}}^{(3)} = \sum_{\lambda_1, \lambda_2, \lambda_3} \{ C(\lambda_1; \lambda_2, \lambda_3) a_{\lambda_1} a_{\lambda_2}^+ a_{\lambda_3}^+$$
$$+ C^*(\lambda_1; \lambda_2, \lambda_3) a_{\lambda_1}^+ a_{\lambda_2} a_{\lambda_3} \} \Delta(\lambda_1 - \lambda_2 - \lambda_3) \tag{7.6}$$

where

$$C(\lambda_1; \lambda_2, \lambda_1 - \lambda_2) = \sum_h 6g^2\mu_B^2 \sqrt{\left(\frac{2S}{N}\right)} \frac{\cos\theta_h \, \sin\theta_h}{R_h^3}$$
$$\times \exp\{i\phi + i(\lambda_1 - \lambda_2)\mathbf{R}_h\}. \tag{7.7}$$

These interaction processes arise from the dipole–dipole term in the Hamiltonian. The physical interpretation of the two terms in eqn (7.1) can be given as follows.

(i) The first term is a splitting process wherein a magnon of wave vector λ_1 is destroyed and two magnons of wave vectors λ_2 and $\lambda_1 - \lambda_2$ are created.

(ii) The second term corresponds to a confluence process wherein two magnons of wave vectors λ_2 and $\lambda_1 - \lambda_2$ are destroyed giving rise to a third magnon of wave vector λ_1.

In all the real processes involving the above interactions energy is conserved, i.e.

$$\hbar\omega_{\lambda_1} = \hbar\omega_{\lambda_2} + \hbar\omega_{\lambda_1 - \lambda_2}.$$

A particular case of interest in the resonance relaxation phenomenon is the one involving the splitting of a uniform-mode magnon into two magnons of opposite momentum and the confluence of the uniform-mode magnon with another magnon to produce a third magnon and their time-conjugate processes. The interaction Hamiltonian is easily written as

$$H_{mm}^{(3)}(\text{split}) = \sum_{\lambda} C(0; \lambda, -\lambda) a_0 a_{\lambda}^{+} a_{-\lambda}^{+} + \text{h.c.} \qquad (7.8)$$

for the splitting process, and

$$H_{mm}^{(3)}(\text{confl}) = \sum_{\lambda} C^{*}(\lambda; 0, \lambda) a_{\lambda}^{+} a_0 a_{\lambda} + \text{h.c.} \qquad (7.9)$$

where the coefficients are particular cases of eqn (7.7)

(c) *Four-magnon interaction processes.* The interaction terms involving four-magnon operators in a ferromagnet will arise from two sources: first from the expansion of the exchange Hamiltonian to higher-order terms in the spin wave operators, and second from the dipolar interaction. The procedure is cumbersome but straightforward in principle. We obtain

$$H_{mm}^{(4)}(\text{exch}) = \sum_{\lambda_1, \lambda_2, \lambda_3, \lambda_4} \frac{zJ}{2N} \left(1 + \frac{1}{8S}\right) \left\{(\gamma_{\lambda_1} + \gamma_{\lambda_2}) - 2\gamma_{\lambda_2 - \lambda_4}\right\}$$
$$\times a_{\lambda_1}^{+} a_{\lambda_2}^{+} a_{\lambda_3} a_{\lambda_4} \Delta(\lambda_1 + \lambda_2 - \lambda_3 - \lambda_4) \qquad (7.10)$$

and

$$H_{mm}^{(4)}(\text{dip}) = \sum_{\lambda_1, \lambda_2, \lambda_3, \lambda_4} \frac{g\mu_B M}{N} \{a_{\lambda_1}^{+} a_{\lambda_2}^{+} a_{\lambda_3} a_{\lambda_4} \Delta(\lambda_1 + \lambda_2 - \lambda_3 - \lambda_4)$$
$$+ a_{\lambda_1}^{+} a_{\lambda_2}^{+} a_{\lambda_3}^{+} a_{\lambda_4} \Delta(\lambda_1 + \lambda_2 + \lambda_3 - \lambda_4) + \text{h.c.}\} \qquad (7.11)$$

in which an approximate expression for the coupling constant in terms of the macroscopic magnetization M is given in the dipolar term.

The four-magnon processes which involve the decay of two uniform-mode magnons together with the creation of two magnons of opposite wave vectors are important in resonance relaxation effects.

We shall defer the calculation of the relaxation rate involving the above interaction processes until later chapters. These will be taken up after we have discussed phonons and phonon-magnon interaction terms. Apart from relaxation effects, the interaction processes discussed in this chapter will lead to important temperature-dependent renormalization of spin-wave modes in ferromagnets (see Oguchi 1960 and Wallace 1966). There will be similar temperature-dependent renormalization effects in antiferromagnets (see Oguchi 1960, Nagai and Tanaka 1969).

7.2. Magnon–magnon renormalization effects in ferromagnets and antiferromagnets

The renormalization of Bloch spin waves due to a two-spin-wave dynamical interaction has been studied in the long-wavelength (low-temperature) limit by Wallace (1966) by using renormalized normal-mode creation (annihilation) operators. In this approach the kinematic interaction is ignored in that it is exponentially small at low temperatures (Dyson 1956). The dynamic interactions are now taken into account after renormalization of the spin-wave modes. The advantage of this procedure is that, whereas in Dyson's approach one has to sum the interactions to all orders to evaluate the leading contribution ($T^{5/2}$ term), in the renormalized operator approach only the first-order corrections due to the residual interaction need be considered. The mathematical procedure underlying the renormalized normal-mode operator technique is given by

$$[H, \xi_\lambda^+] = \hbar\omega_\lambda \xi_\lambda^+ + \chi_\lambda^+ \tag{7.12}$$

where ξ_λ^+ is the approximate normal-mode creation operator and χ_λ^+ is a small correction. The essence of the technique consists in making the remainder operator χ_λ^+ smaller by one order of magnitude in the perturbation parameter. For a ferromagnet one defines a renormalized creation operator

$$\tilde{a}_\lambda^+ = a_\lambda^+ + a_{1\lambda}^+$$

The form of $a_{1\lambda}^+$ is chosen so as to remove the dynamical interaction between pairs of renormalized spin waves. For a Heisenberg ferromagnet the general form of $a_{1\lambda}^+$ is

$$a_{1\lambda}^+ = \frac{1}{N}\sum_{\lambda'\lambda''} \alpha(\lambda, \lambda', \lambda'')a_{\lambda'}^+ a_{\lambda''-\lambda'+\lambda}^+ a_{\lambda''} \tag{7.14}$$

where the coefficients $\alpha(\lambda, \lambda', \lambda'')$ are so chosen that the term χ_λ^+ vanishes, i.e.

$$[H, \tilde{a}_\lambda^+] = \hbar\omega_\lambda \tilde{a}_\lambda^+ + \tilde{\chi}_\lambda^+ \tag{7.15}$$

where

$$\begin{aligned}
\tilde{\chi}_\lambda^+ = \frac{1}{N}\sum_{\lambda'\lambda''} \{&2(J_{\lambda'} - J_{\lambda'-\lambda}) \\
&+ \alpha(\lambda, \lambda', \lambda'')\hbar(\omega_{\lambda'} + \omega_{\lambda''-\lambda'+\lambda} - \omega_{\lambda''} - \omega_\lambda) \\
&+ \frac{2}{N}\sum_{\lambda'''} \alpha(\lambda, \lambda''', \lambda'')(J_{\lambda'} - J_{\lambda'-\lambda'''})\}a_{\lambda'}^+ a_{\lambda''-\lambda'+\lambda}^+ a_{\lambda''}
\end{aligned} \tag{7.16}$$

The condition for $\tilde{\chi}_\lambda{}^+$ to vanish in the first order gives an integral equation for the coefficient. The solution of these integral equations gives us the undetermined coefficients and hence the renormalized creation operators. Writing the entire Hamiltonian in terms of these operators and taking the residual interaction into account, the renormalized statistically averaged spin-wave energy $\hbar\langle\omega_\lambda+\omega_{1\lambda}\rangle$ turns out to be

$$\hbar\langle\omega_\lambda+\tilde{\omega}_{1\lambda}\rangle=g\mu_{\rm B}B+\tfrac{1}{3}zJ\lambda^2a^2$$
$$\times(1-\pi vS^{-1}QZ_{5/2}\theta^{5/2}) \tag{7.17}$$

where

$$Z_q=\sum_{m=1}^{\infty}m^{-q}\exp\left(\frac{-mg\mu_{\rm B}B}{k_{\rm B}T}\right)$$

$$\theta=\frac{3k_{\rm B}T}{4\pi vzJS} \tag{7.18}$$

$$v=a^2\Omega_v{}^{-2/3}$$

Q being the form factor for the lattices in question. The angular bracket $\langle\ldots\rangle$ denotes the statistical-mechanical average of an operator A where

$$\langle A\rangle=\frac{{\rm tr}\,\exp(-\beta H)A}{{\rm tr}\,\exp(-\beta H)}.$$

The negative sign of $\tilde{\omega}_{1\lambda}$ suggests that in the long-wavelength limit the dynamical interaction between two renormalized magnons is attractive. The dependence of the correction on temperature and wave vector follows a $\lambda^2T^{5/2}$ law which should be compared with the $\lambda^2T^{3/2}$ dependence form of Tyablikov (1959) and the $\lambda^2T^{5/2}$ form of Callen (1963). The correction term is real to order $\lambda^2T^{5/2}$ and hence there is no contribution to linewidth in experiments involving renormalized magnons.

Magnon–magnon renormalization effects in antiferromagnets have been discussed by several authors using various levels of approximation. Oguchi (1960) used the usual expansion of the free energy in terms of magnon–magnon interaction parameters. Bloch (1962, 1963) combined this with the minimal property of free energy for some ferromagnetic and antiferromagnetic cubic systems. This involved the introduction of the magnon renormalization approximation (MRA). In this approach the temperature-dependent magnon energies are expressed in terms of the statistical average of the magnon operators themselves. The self-consistent solutions represent magnon energies in the MRA. Another approximation is the random phase approximation (RPA) in which the averages are performed with respect to the unperturbed Hamiltonian. Thus the method is not self-consistent. Nagai

(1969) and Nagai and Tanaka (1969) have calculated the temperature-dependent magnon energies for MnF_2 and FeF_2 using both MRA and RPA methods and compared with experimental data. The experimental data for MnF_2 and FeF_2 seem to lie between the theoretical curves based on these two approximations. It should be noted that the Hamiltonian used by them included magnetic anisotropic terms, namely uniaxial intra-ionic anisotropy for FeF_2 and an inter-ionic dipolar interaction term for MnF_2,

$$H(FeF_2) = 2J \sum_{\langle l,m \rangle} \mathbf{S}_l \cdot \mathbf{S}_m - D\left\{\left(\sum_l S_l^z\right)^2 + \sum_m (S^z)^2\right\} \tag{7.19}$$

The quartic terms in the spin-wave interaction Hamiltonian were decoupled by the RPA so that the resulting Hamiltonian is quadratic in the free-spin-wave operator. More explicitly a typical operator

$$\sum Y_{\lambda_1 - \lambda_2} a_{\lambda_1}^+ a_{\lambda_2} d_{\lambda_3}^+ d_{\lambda_4} \Delta(\lambda_1 - \lambda_2 - \lambda_3 + \lambda_4)$$

$$\approx \sum_{\lambda,q} Y_{\lambda-q}(a_\lambda^+ a_\lambda \langle d_q^+ d_q \rangle$$

$$+ d_\lambda^+ d_\lambda \langle a_q^+ a_q \rangle \tag{7.20}$$

$$- \langle a_\lambda^+ a_\lambda \rangle \langle d_\lambda^+ d_\lambda \rangle)$$

$$+ \text{other possible terms involving}$$
$$\text{two annihilation and two creation operators}$$

The resulting bilinear terms are then diagonalized by the usual canonical transformation. The temperature-dependent magnon energies thus obtained contain various statistical averages $\langle \ldots \rangle$ in the decoupling scheme as parameters to be determined in various approximations such as the free-spin-wave (FSW), RPA, and MRA. For details, reference may be made to the papers of Nagai and Tanaka (1969).

We shall write some expressions relevant to the antiferromagnetic resonance (AFMR) frequency of FeF_2 for which experimental data are available. The renormalized magnon energies $\hbar\tilde{\omega}_\lambda$ in the RPA(R) and MRA(M) are given by

$$\hbar\tilde{\omega}_\lambda(R) = \{H_{1\lambda}^2(R) - H_{2\lambda}^2(R)\}^{1/2} \tag{7.21}$$

where

$$H_{1\lambda}(R) = 2JSz(1 - \mu_R - \omega_R) + \frac{D}{Jz}(1 - \mu_R - \nu_R)$$

$$H_{2\lambda}(R) = 2JSz(1 - \mu_R - \omega_R) Y_\lambda$$

with

$$v_R = \frac{1}{NS} \sum_\lambda \left(\frac{H_{1\lambda}^F}{\hbar\omega_\lambda} \right) \coth \frac{1}{2} \left(\frac{\hbar\omega_\lambda}{k_B T} \right)$$

$$\omega_R = -\frac{1}{NS} \sum_\lambda \frac{H_{2\lambda}^F}{\hbar\omega_\lambda} Y_\lambda \coth \frac{1}{2} \left(\frac{\hbar\omega_\lambda}{k_B T} \right)$$

$$\mu_R = v_R - \frac{1}{2S} \tag{7.22}$$

$$H_{1\lambda}^F = 2JSz \left\{ 1 - \frac{D}{Jz} \left(1 - \frac{1}{2S} \right) \right\}$$

$$H_{2\lambda}^F = 2JSz \, Y_\lambda$$

It should be noted that ω_λ is the free-spin-wave frequency and D is the one-ion unaxial anisotropy constant. Similarly,

$$\hbar\tilde{\omega}_\lambda(M) = \{ H_{1\lambda}^2(M) - H_{2\lambda}^2(M) \} \tag{7.23}$$

where $H_{1\lambda}(M)$ and $H_{2\lambda}(M)$ are in the same form as given in (7.22) except that $H_{1\lambda}^F$ and $H_{2\lambda}^F$ and the frequencies occurring in (7.22) are replaced by $H_{1\lambda}(M)$, $H_{2\lambda}(M)$, and $\omega_\lambda(M)$ respectively. This ensures self-consistency.

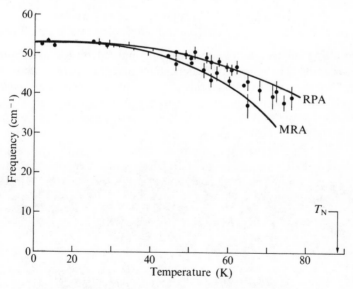

FIG. 7.1. A comparison of the theoretical and experimental results of AFMR in FeF$_2$. (After Nagai and Tanaka 1969.)

The theoretically calculated temperature dependence of the AFMR frequency for $\lambda = 0$ is compared with experimental data for FeF_2 in Fig. 7.1. It is seen that the MRA overestimates the spin-wave interaction and the RPA underestimates it. A similar situation obtains for MnF_2.

Kowalska, Moustafa, and Sokalski (1972) have used the above methods to calculate the temperature-dependent magnon energies in Cr_2O_3 as a function of magnon wave vectors. The agreement is good at low temperatures, but becomes poor in the high-temperature regions. This may be attributed to neglect of the magnon–phonon interaction in the renormalization of magnon energies at high temperatures.

The renormalization effect of the magnon–phonon interaction will be discussed in Chapter 10 for a few systems.

8

PHONONS AND PHONON – MAGNON INTERACTIONS

In earlier chapters we discussed interactions involving spins rigidly anchored to paramagnetic ions which form a framework at rest. However, the ions are never quiescent and the collective motion of ions which are coupled by interionic elastic forces give rise to very important modulations of the magnetic interactions. In fact, we shall see that elementary spin-wave excitations (magnons) form one subsystem which interacts with the other subsystem, namely quantized lattice vibration modes (phonons). This kind of decomposition is permissible if the time of equilibration within each sub-system is shorter than that between the subsystems. This condition is satisfied over a considerable range of temperature in systems of interest.

The subject of lattice dynamics has been adequately covered in many standard books (see Born and Huang 1954). In what follows therefore we shall give a brief discussion of what is relevant to the present treatment.

8.1. Phonons

In a real crystal we have the complex problem of solving the equations of motion of ion cores (nuclei plus inner electronic shells) and valence electrons. This is a formidable task. The simplification arises from the fact that the ratio of the electronic mass to the ionic mass is of the order of 10^{-3}. This renders the ionic motion separable from the electronic motion to a considerable extent. This is the essence of the Born–Oppenheimer factorization that amounts to saying that the electrons follow the ionic motion adiabatically. As a consequence, it can be shown that the ions move in an effective potential field that includes the electronic energy of the valence electrons. The latter, of course, depends parametrically on the instantaneous ionic co-ordinates. However, in the static Born–Oppenheimer approximation one uses the electronic energy corresponding to the equilibrium configuration of the ions. It should be noted that deviations from adiabaticity give rise to electron–lattice interactions which we shall invoke later.

Let us consider a crystal comprising N unit cells with r atoms per unit cell. The unit cell is described by three basis vectors. The co-ordinates of the αth atom in the lth unit cell is denoted by the position vector $\mathbf{R}_{l\alpha}$ and its conjugate momentum by $\mathbf{P}_{l\alpha}$. The lattice Hamiltonian is given by

$$H_{\mathrm{L}} = \sum_{l,\alpha} \frac{\mathbf{P}_{l\alpha}{}^2}{2M_\alpha} + \tfrac{1}{2} \sum_{\substack{l \neq m \\ \alpha\beta}} V(\mathbf{R}_{l\alpha} - \mathbf{R}_{m\beta}) \tag{8.1}$$

where the first term is the kinetic energy and the second term the potential energy for the pairwise interionic interaction; M_α is the mass of the αth atom. The deviation $\delta\mathbf{R}_{l\alpha}$ from the equilibrium configuration $\mathbf{R}_{l\alpha}{}^0$ can be written as

$$\mathbf{R}_{l\alpha} = \mathbf{R}_{l\alpha}{}^0 + \delta\mathbf{R}_{l\alpha}. \tag{8.2}$$

Expanding the interionic potential in powers of $\delta\mathbf{R}_{l\alpha}$ and retaining terms up to second order only (harmonic approximation) we obtain

$$V(\mathbf{R}_{l\alpha} - \mathbf{R}_{m\beta}) = V(\mathbf{R}_{l\alpha}{}^0 - \mathbf{R}_{m\beta}{}^0) + \tfrac{1}{2}\Sigma \delta R_{l\alpha}{}^\mu \Lambda_{l\alpha,m\beta}{}^{\mu,\nu} \delta R_{m\beta}{}^\nu \tag{8.3}$$

where

$$\Lambda_{l\alpha,m\beta}{}^{\mu\nu} = \left(\frac{\partial^2 V_{\mathrm{L}}}{\partial R_{l\alpha}{}^\mu \partial R_{m\beta}{}^\nu} \right)_0 \tag{8.4}$$

μ and ν are the Cartesian indices, and V_{L} denotes the total lattice potential, i.e. the second term of eqn (8.1). The first term is abosrbed in a redefinition of the zero of energy; further $(\partial V_{\mathrm{L}}/\partial R_{l\alpha}{}^\mu) = 0$ from the condition of equilibrium. The lattice Hamiltonian in eqn (8.1) then takes the form

$$H_{\mathrm{L}} = \sum_{l\alpha} \frac{\mathbf{P}_{l\alpha}{}^2}{2M_\alpha} + \tfrac{1}{2} \sum_{\substack{l\alpha,m\beta \\ \mu,\nu}} \delta R_{l\alpha}{}^\mu \Lambda_{l\alpha,m\beta}{}^{\mu,\nu} \delta R_{m\beta}{}^\nu + \dots \tag{8.5}$$

In order to diagonalize the above Hamiltonian we make use of the following co-ordinate transformation:

$$\delta\mathbf{R}_{l\alpha} = \frac{1}{\sqrt{(NM_{\mathrm{c}})}} \sum_{\mathbf{q}s} Q_{\mathbf{q}s} \varepsilon_{\mathbf{q}s}(\alpha) \exp(\mathrm{i}\mathbf{q} \cdot \mathbf{R}_l{}^0). \tag{8.6}$$

Likewise, the momentum $\mathbf{P}_{l\alpha}$ conjugate to the displacement $\delta\mathbf{R}_{l\alpha}$ is described by

$$\mathbf{P}_{l\alpha} = \left(\frac{M_{\mathrm{c}}}{N} \right)^{1/2} \sum_{\mathbf{q}s} P_{\mathbf{q}s} \varepsilon_{\mathbf{q}s}(\alpha) \exp(-\mathrm{i}\mathbf{q} \cdot \mathbf{R}_l{}^0) \tag{8.7}$$

where M_{c} is the mass of the unit cell; $\varepsilon_{\mathbf{q}s}(\alpha)$ is the polarization vector associated with the wave vector $\mathbf{q}$ and the branch index s. In fact these are the eigenvectors of the dynamical matrix obtained by solving the normal-mode problem (see Peierls 1956). The corresponding eigenvalues give the mode-branch eigenfrequencies ω_{qs} as a function of wave vector (dispersion relation). The number of branches is equal to $3r_c$, where r_c is the number of atoms in the unit cell. The wave vector $\mathbf{q}$ spans the N points of the first Brillouin zone, the total number of degrees of freedom being $3r_cN$. The possible values of $\mathbf{q}$ are given by the periodic boundary conditions. The eigenvectors are orthonormalized according to the relations

$$\sum_\alpha M_\alpha {}^* \varepsilon_{qs}(\alpha)\varepsilon_{qs'}{}^*(\alpha) = M_c \delta_{ss'} \tag{8.8}$$

They also satisfy the completeness relations

$$\sum_{q,s} \varepsilon_{q,s}(\alpha)\varepsilon_{qs}{}^*(\alpha') \exp\{i\mathbf{q}\cdot(\mathbf{R}_l{}^0 - \mathbf{R}_{l'}{}^0)\} = \delta_{ll'}\delta_{\alpha\alpha'} \tag{8.9}$$

A proper analysis of the dynamical matrix reveals a classification of the branches according to the dependence of the corresponding frequencies as $\mathbf{q}\to 0$. Thus, we have three acoustic branches (one longitudinal (LA) and two transverse (TA)) with $\omega_{qa}\to 0$ for $q\to 0$. The remaining $3r_c - 3$ branches are known as the optical branches of which $r_c - 1$ are longitudinal optical (LO) and $2r_c - 2$ are transverse optical (TO) branches. For these branches the frequencies tend to non-zero values for $\mathbf{q}\to 0$. The distinction between longitudinal and transverse is strictly valid for certain symmetry directions of the crystal. For a general direction, the situation is rather complex and no such distinction can be made except for low values of $\mathbf{q}$.

First quantization is achieved by treating the conjugate variables $\delta\mathbf{R}_{l\alpha}$ and $\mathbf{P}_{l\alpha}$ as quantum-mechanical operators obeying the equal-time canonical commutation relations

$$[\delta R_{l\alpha}{}^\mu, P_{m\beta}{}^\nu] = i\hbar\delta_{lm}\delta_{\alpha\beta}\delta_{\mu\nu} \tag{8.10}$$

and

$$[\delta R_{l\alpha}{}^\mu, \delta R_{m\beta}{}^\nu] = [P_{l\alpha}{}^\mu, P_{m\beta}{}^\nu] = 0. \tag{8.11}$$

These equations imply the following canonical commutation relations for the normal co-ordinates (Q_{qs}) and conjugate momenta P_{qs}:

$$[Q_{qs}, P_{q's'}] = i\hbar\delta_{qq'}\delta_{ss'} \tag{8.12}$$

$$[P_{qs}, P_{q's'}] = [Q_{qs}, Q_{q's'}] = 0. \tag{8.13}$$

It can be shown that the Hamiltonian (eqn (8.8)) is transferred to

$$H_L = \tfrac{1}{2}\sum_{q,s}\{(P_{qs}{}^*P_{qs}) + \omega_{qs}{}^2 Q_{qs}{}^* Q_{qs}\}. \tag{8.14}$$

We can recast this Hamiltonian in a second-quantized form by introducing the phonon creation and annihilation operators $b_{bs}{}^+$ and b_{qs} by the following canonical transformations:

$$Q_{qs} = -i\left(\frac{\hbar}{2\omega_{qs}}\right)^{1/2} (b_{qs}{}^+ - b_{qs}) \tag{8.15}$$

$$P_{qs} = \left(\frac{\hbar\omega_{qs}}{2}\right)^{1/2} (b_{-qs}{}^+ + b_{qs}) \tag{8.16}$$

With the help of eqns (8.12) and (8.13), it can be shown that the phonon operators obey the well-known Bose commutation relations:

$$[b_{qs}, b_{q's'}{}^+] = \delta_{qq'}\delta_{ss'} \tag{8.17}$$

$$[b_{qs}, b_{q's'}] = [b_{qs}{}^+, b_{q's'}{}^+] = 0 \tag{8.18}$$

In terms of these operators, the lattice Hamiltonian takes the form

$$H_{ph} = \sum_{q,s} \hbar\omega_{qa}(b_{qs}{}^+ b_{qs} + \tfrac{1}{2})$$

$$\equiv \sum_{qs} \hbar\omega_{qs}(N_{qs} + \tfrac{1}{2}) \tag{8.19}$$

which also defines the phonon number operator for a particular mode branch

$$N_{qs} = b_{qs}{}^+ b_{qs}. \tag{8.20}$$

As in the case of magnons the normalized eigenfunctions of the phonon Hamiltonian (cf. eqn (8.19)) are described in the occupation number representation by the Dirac ket

$$|N_{q_1 s_1}, N_{q_2 s_2}, \ldots, N_{q_n s_n}\rangle \tag{8.21}$$

where $N_{q_1 s_1}$, $N_{q_2 s_2}$, etc. are the phonon occupation numbers in a particular mode branch (q, s). The phonon occupation creation and annihilation operators acting on these states give

$$b_{qs}{}^+ |\ldots N_{qs}\ldots\rangle = \sqrt{(N_{qs}+1)} |\ldots(N_{qs}+1)\rangle \tag{8.22}$$

$$b_{qs} |\ldots N_{qs}\ldots\rangle = \sqrt{N_{qs}} |\ldots(N_{qs}-1)\ldots\rangle \tag{8.23}$$

The phonon vacuum state $|\ldots 0 \ldots\rangle$ is defined by the relation

$$b_{qs} |\ldots 0 \ldots|\rangle = 0 \tag{8.24}$$

for all modes and is the ground state in the harmonic approximation. We generate an arbitrary phonon state in the occupation-number representation by the successive application of the phonon creation operators on the vacuum state, i.e.

$$|N_{q_1s_1}, N_{q_2s_2}\cdots\rangle = \frac{1}{(N_{q_1s_1}!N_{q_2s_2}!\cdots)^{1/2}}(b_{q_1s_1}{}^+)^{N_{q_1s_1}}$$

$$\times (b_{q_2s_2}{}^+)^{N_{q_2s_2}}\cdots|\cdots 0\cdots\rangle \tag{8.25}$$

8.2. Phonon magnon interactions

We shall now consider other parts of the crystal Hamiltonian in order to treat the interaction processes involving phonons and magnons. Further, we confine ourselves to magnetic insulators, i.e. there are no itinerant (conduction) electrons. In the electronic part of the Hamiltonian we are therefore concerned with the localized valence electrons which are responsible for magnetism. The effective exchange Hamiltonian for the spin coupling between these localized (unpaired) electrons was derived for a situation where the atoms were at the equilibrium positions. Thus $J_{eff}(R_{lm})$ depends only on the equilibrium separation between the two paramagnetic atoms involved. At a finite temperature the deviations from this equilibrium distance due to lattice vibrations must be taken into account. We shall obtain additional terms involving modulation of the effective exchange interaction due to lattice vibration modes. The modulation may arise in two ways. First, the oscillating crystal field may admix low-lying orbital excited states into the ground state of the magnetic ion. This in turn modulates the exchange integral. Secondly, the effective distance-dependent exchange integral may be directly modulated by the relative movement of the magnetic ions. In a phenomenological treatment, the two effects are inextricably mixed. We shall consider the orbital mechanism first.

For simplicity, we consider a magnetic insulator having one magnetic ion per unit cell with one unpaired electron. The unpaired electron moves in the oscillating crystal field of the neighbouring ions. Let us write the Hamiltonian of these electrons moving in the force field of ion cores at their instantaneous positions. In the first quantization representation we have

$$H_{el} = \sum_l \frac{\mathbf{p}_{l0}{}^2}{2m} + \sum_{l,l'\alpha'} U(\mathbf{r}_{l0} - \mathbf{R}_{l'\alpha'}) \tag{8.26}$$

where $\mathbf{p}_{l0}{}^2/2m$ is the kinetic energy of the electron specific to the magnetic ion in the lth unit cell denoted $l0$, and $U(\mathbf{r}_{l0} - \mathbf{R}_{l'\alpha'})$ is its potential energy at $\mathbf{r}_{l0}$ due to the ion core at $\mathbf{R}_{l'\alpha'}$. Referred to the equilibrium positions (e.g. $\mathbf{R}_{l'\alpha'}{}^0$) of the ion cores the Hamiltonian for the electron (labelled $l0$) is rewritten as

$$H_{el}(l0) = \frac{\mathbf{p}_{l0}{}^2}{2m} + U(\mathbf{r}_{l0} - \mathbf{R}_{l0}{}^0) + V_{cf}{}^0 + V_{el} \tag{8.27}$$

where

$$V_{cf}^{0} = \sum_{\substack{m\beta \\ \beta \neq 0}} U(\mathbf{r}_{l0} - \mathbf{R}_{m\beta}^{0}) \tag{8.28}$$

and

$$V_{el} = V_{cf} - V_{cf}^{0} = \sum_{h} \frac{\partial V_{cf}}{\partial \mathbf{R}_{h}} \cdot \delta \mathbf{R}_{h}$$

$$+ \frac{1}{2} \sum_{hh'} \delta \mathbf{R}_{h'} \cdot \left(\frac{\partial^{2} V_{cf}}{\partial \mathbf{R}_{h} \partial \mathbf{R}_{h'}} \right) \cdot \delta \mathbf{R}_{h'} + \tag{8.29}$$

$$\equiv \sum_{h} \mathbf{V}^{h} \cdot \delta \mathbf{R}_{h} + \frac{1}{2} \sum_{hh'} \delta \mathbf{R}_{h} \cdot \mathbf{V}^{hh'} \cdot \delta \mathbf{R}_{h} + \cdots .$$

Here $\mathbf{R}_{h} = \mathbf{R}_{l0} - \mathbf{R}_{i'\alpha'}$ is the distance vector connecting the atoms at $l0$ and $l'\alpha'$; V_{cf}^{0} denotes the magnetic-electron other-ion interaction potential when the ions are in their equilibrium positions. In effect, this represents the static crystal field experienced by the electron of the magnetic atom at $\mathbf{R}_{l0}$. On the other hand, V_{el} (cf. eqn (8.29)) represents the interaction between this electron and the oscillating crystal field; explicitly, it is written as a Taylor series expansion in powers of the relative displacement vectors $\delta \mathbf{R}_{h}$ etc.

Now in the chapter dealing with the exchange interaction, the effective exchange Hamiltonian was derived in terms of those orthonormal sets of localized orbitals which were eigenstates of the Hartree–Fock (HF) Hamiltonian of the crystal. However, the perturbation term V_{el} is not included in this HF Hamiltonian although $U(\mathbf{r}_{l0} - \mathbf{R}_{l0}^{0}) + V_{cf}$ is included. The eigenfunction of the unperturbed HF Hamiltonian will be modified by the inclusion of the perturbation V_{el}. We envisage that the perturbation V_{el} admixes the low-lying excited orbital states into the ground state $\phi_{m'}$. Thus the solution of

$$(H_{em}^{0} + V_{el}) \psi_{m} = E_{m} \psi_{m} \tag{8.30}$$

is given by first-order perturbation theory as

$$\psi_{m} = \phi_{m} + \sum_{\mu} (V_{el})_{\mu m} \frac{\phi_{\mu}}{E_{m} - E_{\mu}} \tag{8.31}$$

where ϕ_{μ} is the excited orbital, $(V_{el})_{\mu m}$ is the matrix element of V_{el} connecting states ϕ_{m} and ϕ_{μ} and $\Delta E_{\mu m} = E_{m} - E_{\mu}$ is the corresponding energy denominator. It should be noted that $(V_{el})_{\mu m}$ involves lattice displacements which will be explicitly displayed later. The use of time-independent perturbation theory in eqn (8.31) is justified within the quasistatic approximation.

Next, we reformulate the effective exchange Hamiltonian for magnetically coupled systems in terms of the perturbed orbitals ψ_m (cf. eqn (8.31)). In addition to the exchange Hamiltonian derived in Chapters 3 and 4, we shall obtain extra terms which involve lattice displacements. The total Hamiltonian will now have the form

$$H = \text{constant} + H_L + H_S + H_Z + H_{an} + H_{dip} + H_{SL} \tag{8.32}$$

where $H_L (\equiv H_{ph})$ is the lattice (phonon) part of the Hamiltonian already given (cf. eqn (8.19)). The effective exchange Hamiltonian corresponding to the equilibrium separation of the paramagnetic atoms is denoted by H_S:

$$H_S = -2 \sum_{m<n} J_{eff}(R_{mn}^{0}) S_m \cdot S_n. \tag{8.33}$$

H_Z, H_{an}, and H_{dip} are the Zeeman, anisotropy and dipolar contributions which have been explained in previous chapters. The spin-lattice interaction terms are represented by H_{SL} (see Sinha and Upadhyaya 1962):

$$H_{SL} = 8 \sum_{m<n} \sum_{h} (J_M{}^h \cdot \delta R_h) S_m \cdot S_n + \text{higher-order terms} \tag{8.34}$$

where $J_M{}^h$ is the gradient of the exchange integral with respect to the lattice displacement. Its explicit form can be written as

$$J_M{}^h = \sum_{\mu} J_{mn}{}^{n\mu} \langle \phi_\mu | V^h | \phi_m \rangle \Delta E_{\mu m} \tag{8.35}$$

where $J_{mn}{}^{n\mu}$ is an effective exchange integral involving one excited orbital ϕ_μ and the ground-state orbital ϕ_m induced by $\langle \phi_\mu | V^h | \phi_m \rangle$, the matrix element of the oscillating crystal field. Earlier, we have seen that the effective exchange integral is the resultant of direct exchange, transfer effects, exchange polarization, and correlation effects. The modulated exchange integral written may involve all these processes except that one of the orbitals is an excited-state orbital because of the phonon-induced effects mentioned above. In the present formulation single-ion spin–phonon processes arising from spin–lattice effects have been ignored (Van Vleck 1940; cf. Chapter 2). In exchange-coupled systems they are weaker than the processes considered above.

An alternative phenomenological formulation of spin-lattice interaction involves the expansion of the effective exchange energy in powers of the ionic displacements or strain tensor (Akhiezer 1946)

$$H_{SL} = -2 \sum_{\substack{mn \\ m<n}} \sum_{h} \{(\delta R_h) \cdot \nabla J_{eff}(R_{mn})\} S_m \cdot S_n \tag{8.36}$$

However, this formulation involves the condition that the electrons are tightly bound to the ion cores (Pytte 1965), i.e. the electrons move rigidly with the ions and there is no modification of the electronic states of the ions due to crystal-field oscillations. A similar development of the dipole–dipole interaction terms can be assumed.

The formulation given in eqn (8.34) is an atomistic description and includes the modification of the atomic orbital function due to crystal-field oscillations. Also, it can incorporate the anisotropic nature of the modulated interaction in case the orbitals involved (excited or ground state) have a specific spatial disposition.

The next step is to re-express the spin–lattice Hamiltonian H_{SL} in terms of phonon and magnon operators. For this purpose we make use of the appropriate transformations on the spin and lattice displacement operators, i.e.

$$\delta\mathbf{R}_h = \delta\mathbf{R}_l - \delta\mathbf{R}_{l'}$$

with

$$\delta\mathbf{R}_l = \frac{1}{\sqrt{N}} \sum_{qs} \mathbf{g}_{qs}(b_{qs}{}^+ - b_{-qs})\exp(i\mathbf{q}\cdot\mathbf{R}_l{}^0) \tag{8.37a}$$

and

$$\mathbf{g}_{qs} = -i\boldsymbol{\varepsilon}_{qs}(0)\left(\frac{\hbar}{2M_c\omega_{qs}}\right)^{1/2}. \tag{8.37b}$$

For simplicity, we have idealized the system as consisting entirely of magnetic atoms. The same spin-deviation, spin-wave, and canonical transformations are used for the spin operators as for the pure magnon parts (see Chapter 5). In what follows we shall write the phonon–magnon interaction terms separately for each type of magnetic ordering, namely ferromagnetic antiferromagnetic, and ferrimagnetic systems. It should be noted in passing that the strain field ε_s associated with the longitudinal phonon is given by the divergence of the displacement field (i.e. eqn (8.37)).

8.3. Interaction Hamiltonian

8.3.1. *Ferromagnets*
The magnon–phonon interaction Hamiltonian turns out to be (Sinha and Upadhyaya 1962)

$$H_{mp}(\text{ferro}) = \sum_{\lambda,q} \phi_{\lambda,q} a_{\lambda-q}{}^+ a_\lambda (b_{qs}{}^+ - b_{-qs}) \tag{8.38}$$

where

$$\phi_{\lambda,q} = \frac{8S}{\sqrt{N}} \sum_h (\mathbf{J}_M{}^h \cdot \mathbf{g}_{qs})\{\exp(-i\mathbf{q}\cdot\mathbf{R}_h)-1\}\{\exp(i\lambda\cdot\mathbf{R}_h)-1\} \tag{8.39}$$

The interaction terms given in eqn (8.38) are essentially two-magnon one-phonon inelastic processes. A magnon of wave vector λ is destroyed and another magnon of wave vector $\lambda - q$ is created with the emission or absorption of a phonon. In writing these terms we have selected only the normal processes (i.e. the reciprocal lattice vector occurring in the interference condition has been set equal to zero).

8.3.2. *Two sublattice antiferromagnets*
It has been shown earlier that the elementary spin-wave excitations in a two-sublattice antiferromagnet consist of two branches α and β. The corresponding magnon operators were designated by the creation and annihilation operators $(\alpha_\lambda^+, \alpha_\lambda)$ and $(\beta_\lambda^+, \beta_\lambda)$. The magnon–phonon interaction terms which emerge after the relevant canonical transformations involve both these branches. The expression is given by (Upadhyaya and Sinha 1963)

$$
\begin{aligned}
H_{mp}(\text{antiferro}) = \sum_{\lambda, qs} \{ &A_{\lambda, qs}(\alpha_\lambda \alpha_{\lambda-q}^+ b_{qs}^+ - \alpha_\lambda^+ \alpha_{\lambda-q} b_{qs}) \\
+ &B_{\lambda, qs}(\alpha_\lambda \beta_{\lambda-q} b_{qs}^+ - \alpha_\lambda^+ \beta_{\lambda-q}^+ b_{qs}) \\
+ &A_{\lambda, qs}(\beta_\lambda \beta_{\lambda-q}^+ b_{qs} - \beta_\lambda^+ \beta_{\lambda-q} b_{qs}) \}
\end{aligned}
\tag{8.40}
$$

where the coupling constants for the longitudinal acoustic modes are given by

$$
\begin{aligned}
A_{\lambda q} = \frac{4Sz}{\sqrt{N}} \sum_h (\mathbf{J}_M^h \cdot \mathbf{g}_q) \{ &(Y_{\lambda-q} - Y_\lambda)\sinh(\theta_{\lambda-q} - \theta_\lambda) \\
+ &(1 - Y_q)\cosh(\theta_{\lambda-q} - \theta_\lambda) \}
\end{aligned}
\tag{8.41}
$$

$$
\begin{aligned}
B_{\lambda q} = \frac{4Sz}{\sqrt{N}} \sum_h (\mathbf{J}_M^h \cdot \mathbf{g}_q) \{ &(Y_{\lambda-q} - Y_\lambda)\cosh(\theta_{\lambda-q} - \theta_\lambda) \\
+ &(1 - Y_q)\sinh(\theta_{\lambda-q} - \theta_\lambda) \}.
\end{aligned}
\tag{8.42}
$$

In the above equations θ_λ, Y_λ, and Y_q have the same meaning as given earlier during the diagonalization procedure for antiferromagnets. It should be noted that terms involving only creation (destruction) of three bosons have been omitted in that we shall be concerned with lowest-order energy-conserving relaxation processes.

8.3.3. *Two sublattice ferrimagnet*
The calculation is similar to the two-sublattice antiferromagnet except that the two spin-wave branches referred to earlier as 'acoustic' (designated by α) and 'optical' (designated by β) are no longer degenerate. The magnon–

phonon interaction terms look similar to the antiferrimagnetic case; however, the coupling constants are different. The interaction Hamiltonian is given by (Joshi and Sinha 1965)

$$H_{mp}(\text{ferri}) = \sum_{\lambda q} \{ A_{\lambda q}'(\alpha_\lambda \alpha_{\lambda-q}{}^+ b_q{}^+ - \alpha_\lambda{}^+ \alpha_{\lambda-q} b_q)$$

$$+ B_{\lambda q}'(\alpha_\lambda \beta_{\lambda-q} b_q{}^+ - \alpha_\lambda{}^+ \beta_{\lambda-q}{}^+ b_q) \tag{8.43}$$

$$+ C_{\lambda q}'(\beta_\lambda \beta_{\lambda-q}{}^+ b_q - \beta_\lambda{}^+ \beta_{\lambda-q} b_q{}^+) \}$$

where the coupling constants are defined as follows:

$$A_{\lambda q}' = D_q \{ (\gamma_{\lambda-q} - \gamma_\lambda)(S_A S_B)^{1/2} \cosh(\theta_{\lambda-q} - \theta_\lambda)$$
$$+ (1 - \gamma_q)(S_B \cosh \theta_\lambda \cosh \theta_{\lambda-q} - S_A \sinh \theta_\lambda \sinh \theta_{\lambda-q}) \} \tag{8.44}$$

$$B_{\lambda q}' = D_q \{ (\gamma_{\lambda-q} - \gamma_q)(S_A S_B)^{1/2} \cosh(\theta_{\lambda-q} - \theta_\lambda)$$
$$+ (1 - \gamma_q)(S_B \cosh \theta_\lambda \sinh \theta_{\lambda-q} - S_A \sinh \theta_\lambda \tag{8.45}$$
$$\cosh \theta_{\lambda-q})$$

and

$$C_{\lambda q} = D_q - \{ (\gamma_{\lambda-q} - \gamma_\lambda)(S_A S_B)^{1/2} \sinh(\theta_{\lambda-q} - \theta_\lambda)$$
$$+ (1 - \gamma_q)(S_A \cosh \theta_\lambda \cosh \theta_{\lambda-q} - S_B \sinh \theta_\lambda \sinh \theta_{\lambda-q}) \} \tag{8.46}$$

with

$$D_q \equiv \frac{4}{\sqrt{N}} \sum_h (\mathbf{J}_M{}^h \cdot \mathbf{g}_q). \tag{8.47}$$

The first term of eqn (8.43) represents the interaction of phonons with magnons of the lower-lying (acoustic) branch whereas the last term refers to the higher (optical) branch. The middle term connects magnons of the two branches.

The magnon–phonon interaction processes considered above involve the acoustic phonons only. At somewhat elevated temperatures interactions involving optical phonons will also become important. This can be formulated by taking into account the antiphase vibration of the cations (magnetic ions) and the diamagnetic ligand ions (Shukla and Sinha 1967). In fact, in ionic crystals the interactions with optical phonons will be stronger.

In ionic magnetic insulators there is an additional mechanism which involves a Zeeman-type coupling of the transverse optical phonons with appropriate magnon modes. This occurs via the near-zone (induction) magnetic field associated with TO phonons. This type of spin–phonon interaction is given by (Kumar and Sinha 1967a)

$$H_{SP} = \sum_{qt} G_{qt}(\mathbf{T}_{qt} \cdot \mathbf{S}_l)(b_{qt}{}^+ - \mathbf{b}_{-q})\exp(i\mathbf{q} \cdot \mathbf{R}_l) \qquad (8.48)$$

with

$$G_{qt} = -i\left(\frac{4\pi g\mu_B N e^* c}{3\omega_{qt}\Omega_v}\right)\left(\frac{h}{2MN\omega_{qt}}\right) \qquad (8.49)$$

and

$$\mathbf{T}_{qt} = \frac{\mathbf{q} \times \varepsilon_{qt}}{|\mathbf{q}|} \qquad (8.50)$$

where e^* is the effective ionic charge and Ω_v is the volume. By developing the spin operator $\mathbf{S}_l$ in terms of magnon variables for the appropriate system, the above interaction gives rise to various magnon–phonon processes (one-magnon one-phonon, two-magnon one-phonon). These are likely to be important for ferrimagnets only, for reasons of energy conservation (Kumar and Sinha 1967b).

9

MAGNON – MAGNON RELAXATION EFFECTS

In this chapter we shall discuss the approach to equilibrium of the Bose gas consisting of magnons which is slightly perturbed from its thermal equilibrium distribution. This equilibration is brought about by the mutual interaction of magnons. In the first instance we shall be interested only in an average relaxation time. We denote the equilibrium distribution by the magnon occupation number $n_\lambda{}^0$ and the deviation from this by δn_λ defined by

$$\delta n_\lambda = n_\lambda - n_\lambda{}^0 \tag{9.1}$$

where n_λ is the perturbed distribution. The relaxation time $\tau_\lambda{}^{mm}$ for a particular magnon mode λ follows from the Boltzmann rate equation in the relaxation-time approximation (see Akhiezer, Baryakhter, and Peletminskii 1968):

$$\dot{n}_\lambda = -\frac{1}{\tau_\lambda{}^{mm}}(n_\lambda - n_\lambda{}^0) = \frac{-\delta n_\lambda}{\tau_\lambda{}^{mm}}. \tag{9.2}$$

Our aim is to evaluate the relaxation frequency $1/\tau_\lambda{}^{mm}$ averaged over all modes, i.e.

$$\frac{1}{\tau_\lambda{}^{mm}} = \frac{\Sigma_\lambda 1/\tau_\lambda{}^{mm} n_\lambda{}^0}{\Sigma_\lambda n_\lambda{}^0}. \tag{9.3}$$

The overall relaxation frequency will be the sum of the frequencies due to various magnon–magnon interaction processes, i.e.

$$\frac{1}{\tau_\lambda{}^{mm}} = \sum_i \frac{1}{\tau_\lambda{}^{mm(i)}} \tag{9.4}$$

where i refers to the various magnon–magnon interaction processes given in Chapter 7. In the following we shall consider only the lowest-order momentum and energy conserving processes. These are three-magnon splitting and confluence processes. In the first Born approximation the probability per unit time $W(i \rightarrow f)$ of transition connecting the initial ($|i\rangle|$) and the final ($|f\rangle$) states is given by the well-known Golden rule

$$W(i \rightarrow f) = \frac{2\pi}{\hbar} |\langle f | H_{mm} | i \rangle|^2 \delta(E_i - E_f) \tag{9.5}$$

where H_{mm} is the magnon–magnon interaction Hamiltonian and the Dirac delta function $\delta(E_i - E_f)$ ensures energy conservation.

9.1. Relaxation due to three-magnon processes in ferromagnets

Making use of H_{mm} appropriate to the splitting and the confluence processes (cf. eqn (7.7)), we can write the matrix elements for the confluence and the splitting processes as

$$\langle (n_{\lambda_1} - 1), (n_{\lambda_2} - 1), (n_{\lambda_3} + 1) | H_{mm}^{confl}(3) | n_{\lambda_1}, n_{\lambda_2}, n_{\lambda_3} \rangle$$
$$= C(\lambda_1, \lambda_2; \lambda_3) \{ n_{\lambda_1} n_{\lambda_2} (n_{\lambda_3} + 1) \}^{1/2} \Delta(\lambda_1 + \lambda_2 - \lambda_3) \quad (9.6)$$

and

$$\langle (n_{\lambda_1} - 1), (n_{\lambda_2} + 1)(n_{\lambda_3} + 1) | H_{mm}^{split}(3) | n_{\lambda_1}, n_{\lambda_2}, n_{\lambda_3} \rangle$$
$$= C(\lambda_1, \lambda_2, \lambda_3) \{ n_{\lambda_1} (n_{\lambda_2} + 1)(n_{\lambda_3} + 1) \}^{1/2} \Delta(\lambda_1 - \lambda_2 - \lambda_3). \quad (9.7)$$

The decay rate $\dot{n}_\lambda$ per unit time due to collisions involving the confluence process is given as

$$\dot{n}_\lambda(confl) = \frac{2\pi}{\hbar} \sum_{\lambda_2 \lambda_3} |C(\lambda_3; \lambda_1, \lambda_2)|^2 \{ n_{\lambda_1} n_{\lambda_2} (n_{\lambda_3} + 1)$$
$$- (n_{\lambda_1} + 1)(n_{\lambda_2} + 1)(n_{\lambda_3}) \} \Delta(\lambda_1 + \lambda_2 - \lambda_3) \delta(E_{\lambda_1} + E_{\lambda_2} - E_{\lambda_3}). \quad (9.8)$$

We make use of the relation (9.1) for $\dot{n}_{\lambda_1}$. Further, making use of the condition for equilibrium, we obtain

$$n_{\lambda_1}{}^0 n_{\lambda_2}{}^0 (n_{\lambda_3}{}^0 + 1) = (n_{\lambda_1}{}^0 + 1)(n_{\lambda_2}{}^0 + 1) n_{\lambda_3}{}^0 \quad (9.9)$$

Combining this with eqn (9.8), we obtain

$$\frac{1}{\tau_\lambda^{mm}(confl)} = \sum_{\lambda_2 \lambda_3} \frac{2\pi}{\hbar} |C(\lambda_3; \lambda_1, \lambda_2)|^2$$
$$\times (n_{\lambda_2}{}^0 - n_{\lambda_3}{}^0) \Delta(\lambda_1 + \lambda_2 - \lambda_3) \delta(E_{\lambda_1} + E_{\lambda_2} - E_{\lambda_3}). \quad (9.10)$$

Similarly, the decay rate due to the three-magnon splitting process is found to be

$$\frac{1}{\tau_{\lambda_1}^{mm}(split)} = \sum_{\lambda_2 \lambda_2} \frac{2\pi}{\hbar} |C(\lambda_1; \lambda_2, \lambda_3)|^2$$
$$\times (n_{\lambda_2}{}^0 + n_{\lambda_3}{}^0 + 1) \Delta(\lambda_1 - \lambda_2 - \lambda_3) \delta(E_{\lambda_1} - E_{\lambda_2} - E_{\lambda_3}). \quad (9.11)$$

The mean three-magnon relaxation frequency given by the thermal average of the sum of the two processes is

$$\frac{1}{\tau^{mm(3)}} = \sum_{\lambda_1} \frac{n_{\lambda_1}{}^0 (1/\tau_{\lambda_1}{}^{mm}(confl) + 1/\tau_{\lambda_1}{}^{mm}(split)}{\sum_{\lambda_1} n_{\lambda_1}{}^0} \quad (9.12)$$

The specific form of the coupling constant $C(\lambda_1; \lambda_2, \lambda_3)$ can be obtained from eqn (7.7). However, it is convenient to use a simpler approximate form derived from macroscopic considerations. Thus

$$C(\lambda_1; \lambda_2, \lambda_1 - \lambda_2) \approx \frac{g\mu_B M}{\sqrt{N}} \qquad (9.13)$$

where M is the macroscopic magnetization. We shall not give the details of the calculations here. It can be found elsewhere (Alkhiezer et al. 1968). For an ideal ferromagnet we use a quadratic dispersion relation in the long-wavelength approximation, namely

$$E_\lambda = 2JSa^2\lambda^2 = k_B\theta_c a^2 \lambda^2. \qquad (9.14)$$

The final result is

$$\frac{1}{\tau^{mm(3)}} = \frac{(g\mu_B M)^2}{\hbar\theta_c k_B} \left(\frac{T}{\theta_c}\right)^{1/2} \left\{\ln\left(\frac{g\mu_B M}{k_B T}\right)\right\}^2 \qquad (9.15)$$

for $g\mu_B M \ll k_B T$, and

$$\frac{1}{\tau^{mm(3)}} = \frac{(g\mu_B M)^{5/2}}{\hbar(k_B\theta_c)^{3/2}} \exp\left(-\frac{2g\mu_B M}{k_B T}\right) \qquad (9.16)$$

for $g\mu_B T \gg K_B T$. The above gives the three-magnon relaxation frequency relevant to the equilibration process in the absence of an external magnetic field. For $\theta_c \sim 10^3$ K, $g\mu_B M \sim 0.1$ erg, $T = 10$ K, $1/\tau^{mm}(3)$ as obtained from eqn (9.15) turns out to be 10^7 s^{-1}. The calculations outlined above are for an ideal ferromagnet.

To interpret the linewidth of spin-wave resonance experiments it is important to know the relaxation frequency of the particular magnon mode excited selectively by the radiofrequency field in the presence of an external static magnetic field. In this situation one needs to know the magnon dispersion relation in the presence of the Zeeman term. It can be shown with the help of eqns (5.29) and (5.33) that the dispersion relation takes the approximate form (Sparks 1964)

$$E_\lambda = 2JSa^2\lambda^2 + g\mu_B B + 4g\mu_B M \sin^2\theta_\lambda. \qquad (9.17)$$

The relaxation frequencies for the confluence and the splitting processes can be calculated with the help of eqns (9.10) and (9.11) by feeding eqn (9.17) into the energy expression. For very-long-wavelength magnons (say for $2J Sa^2\lambda_1^2 \ll E_{\lambda_1}$ and $k_B T > E_{\lambda_1} + E_{\lambda_2}$ etc.), one obtains

$$\frac{1}{\tau_{\lambda_1}^{mm}} (\text{confl}) = \frac{(4\pi g\mu_B M)^2 \lambda_1 a(k_B T)}{24\pi S E_{\lambda_1}(2JS)}$$
$$\times (1 + \tfrac{17}{2}\sin^2\theta_{\lambda_1} - \tfrac{35}{4}\sin^4\theta_{\lambda_1})F(E_{\lambda_1}, \theta_{\lambda_1}) \qquad (9.18)$$

where θ_{λ_1} is the angle between λ_1 and the z axis (direction of the external magnetic field) and $F(E_{\lambda_1}, \theta_{\lambda_1})$ is the Schlomann factor (see Keffer 1966).

For two common experimental situations, namely $\theta_\lambda = 0$ and $\theta_\lambda = \pi/2$, the values are unity and $(g\mu_B H + \frac{4}{3}\pi g\mu_B M)/E_\lambda$ respectively.

The above expression shows the dependence of $1/\tau_\lambda^{mm}$ on the wave vector λ and the angle θ_λ. The relaxation frequency increases initially but drops off for large values of λ_1. Thus there is a broad hump. Under the same approximation the splitting process gives

$$\frac{1}{\tau_{\lambda_1}^{\,mm}}(\text{split}) = \frac{k_B T}{64\pi Sh}\left(\frac{4g\mu_B M}{2JS}\right) F\left(H_{\text{sphere}}\right) \tag{9.19}$$

where $F\left(H_{\text{sphere}}\right)$ is a complicated correction factor. The above expression is valid for H_{sphere} lying between 0 and $\frac{4}{3}\pi M$ and $\theta_{\lambda_1} = \frac{1}{2}\pi$.

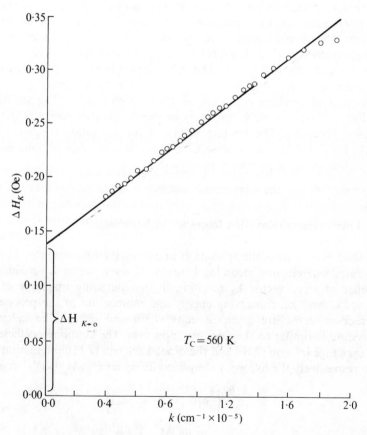

FIG. 9.1. Room-temperature measurements of the parallel pumping relaxation frequency (linewidth) on pure YIG as a function of magnon wave number k. (After Le Craw and Spencer 1962.)

It should be noted that the confluence process does not relax the uniform-mode magnon; also the splitting process cannot relax magnons with λ less than a threshold value for reasons of energy-momentum conservation (Keffer 1966).

The development of the parallel pumping technique (i.e. when a large radiofrequency field is applied parallel to the bulk magnetization) has made it possible to excite directly magnons of selected wave vector at an angle θ of $\pi/2$. These modes are excited when the radiofrequency field exceeds a certain critical value proportional to the relaxation frequency of the mode in question. This provides a direct measurement of the relaxation frequency which is proportional to line width (see Morgenthaler 1960, Schlomann et al. 1960). This technique excludes the two-magnon surface-scattering contributions to relaxation in that the two-magnon diagonalized modes are involved in the excitation. Thus the main contributing factors are the bulk processes such as three-magnon and magnon–phonon processes (see Chapter 10). Room-temperature measurements of the parallel pumping relaxation frequency on pure YIG as a function of magnon wave vector and $\theta = \pi/2$ are shown in Fig. 9.1. The initial linear increase of the relaxation frequency with the magnon wave vector is due to the linear part of the three-magnon confluence process as given in eqn (9.18). The subsequent bending for larger wave vectors may be due to the dominance of the four-magnon processes. The limiting values of the relaxation frequency (linewidth) for $\lambda_1 = 0$ appear to arise from other sources such as four-magnon and two-magnon one-phonon processes.

9.2. Four-magnon relaxation frequency in ferromagnets

We shall now discuss the relaxation frequency for four-magnon scattering processes wherein one incoming magnon of wave vector λ_3 collides with another of wave vector λ_4 resulting in two outgoing magnons of wave vectors λ_1 and λ_2, conserving energy and momentum in the process. The interaction terms are given in eqns (7.10) and (7.11). The calculation procedure is similar to the three-magnon case. The coupling coefficient for the exchange (cf. eqn (7.10) and the dipolar (cf. eqn (7.11)) interaction terms take respectively the following simplified forms for $(g\mu_B M/\theta_c k_B)^{1/2} \ll a\lambda \ll 1$:

$$\frac{k_B \theta_c}{N}\left\{\frac{1}{4}a^2(\lambda_1 \cdot \lambda_2 + \lambda_3 \cdot \lambda_4)\right\}$$

$$\frac{g\mu_B M}{N}$$

$$(9.20)$$

Thus we obtain

$$\frac{1}{\tau_\lambda{}^{mm}(4)} = \frac{k_B\theta_c}{\hbar}\left(\frac{T}{\theta_c}\right)^{5/2} (a\lambda)^3 \text{ for } k_BT < g\mu_B M \ll E_\lambda$$

$$\frac{1}{\tau_\lambda{}^{mm}(4)} = \frac{(g\mu_B M)}{k_B\theta_c}\left(\frac{T}{\theta_c}\right)^2 \text{ for } k_B\theta_c a^2\lambda^2 < g\mu_B B \ll k_BT.$$

(9.21)

The mean relaxation frequency due to these processes for the case $g\mu_B M \ll$ $\ll k_B\theta_c$ (i.e. when exchange dominates) is found to be

$$\frac{1}{\tau_\delta{}^{mm}(4)} = \frac{k_B\theta_c}{\hbar c}\left(\frac{T}{\theta_c}\right)^4$$

(9.22)

It should be noted that the four-magnon exchange process (cf. eqn (9.20)) cannot relax the uniform magnon mode in that the exchange Hamiltonian commutes with both the total spin and its z component. This process will not be important for ferromagnetic resonance relaxation.

9.3. Magnon–magnon relaxation in antiferromagnets

For an ideal antiferromagnet the dipolar contribution is non-existent in that the macroscopic magnetization is zero. Thus the interaction process emanates from the higher-order expansion of the exchange terms. At low temperature the dominat four-magnon processes comprise terms such as $\alpha_{\lambda_1}{}^+\alpha_{\lambda_2}{}^+\alpha_{\lambda_3}\alpha_{\lambda_4}$, $\beta_{\lambda_1}{}^+\beta_{\lambda_2}{}^+\beta_{\lambda_3}\beta_{\lambda_4}$, and $\alpha_{\lambda_1}{}^+\alpha_{\lambda_2}\beta_{\lambda_3}{}^+\beta_{\lambda_4}$. In the absence of an external magnetic field their contributions are comparable because the two spin-wave branches are degenerate. These processes do relax the uniform mode ($\lambda=0$) magnons as the canonical transformations involved mix the anisotropy and the exchange terms. The final result is

$$\frac{1}{\tau_{\lambda=0}{}^{mm}(4)} = \frac{7.5}{10^4}\left(\frac{z^3}{S^2}\right)\omega_H\left(\frac{\omega_A}{\omega_c}\right)\frac{e^{-X}}{X}$$

(9.23)

where $X = \hbar\omega_H/k_BT$.

For $k_BT > \hbar\omega_H$ the relaxation frequency is proportional to T^2. Genkin and Fain (1962) estimate that $\tau_{\lambda=0}{}^{mm}$ (AF) is of the order of 10^{-10} s for MnF_2 at $T \sim 10$ K.

At higher temperatures towards the Néel temperature T_N higher-order processes involving six or more magnons become progressively more important. Good agreement with experiments on MnF_2, FeF_2, Rb_2MnF_4 and K_2MnF_4 has been obtained at temperatures up to 0·8 T_N (Rezende and White 1976).

10

MAGNON–PHONON RELAXATION

The various magnon–phonon interaction mechanisms for ferromagnetic, antiferromagnetic, and ferrimagnetic systems have been discussed in Chapter 8. In this chapter we consider the calculation of the magnon–phonon relaxation frequencies $1/\tau^{mp}$ for these systems. This will characterize the rate of flow of energy from magnons to phonons. We treat the magnons and the phonons as two subsystems. In this chapter only those systems are considered for which the equilibration time for each subsystem (τ^{mm} and τ^{pp}) is short compared with the inter-subsystem relaxation time τ^{mp} (see Akhiezer *et al.* 1968). This enables us to define two slightly different temperatures for the two subsystems, *viz.* T_m for magnons and T_p for phonons. This corresponds to the two-thermal-reservoir model of Casimir and du Pré (1938). However, it is possible to excite either of the subsystems by external agencies, e.g. by irradiation with electromagnetic or ultrasonic fields.

Let us consider the situation where $T_m = T$ and $\Delta T = T_m - T_p > 0$ which corresponds to spin-wave excitation. The eigenstates of the diagonal parts of the magnon and the phonon systems have been defined earlier. In the occupation-number representation, the eigenstates for the combined system can be described by

$$|n_{\lambda_1}, n_{\lambda_2}, \ldots; N_{q_1 s_1}, N_{q_2 s_2}\rangle \qquad (10.1)$$

together with its straightforward generalization to antiferromagnets and ferrimagnets. In the following sections we consider the calculation of magnon–phonon relaxation frequencies in the three systems.

10.1. Ferromagnets

The rate of increase $\dot{Q}$ of phonon energy due to the inflow of energy from the magnon system is expressed as (Sinha and Upadhyaya 1962)

$$\dot{Q} = \sum_{qs} \hbar\omega_{qs} \langle \dot{N}_{qs} \rangle$$

$$\sum_{\lambda, qs} \left(\frac{2\pi}{\hbar}\right) |\Phi_{\lambda, qs}|^2 \hbar\omega_{qs} \{(n_{\lambda-q}+1)n_\lambda(N_{qs}+1)$$

$$-(n_{\lambda-q})(n_\lambda+1)N_{qs}\}\delta(E_{\lambda-q}+\hbar\omega_{qs}-E_\lambda) \qquad (10.2)$$

where we have considered the three-boson interaction processes that involve the emission or absorption of the phonon along with the scattering of a magnon (cf. eqn (8.38)). In the above expression the phonon occupation number N_{qs} and the magnon occupation number n_λ correspond to their respective temperatures, i.e.

$$n_\lambda = \left\{ \exp\left(\frac{E_\lambda}{k_B T_m}\right) - 1 \right\}^{-1}$$

and

$$N_{qs} = \left\{ \exp\left(\frac{\hbar\omega_{qs}}{k_B T_p}\right) - 1 \right\}^{-1}.$$

As we have taken $T_m = T$ and $T_p = T - \Delta T$, we can re-express eqn (10.2) by expanding in powers of ΔT. On retaining terms up to first order in ΔT, we obtain

$$\dot{Q} = \frac{2\pi}{h} \frac{\Delta T}{T^2} \sum_{\lambda, qs} \frac{(\hbar\omega_{q,s})^2}{k_B} |\phi_{\lambda, qs}|^2$$

$$\times \exp\left(\frac{E_\lambda}{k_B T}\right) F(\lambda, qs)\delta(E_{\lambda-q} + \hbar\omega_{qs} - E_\lambda) \tag{10.3}$$

where

$$F(\lambda, qs) \equiv (n_{\lambda-q}{}^0)(n_\lambda{}^0)(N_{qs}{}^0) \tag{10.4}$$

i.e. the product of the equilibrium Bose factors for temperature T. For longitudinal acoustic phonons we use the well-known Debye approximation $\omega_q(LA) = v_s q$, where v_s is the velocity of sound. The coupling constant $\phi_{\lambda q}$ in the long-wavelength region is given by the simple form (Sinha and Upadhyaya 1962)

$$\phi_{\lambda q} \approx -i \frac{4}{\sqrt{(N)}} \left(\frac{\hbar}{2\omega_q M}\right)^{1/2} (2\lambda q a^2 \cos^2\theta_{\lambda, q}) 2SJ_M. \tag{10.5}$$

Making use of these approximations and performing the summation (integration), we obtain (in the low-temperature region)

$$\dot{Q} = \frac{2^9 \times 3N}{\pi^3} S^2 (J_M)^2 \left(\frac{\hbar}{Mk_B}\right)^2 \frac{\Delta T}{T^2} \frac{T^6}{\theta_D{}^2 \theta_C{}^4} \exp\left(-\frac{\theta_D{}^2}{4\theta_C{}^T}\right) \tag{10.6}$$

where θ_D is the Debye temperature of the solid.

The relaxation frequency for thermalization is given by

$$\frac{1}{\tau^{mp}} = \dot{Q}\left(\frac{1}{C_m} + \frac{1}{C_p}\right)\frac{1}{\Delta T} \tag{10.7}$$

where C_m and C_p are the heat capacities of the magnon and the phonon systems respectively. These are given by

$$C_m \text{ (ferro)} = \frac{15}{32} \frac{1}{\pi^{3/2}} k_B N \left(\frac{T}{\theta_C} \right)^{3/2}$$

$$C_p \text{ (Debye)} = \frac{12\pi^4}{5} k_B N \left(\frac{T}{\theta_D} \right)^3$$

(10.8)

Substituting in eqn (10.7), we obtain

$$\frac{1}{\tau^{mp}} \text{ (ferro)} = \frac{3 \times 2^9}{\pi^3} S^2 (J_M)^2 \left(\frac{\hbar}{M k_B^2} \right) \frac{T^4}{\theta_D^2 \theta_C^4} \left(\frac{\theta_C}{T} \right)^{3/2}$$
$$\times \left(11 + \frac{(\theta_D^2/\theta_C T)^{3/2}}{234} \right) \exp\left(-\frac{\theta_D^2}{4\theta_C T} \right)$$

(10.9a)

for $T \ll \theta_D^2/\theta_C$ and

$$\frac{1}{\tau^{mp}} \text{ (ferro)} \approx 4 \left(\frac{\hbar}{M k_B^2} \right) \left(\frac{\theta_D^2}{\theta_C^4} \right) S^2 (J_M)^2$$

(10.9b)

for $T \gg \theta_D^2/\theta_C$.

For a typical ferromagnet, estimates with $\theta_C \sim 10^3$ K, $\theta_D = 500$ K and $J_M \sim 10^{-6}$ dyn give

$$\tau^{mp} \text{(ferro)} \sim 10^{-6} \text{s} \qquad \text{at 10 K.}$$

The presence of the exponential factor in eqn (10.9a) suggests that only those magnons whose energy is larger than $k_B \theta_D^2/4\theta_C$ are capable of emitting phonons.

The above relaxation frequency is connected with the energy transfer between the spin and lattice subsystems. One can also define an occupation-number relaxation frequency for an individual mode as well as an average (thermal) relaxation frequency. This was the kind of calculation we carried out in Chapter 9. The number relaxation frequency $1/\tau^{mp}$ (number) is found to be (Akhiezer *et al.* 1968)

$$\frac{1}{\tau^{mp}} \text{(number)} = \frac{\theta_C}{\hbar} \frac{k_B^2 T}{M v_s^2} \left(\frac{T}{\theta_C} \right)^{5/2} \exp\left(-\frac{\theta_D^2}{4\theta_C T} \right)$$

(10.10a)

for $T \ll \theta_D^2/\theta_C$ and

$$\frac{1}{\tau^{mp}} \text{(number)} \approx \frac{\theta_C}{\hbar} \frac{k_B^2 T}{M v_s^2} \left(\frac{T}{\theta_C} \right)^{5/2}$$

(10.10b)

for $T \gg \theta_D^2/\theta_C$.

The expressions (10.9) and (10.10) show some minor differences in the temperature dependence. This is connected with the fact that the two relaxation frequencies describe physically different effects, namely the energy and the number relaxation processes.

10.2. Antiferromagnets

We invoke the interaction terms derived for a two-sublattice antiferromagnet in Chapter 8. The transition probabilities for the three types of processes (cf. eqns (8.40), (8.41), and (8.42)) involving interaction with the magnons of the two branches can be calculated by the procedure indicated above. The only point to remember is that we deal with two types of occupation numbers $n_\lambda{}^+$ and $n_\lambda{}^-$ corresponding to the two magnon branches.

Thus the rate of transfer of energy from the magnon to the phonon subsystem can be written as (Upadhyaya and Sinha 1963)

$$\dot{Q} = \dot{Q}_{(++)} + \dot{Q}_{(+-)} + \dot{Q}_{(--)}$$

$$\equiv \sum_{qs} \hbar \omega_{qs} (\dot{N}_{qs(++)} + \dot{N}_{qs(+-)} + \dot{N}_{qs(--)})$$

$$= \frac{2\pi}{\hbar} \sum_{qs} \hbar \omega_{qs} [\, |A_{\lambda,qs}|^2 \{ n_\lambda{}^+ (n_{\lambda-q}{}^+ + 1)(N_{qs} + 1)$$

$$- (n_\lambda{}^+ + 1) n_{\lambda-q}{}^+ N_{qs} \} \; \delta(E_{\lambda-q}{}^+ + \hbar \omega_{qs} - E_\lambda{}^+) \qquad (10.11)$$

$$+ |B_{\lambda,qs}|^2 \{ n_\lambda{}^+ n_{\lambda-q}{}^- (N_{qs} + 1)$$

$$- (n_\lambda{}^+ + 1)(n_{\lambda-q}{}^- + 1) N_{qs} \} \delta(E_{\lambda-q}{}^- - \hbar \omega_{qs} + E_\lambda{}^+)$$

$$+ |A_{\lambda,qs}|^2 \{ (n_\lambda{}^- + 1) n_{\lambda-q}{}^- (N_{qs} + 1)$$

$$- n_\lambda{}^- (n_{\lambda-q}{}^- + 1) N_{qs} \} \delta(E_\lambda{}^- + \hbar \omega_{qs} - E_{\lambda-q}{}^-) \,].$$

In order to simplify the calculation, we shall henceforth neglect the Zeeman and anisotropy terms, i.e.

$$E_\lambda{}^+ = E_\lambda{}^- = E_\lambda = k_B \theta_C a \lambda.$$

Also for the LA phonons $\hbar \omega_{qs} = k_B \theta_D a q$ and so the same Bose distribution factor can be used for the magnons of the two branches, i.e. $n_\lambda{}^+ = n_\lambda{}^- = n_\lambda = \{\exp(E_\lambda/k_B T) - \}^{-1}$. For the explicit evaluation of the summation (integral) involved in eqn (10.11), one must take into account the energy and momentum conservation conditions. For the three energy transfer channels envisaged above, this implies the following conditions:

(l) for channels $\dot{Q}_{(++)}$ and $\dot{Q}_{(--)}$, we must have $\theta_D < \theta_C$;
(ii) for channels $\dot{Q}_{(+-)}$, we must have $\theta_D > \theta_C$.

For most of the physical systems of intere $\theta_D > \theta_C (\sim \theta_N)$, and accordingly we confine our attention to $\dot{Q}_{(+-)}$ which involves the confluence of two magnons, one from each branch, with the creation of a phonon and the conjugate process. The result of the calculation is

$$\frac{1}{\tau_{(+-)}{}^{mp}(AF)} = \dot{Q}_{(+-)}\left[\frac{1}{C_m} + \frac{1}{C_p}\right] = RT^5 \tag{10.12}$$

where

$$R = \frac{10^4}{\pi^3} \frac{\hbar}{Mk_B{}^3}\left(\frac{1}{4} + \frac{\zeta^3}{234}\right) \times \left(2 \cdot 52\zeta^2 + \frac{2 \cdot 53}{\zeta^2} - 5 \cdot 05\right) \tag{10.13}$$

with $\zeta \equiv (\theta_D/\theta_C) \gtrsim 1$ and we have used the magnon heat capacity $C_m = 4Nk_B(T/\theta_C)^3$.

The above shows a simple power-law temperature dependence of the magnon–phonon relaxation frequency in antiferromagnets. Estimates for MnF_2 show that $1/\tau^{mp}(AF) \sim 10^7 s^{-1}$ at 10 K.

It should be noted that the spin-wave band gap arising from the Zeeman term has been neglected. Its inclusion will result in some minor changes to the estimate. It can be seen from eqn (10.12) that the relaxation frequency vanishes for $\theta_D = \theta_C$ for this channel.

10.3. Ferrimagnets

The interaction processes involving acoustic phonons were given in Chapter 8 for the two sublattice ferrimagnet. The main difference compared with an antiferromagnet arises because the two magnon branches α and β are no longer degenerate for $B = 0$ but are separated by a gap of the order of the exchange energy. Therefore the $\dot{Q}_{+-}$ process which involves the creation (destruction) of one magnon from each branch with the destruction (creation) of an acoustic (LA) phonon will not conserve energy. Thus, only the interaction processes leading to $\dot{Q}_{++}$ and $\dot{Q}_{--}$ are considered (Joshi and Sinha 1965).

In the long-wavelength approximation the coupling constants reduce to

$$|A_{\lambda q}|^2 = |C_{\lambda q}|^2 = \frac{16}{N}\frac{\pi\hbar}{\omega_q M}|J_M|^2\frac{(S_A{}^2 + S_B{}^2)}{64}a^4q^4. \tag{10.14}$$

Following the procedure discussed earlier, we obtain

$$\dot{Q} = \dot{Q}_{\alpha\alpha} + \dot{Q}_{\beta\beta} = \frac{2\pi}{\hbar}\frac{\Delta T}{T^2}\sum_{\lambda, q}\left(\frac{\hbar\omega_q}{k_B}\right)^2\left\{F^\alpha(\lambda, q)|A_{\lambda q}|^2\exp\left(\frac{E_\lambda{}^\alpha}{k_B T}\right)\right.$$

$$\left.\delta(E_{\lambda-q}{}^\alpha + \hbar\omega_q - E_\lambda{}^\alpha) + F^\beta(\lambda, q)|C_{\lambda q}|^2\exp\left(\frac{E_\lambda{}^{-q}}{k_B T}\right)\delta(E_\lambda{}^\beta + \hbar\omega_q - E_{\lambda-q}{}^\beta)\right\}$$

$$\tag{10.15}$$

where the superscripts α and β refer to the lower and the higher branches respectively. Here we have distinguished between the Bose distribution functions for the two branches i.e.

$$F^{\alpha,\beta}(\lambda, \mathbf{q}) \equiv (n_{\lambda,\mathbf{q}}{}^{\alpha,\beta})^0 (n_\lambda{}^{\alpha,\beta})^0 (N_{\mathbf{q}s}{}^0). \qquad (10.16)$$

On integration, we finally obtain

$$\dot{Q} = \frac{718{\cdot}8}{\pi^2} \left(\frac{\hbar}{Mk_B}\right) (S_A{}^2 + S_B{}^2) |J_M|^2 \frac{T^6 \Delta T}{\theta_C{}^2 \theta_D{}^6}$$

$$\times \exp\left(-\frac{\theta_D{}^2}{4\theta_C{}^T}\right) \left[1 + \exp\left\{-\frac{4(S_A - S_B)^2}{S_A S_B} \frac{\theta_C}{T}\right\}\right]$$

$$(10.17)$$

where

$$k_B \theta_C \approx 4 J_{AB} \frac{S_A S_B}{|S_A - S_B|}.$$

In the low-temperature region the second term in square brackets in eqn (10.17), which arises from the interaction of phonons with the higher magnon branch, will be negligible compared with the first term. This simply reflects the fact that the higher branch is not sufficiently populated in this temperature region. We shall therefore neglect this and evaluate the relaxation frequency $1/\tau^{mp}(\text{ferri})$ for the acoustic branches of the magnons and phonons. Using

$$C_m \approx \frac{Nk_B}{18{\cdot}69} \left(\frac{T}{\theta_C}\right)^{3/2}$$

we obtain

$$\frac{1}{\tau^{mp}}(\text{ferri}) = \dot{Q}_{\alpha\alpha} \left(\frac{1}{C_m} + \frac{1}{C_{ph}}\right)$$

$$= \frac{718{\cdot}8}{2} \left(\frac{\hbar}{Mk_B{}^2}\right) (S_A{}^2 + S_B{}^2)$$

$$(10.18)$$

$$\times |J_M|^2 \frac{T^6}{\theta_C{}^2 \theta_D{}^2} \exp\left(-\frac{\theta_D{}^2}{4\theta_C T}\right) \left\{18{\cdot}69 \left(\frac{\theta_C}{T}\right)^{3/2} + \frac{1}{234} \frac{\theta_D}{T}\right\}.$$

For a typical choice of values for the relevant parameters, i.e. $M = 55$, $S_A = 2$, $S_B = 5/2$, $\theta_C = 200$ K, $\theta_D = 200$ K and $J_M \sim 10^{-7} - 10^{-6}$ dyn, we obtain

$$\tau^{mp}(\text{ferri}) \sim 10^{-5} - 10^{-7} \text{ s}$$

at 10 K.

10.4. Interaction of magnons with optical phonons

Magnon–phonon interaction processes involving optical phonons in two-sublattice ferrimagnetic and antiferromagnetic systems have been considered by several workers (Kasuya and Le Craw 1961, Shukla and Sinha 1967). We shall consider one of the mechanisms that takes account of the antiphase relative oscillation (LO) of a paramagnetic ion and its nearest-neighbour ligand ions. The antiphase motion of the ligand ions will give rise to phonon-induced mixing of the orbital states of the paramagnetic ion. Thus one reformulates the exchange coupling between paramagnetic atoms in terms of such modified orbital functions.

The magnon–phonon interaction terms have a similar structure, as discussed earlier, except that the coupling coefficients with respect to the wave-vector dependence are different. For a simple antiferromagnet the $\dot{Q}_{(+-)}$ process will again be important and the relevant relaxation frequency is (Shukla and Sinha 1967):

$$\frac{1}{\tau^{mp}}(\mathrm{AF}) \approx \frac{4 \times 10^{-2}}{\pi^3} \frac{\hbar}{M k_B^2} S^2 J_M^2 \frac{\theta_E^8}{\theta_C^5} \frac{\exp(-\theta_E/T)}{T^5} \tag{10.19}$$

where θ_E is the Einstein temperature. It should be noted that we have assumed that $1/C_m \gg 1/C_{LO} \gg 1/C_{LA}$, which is true at low temperatures where C_{LO} is the heat capacity contribution of the LO phonon mode.

We obtain similar expressions for ferrimagnets (Shukla and Sinha 1967):

$$\frac{1}{\tau_0^{mp}}(\mathrm{ferri}) = \frac{\dot{Q}_{\alpha\beta}}{T}\left(\frac{1}{C_m(\mathrm{ferri})}\right)$$

$$= \frac{3 \cdot 11}{\pi^3}\left(\frac{\hbar}{M k_B^2}\right)\frac{S_A S_B(S_A^2 + S_B^2)}{|S_A - S_B|^2}$$

$$\times \frac{\theta_E}{\theta_C} J_M^2 \left(\frac{\theta_E}{\theta_C}\right)^3 \frac{\exp(-\theta_E/T)}{T^{7/2}} \tag{10.20}$$

for $T < \theta_C < \theta_E$, where

$$r = \frac{4|S_A - S_B|^2}{S_A S_B}.$$

In the above only one optical phonon (LO) branch has been taken into account.

10.5. Relaxation of single magnon modes

In spin-wave resonance experiments, a single magnon mode (wave vector λ which may or may not be equal to zero) is excited. In the previous chapters we have discussed magnon–magnon relaxation process. Here we consider the effect of the magnon–phonon interaction process in relaxing these excited modes. These are important in explaining the temperature dependence of the ferromagnetic resonance linewidth. These are essentially the two-magnon one-phonon processes given earlier. In the Kasuya–Le Craw (1961) process the confluence of a uniform-mode magnon with a phonon (acoustic) yields another magnon. In the temperature region where $k_B T \gg \hbar\omega_{q_2}$, this process gives for the relaxation frequency $(1/\tau_{\lambda=0}{}^{mp})$ of the uniform mode

$$\frac{1}{\tau_{\lambda=0}{}^{mp}} \propto q_2 \frac{\{(\hbar\omega_{q_2})^2/k_B{}^2 T\} \exp(\hbar\omega_{q_2}/k_B T)}{[\exp(\hbar\omega_{q_2}/k_B T)-1]^2}. \tag{10.21}$$

where

$$q_2 = \frac{\hbar v_s}{2 J_{eff} S_{eff} a^2}.$$

This predicts an almost linear increase of the relaxation frequency with temperature in the region $k_B T \gg \hbar\omega_{q_2}$. It gave a good agreement with the linewidth in yttrium iron garnet (YIG).

Most of these ferrimagnetic insulators are ionic crystals. It is expected that interaction with optical phonons will be much stronger. In fact, this kind of interaction has been found to be important in europium iron garnet (EuIG) (Sinha and Le Craw 1971). The Eu^{3+} ions have low-lying excited states. Thus the phonon-modulated exchange interaction processes become rather important when Eu^{3+} ions are involved.

The relevant interaction Hamiltonian for the uniform-mode relaxation process can be written as (Sinha and Le Craw 1971)

$$H_{mp}{}^0(\text{truncated}) = \sum_q B_{0q}(\alpha_0 \beta_q b_{q0}{}^+ - \alpha_0{}^+ \beta_q{}^+ b_{q0}) \tag{10.22}$$

with

$$|B_{0q}|^2 = B_0{}^2 a^2 q^2$$

where $b_{q0}{}^+$ and b_{q0} are the phonon operators for the LO mode of the wave vector q and

$$B_0{}^2 = 8z \frac{\hbar}{NM\omega_0} \frac{4(S_A S_B)(S_A{}^2 + S_B{}^2)}{|S_A - S_B|^2} (J_M)^2 \tag{10.23}$$

where ω_0 is the LO mode frequency which is assumed to be flat. This is a confluence of an acoustic (uniform-mode) magnon with an optical magnon to give an optical phonon. The relaxation frequency is given by

$$\frac{1}{\tau_{\lambda=0}{}^{mp}} \propto \omega_H J_M{}^2(T) \exp\left(\frac{\theta_E}{T}\right) \left\{\exp\left(\frac{\theta_E}{T}\right)-1\right\}^{-2} \frac{T^{-1}}{g_{eff}(T)} \tag{10.24a}$$

where ω_H is the operating frequency. It is to be noted that $J_M(T)$ and the effective g factors become temperature dependent because one has to take a thermal average over low-lying excited states. The above expression is valid over the entire temperature region. In the low-temperature region it becomes,

$$\omega_H \exp\left(-\frac{\theta_E}{T}\right) T^{-1}. \qquad (10.24b)$$

A comparison of the theoretical curve for the linewidth based on the above expression is given in Fig. 10.1 together with the experimental points. The temperature and frequency dependence of the linewidth are in reasonable agreement with experimental data.

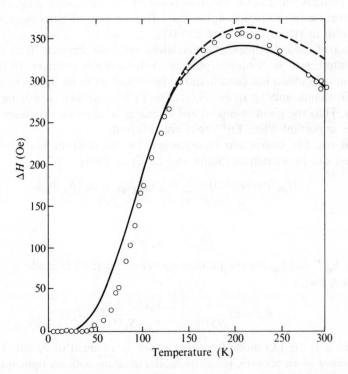

FIG. 10.1. A comparison of the theoretically calculated temperature-dependent linewidth with experimental points for EuIG: solid curve, theory using $Z(T)^{-1}$; broken curve, theory using $M(T)$; points experimental values. (After Sinha and Le Craw 1971).

10.6. Renormalization effects of magnon–phonon interactions

So far we have discussed some of the kinetic effects arising from the magnon–phonon interaction processes. These interaction processes can also lead to renormalization of the magnon and phonon energies which will depend on temperature. We shall give the results for an ideal Heisenberg ferromagnet (Pytte 1965, Bakre, Joshi, and Sinha 1967).

In the weak-coupling approximation the simplest approach is to eliminate the magnon–phonon interaction terms by a suitable canonical transformation. Thus, if we write the Hamiltonian as (considering acoustic phonons only)

$$H = H_0 + H_1$$

where

$$H_0 = \sum_\lambda E_\lambda (a_\lambda^+ a_\lambda + \tfrac{1}{2}) + \sum_q \hbar\omega_q (b_q^+ b_q + \tfrac{1}{2}) \equiv H_m + H_p \qquad (10.25)$$

and

$$H_1 = \sum_{\lambda q} \phi_{\lambda q}(a_{\lambda-q}^+ a_\lambda b_q^+ - a_{\lambda-q} a_\lambda^+ b_q). \qquad (10.26)$$

The transformed Hamiltonian is

$$H_T = H_0 + H_1 + i[H_0, S] + i[H_1, S] + \dots \qquad (10.27)$$

where the generator S is chosen such that

$$H_1 = -i[H_0, S] \qquad (10.28)$$

which gives

$$S = \sum_{\lambda q} (B_{\lambda q} a_\lambda^+ a_{\lambda-q} b_q^+ + B_{\lambda q}^* a_\lambda a_{\lambda-q}^+ b_q) \qquad (10.29)$$

where

$$B_{\lambda q}^* = B_{\lambda q} = \frac{i\phi_{\lambda q}}{E_{\lambda-q} - E_\lambda + \hbar\omega_q}. \qquad (10.30)$$

This gives the renormalized magnon energy up to second order as

$$\tilde{E}_\lambda(\text{renormalized}) = E_\lambda - 4 \cdot 27 \, \pi^2 \frac{\hbar a^5}{Mv_s} \frac{S^2(J_M)^2}{k_B \theta_C} \left(\frac{k_B T}{\hbar v_s}\right)^4 \lambda^2. \qquad (10.31)$$

Thus, in addition to a constant shift, we obtain a correction which is proportional to T^4. Pytte (1965) has made a detailed investigation of the renormalization effects and finds a similar correction term.

Some interesting magnon–phonon renormalization effects have recently been observed in FeF_2 by inelastic neutron-scattering measurements at low temperatures (Rainford, Houmann, and Guggenheim 1972). The results suggest that there is a strong interaction between magnon and phonon excitations. This kind of strong interaction is not observed in MnF_2 which has the same chemical and magnetic structure. Recalling that Mn^{2+} is a $3d^5(^6S)$ ion, while Fe^{2+} is a $3d^6(^5D)$ ion, it would appear that a spin–phonon interaction mechanism of the Van Vleck type dominates in the latter system. This involves the orbit–lattice (H_{OL}) interaction via modulation of the crystal field and the intra-ionic spin–orbit interaction (H_{SO}). It is also linear in the spin and phonon variables. A detailed theoretical explanation of the experimental results for FeF_2 in terms of the above mechanism has been given by Lovesey (1972). The crystal-field parameters were obtained from earlier measurements. To calculate the renormalized excitation energies one needs the unperturbed magnon and phonon dispersion relations. For magnons, Lovesey chose the relevant parameters so as to make the magnon energy agree with the observed values at certain special points of Brillouin zone, namely near the centre and the boundary where the effect of interaction is small. On the other hand, for

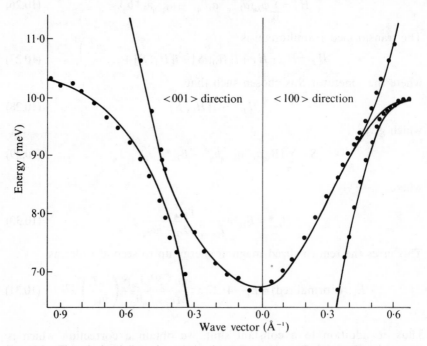

FIG. 10.2.   The calculated dispersion relation for FeF_2 together with experimental data at 4·2 K. (After Lovesey 1972.)

phonons a term which is cubic in phonon wave vector was included as suggested by the phonon spectra of TiO_2. The calculated dispersion relation for the excitation energy is shown in Fig. 10.2 together with experimental data for FeF_2. The agreement between theory and experiment seems to support the interaction mechanism used.

11

NEUTRON–MAGNON INTERACTIONS

The availability of a high flux of thermal neutrons (wavelength of the order of interatomic distances in solids) from nuclear reactors has made it possible to probe the spectra of elementary excitations in solids. In contrast to other probes, it is possible to span a substantial portion of the Brillouin zone using thermal neutrons. Although there are many aspects of neutron interactions in magnetic crystals, e.g. neutron diffraction (determination of static magnetic structure, see Izyumov and Ozerov 1970) and neutron inelastic scattering (dynamic structure, see Kothari and Singwi 1959), we shall confine our attention to the problem of the inelastic scattering of neutrons by spin waves in magnetically ordered solids. We shall ignore neutron interactions with atomic nuclei. The magnetic interaction of slow neutrons with an atom comprises two parts, one involving spin moment and the other involving orbital atomic transitions. The second interaction is possible for atomic systems having orbital angular momentum, i.e. $L \neq 0$ (Joshi and Sinha 1967). The majority of theoretical work concerns interactions involving spin only moments, i.e. atoms in an orbital singlet ground state (Elliot and Lowde 1955). Therefore we shall consider the spin-only situation and formulate the basic interaction process.

11.1. Formulation of spin-only interaction terms

The interaction between the neutron and the electron spins is of purely electromagnetic origin and follows from the low-energy limit of the Dirac equation. The interaction Hamiltonian $\Sigma_l H_{en}{}^l$ is (see de Gennes 1963, Kittel 1963)

$$\sum_l H_{en}{}^l = -\sum_l \boldsymbol{\mu}_c{}^l \cdot \text{curl } \mathbf{A}_n \tag{11.1}$$

with the vector potential $\mathbf{A}_n$ given by

$$\mathbf{A}_n = \text{curl}\left(\frac{\boldsymbol{\mu}_n}{|\mathbf{r}_n - \mathbf{r}_c{}^l|}\right) \tag{11.2}$$

where $\boldsymbol{\mu}_c{}^l$ and $\boldsymbol{\mu}_n$ are the electron and the neutron spin magnetic moments respectively, and $\mathbf{r}_n$ and $\mathbf{r}_e{}^l$ are the co-ordinates of the neutron and the magnetic electron localized at site l.

11.2. Differential scattering cross-section for one-magnon (absorption or emission) processes

The differential scattering cross-section for the collision of the neutron with a magnetic system is given by the general expression

$$\frac{d^2\sigma}{d\Omega d\omega} = \left(\frac{m_n}{2\pi\hbar^2}\right)^2 \frac{k'}{k} \sum_{\substack{\sigma\sigma' \\ ms,m's'}} p_\sigma, p_{ms} |\langle \mathbf{k}'\sigma', m's' | \sum_l H_{en}{}^l | \mathbf{k}\sigma, ms\rangle|^2$$

$$\times \delta\left(\frac{E_{ms} - E_{m's'}}{\hbar} + \omega\right) \tag{11.3}$$

where ms and $m's'$ denote the initial and the final spin-orbital states of the magnetic system and $\mathbf{k}\sigma$ and $\mathbf{k}'\sigma'$ are the initial and the final wave vectors and spin projections of the neutron. Here $\hbar\omega$ and $\hbar\mathbf{q}$ are the energy-momentum transfers to neutrons i.e.

$$\hbar\mathbf{k}' - \hbar\mathbf{k} = \hbar\mathbf{q}$$

$$E_{k'} - E_k \equiv \frac{\hbar^2}{2m_n}(k'^2 - k^2) = \hbar\omega \tag{11.4}$$

where $d\Omega$ is the element of the solid angle through which the neutron is scattered, p_σ and p_{ms} represent respectively the statistical weights of the initial neutron spin and the initial state of the magnetic system, and m_n is the mass of the neutron. The state of the magnetic system characterized by the symbol $|ms\rangle$ comprises the spin-orbital states of the paramagnetic ions, i.e.

$$|ms\rangle = \sum_P (-1)^P P\phi_1(\xi_1)\phi_2(\xi_2) \dots \phi_N(\xi_N) \tag{11.5}$$

where ξ denotes the space and spin co-ordinates, P is the permutation operator, and $\phi_1(\xi)$ is the spin-orbital state at site 1. In computing the matrix elements we shall ignore orbital transitions.

The interaction processes in eqn (11.1) can be written in terms of spin operators by noting that

$$\mu_e{}^l = -\frac{|e|\hbar}{m_e c}\mathbf{s}_e{}^l$$

$$\mu_n = -\frac{|g_n||e|\hbar}{m_n c}\mathbf{s}_n \tag{11.6}$$

where $g_n = -1\cdot 91$. Thus the interaction term becomes

$$H_{en}{}^l = -B_n \sum_l \mathbf{s}_e{}^l \cdot \nabla \times \left(\nabla \times \frac{\mathbf{s}_n}{|\mathbf{r}_n - \mathbf{r}_e{}^l|}\right) \tag{11.7}$$

where

$$B_n = \frac{e^2 \hbar^2 g_n}{m_e m_n c^2}. \tag{11.8}$$

Thus the matrix element of the interaction Hamiltonian for plane-wave neutron states and with the above definition of $|ms\rangle$ can be written as

$$\langle \mathbf{k}'\sigma'm's'| \sum_l H_{en}{}^l |\mathbf{k}\sigma ms\rangle \tag{11.9}$$

$$= -B_n \langle \sigma's'|F(q_\lambda) \sum_l \exp(i\mathbf{q}\cdot\mathbf{R}) \int d^3r \exp(-i\mathbf{q}\cdot\mathbf{r}) \mathbf{s}_e{}^l \cdot \nabla \times \nabla \times \frac{\mathbf{s}_n}{r} \rangle$$

where the magnetic form factor

$$F(q) = \int |\phi_l(r_e)|^2 \exp(i\mathbf{q}\cdot\mathbf{r}_e) d^3r_e \tag{11.10}$$

assuming that all magnetic ions are identical and there is no orbital excitation. The integral in eqn (11.9) becomes

$$\int d^3r \exp(-i\mathbf{q}\cdot\mathbf{r}) \mathbf{s}_e{}^l \cdot \nabla \times \left(\nabla \times \frac{\mathbf{s}_n}{r} \right) = 4\pi \mathbf{s}_n \cdot \mathbf{s}_{e\perp}{}^l$$

where $\mathbf{s}_{e\perp}{}^l$ is the component of $\mathbf{s}_e{}^l$ normal to $\mathbf{q}$. Thus

$$\langle \mathbf{k}'\sigma'm's'| \sum_l H_{en}{}^l |\mathbf{k}\sigma ms\rangle \tag{11.11}$$

$$= 4\pi B_n F(q) \sum_l \exp(i\mathbf{q}\cdot\mathbf{R}) \langle \sigma's'|\mathbf{s}_n \cdot \mathbf{s}_{e\perp}{}^l |\sigma s\rangle.$$

Squaring the above matrix elements and substituting in eqn (11.3), carrying out the summation, and averaging over the final and initial neutron spin states, we obtain for the case of unpolarized neutrons

$$\frac{d^2\sigma}{d\Omega d\omega} = \left(\frac{e^2 g_n}{m_e c^2} \right)^2 \frac{k'}{k} \sum_{lm} \exp\{i\mathbf{q}\cdot(\mathbf{R}_l - \mathbf{R}_m)\} |F(q)|^2 \tag{11.12}$$

$$\times \langle \mathbf{s}_{e\perp}{}^l \cdot \mathbf{s}_{e\perp}{}^m \rangle \delta\left(\frac{E_k - E_{k'}}{\hbar} + \omega \right).$$

Introducing the integral representation of the δ function, writing

$$\mathbf{s}_{e\perp}{}^m(0) = \exp\left(-\frac{iHt}{\hbar} \right) \mathbf{s}_{e\perp}{}^m(t) \exp\left(\frac{iHt}{\hbar} \right)$$

and making use of the cyclic invariance of the trace, we obtain

$$\frac{d^2\sigma}{d\Omega d\omega} = \left(\frac{e^2 g_n}{m_e c^2}\right)^2 \frac{k'}{k} |F(\mathbf{q})|^2 \sum_{lm} \exp\{i\mathbf{q}\cdot(\mathbf{R}_l - \mathbf{R}_m)\}$$

$$\times \frac{1}{2\pi} \int_{-\infty}^{\infty} dt \, \exp(-i\omega t)\langle \mathbf{s}_{e\perp}{}^l(0)\cdot\mathbf{s}_{e\perp}{}^m(t)\rangle.$$

(11.13)

This is a standard expression for the differential scattering cross-section (e.g. Kittel 1963). In the above we have treated the moment-bearing atoms as static at the respective equilibrium positions. However, atoms are never quiescent and the factor $\exp\{i\mathbf{q}\cdot(\mathbf{R}_1 - \mathbf{R}_m)$ should be replaced explicitly as

$$\exp\{i\mathbf{q}\cdot(\mathbf{R}_l - \mathbf{R}_m)\}\,|\langle\exp\{i\mathbf{q}\cdot(\delta\mathbf{R}_l)\rangle|^2\}$$

where $\delta\mathbf{R}_l$ is the displacement of the atom in question. This can be rewritten as

$$|\langle\exp(i\mathbf{q}\cdot\mathbf{R}_l)\rangle|^2 = \exp(-2W_q)$$

where $\exp(-2W_q)$ is the well-known thermal factor with

$$W_q = \frac{\hbar}{2MN} \sum_{q's'} \frac{\langle\mathbf{q}\cdot\boldsymbol{\varepsilon}_{q's'}\rangle^2}{\omega_{q's'}} \frac{1}{2}\coth\left(\frac{\hbar\omega_{q's'}}{2 k_B T}\right).$$

In all following expressions this reduction factor is implicitly present.

For a ferromagnetically ordered system we can re-express the operators involved in the spin–spin correlation function in terms of the magnon operators. For this purpose we note that

$$\langle\mathbf{s}_{e\perp}{}^l(0)\cdot\mathbf{s}_{e\perp}{}^m(t)\rangle$$

$$= \langle\{\mathbf{s}_e{}^l(0)\cdot\mathbf{q}\}\frac{\mathbf{q}}{q^2}\cdot[\mathbf{s}_e{}^m(t) - \{\mathbf{s}_e{}^m(t)\cdot\mathbf{q}\}\frac{\mathbf{q}}{q^2}]\rangle$$

(11.14)

$$= \langle\mathbf{s}_e{}^l(0)\cdot\mathbf{s}_e{}^m(t) - \{\mathbf{s}_e{}^l(t)\cdot\mathbf{q}\}\{\mathbf{s}_e{}^m(t)\cdot\mathbf{q}\}/q^2\rangle$$

Next we introduce the magnon operators and retain only one-magnon terms (See Chapter 5). We obtain

$$\langle\mathbf{s}_e{}^l(0)\cdot\mathbf{s}_e{}^m(t)\rangle = \frac{S}{N} \sum_{lm\lambda\lambda'} \langle a_\lambda(0)a_{\lambda'}{}^+(t)\exp\{i(\lambda\cdot\mathbf{R}_l - \lambda'\cdot\mathbf{R}_m)\}$$

$$+ a_\lambda{}^+(0)a_{\lambda'}(t)\exp\{-i(\lambda\cdot\mathbf{R}_l - \lambda'\cdot\mathbf{R}_m)\}$$

(11.15)

$$+ \frac{1}{2q^2}\{a_\lambda(0)\exp(i\lambda\cdot\mathbf{R}_l)q^- + a_\lambda{}^+(0)\exp(-i\lambda\cdot\mathbf{R}_l)q^+\}$$

$$\times \{a_{\lambda'}(t)\exp(i\lambda'\cdot\mathbf{R}_m)q^- + a_{\lambda'}{}^+(t)\exp(-i\lambda'\cdot\mathbf{R}_m)q^+\}\rangle$$

$$+ \text{higher-order terms.}$$

where $q^{\pm} = q_x \pm iq_y$. Noting that

$$a_\lambda(t) = a_\lambda(0)\exp(-i\omega_\lambda t)$$
$$a_\lambda^+(t) = a_\lambda^+(0)\exp(i\omega_\lambda t)$$

assuming

$$\langle a_\lambda^+(0)a_{\lambda'}(0)\rangle = n_\lambda^0 \delta_{\lambda\lambda'} \tag{11.16}$$

substituting eqn (11.15) into (11.13), and carrying out the site summation and time integration, we obtain

$$\frac{d^2\sigma}{d\Omega d\omega} = \left(\frac{e^2 g_n}{m_e c^2}\right)^2 \frac{SN}{2}\frac{k'}{k}|F(\mathbf{q})|^2 \{\delta(\omega - \omega_\mathbf{q})(1 + n_\mathbf{q}^0)(1 + \hat{q}_z^2)$$
$$+ \delta(\omega + \omega_\mathbf{q})n_\mathbf{q}^0(1 + \hat{q}_z^2)\} \tag{11.17}$$

where $\hat{q}_z$ is the z component of the unit vector along $\mathbf{q}$. The above expression is for normal processes. If we include Umklapp processes as well, the expression is modified to

$$\frac{d^2\sigma}{d\Omega d\omega} = \left(\frac{e^2 g_n}{m_e c^2}\right)^2 \frac{SN}{2}\frac{k'}{k} \sum_\mathbf{g} |F(\mathbf{q})|^2 \{\delta(\omega - \omega_\lambda)(1 + n_\lambda^0)$$
$$\times (1 + \hat{q}_z^2) + \delta(\omega + \omega_\lambda)n_\lambda^0(1 + \hat{q}_z^2)\}\Delta(\mathbf{q} + \lambda + \mathbf{g}) \tag{11.18}$$

where $\mathbf{g}$ is a reciprocal lattice vector.

If the incident neutrons are in a definite state of polarization, the above expression is modified. Some additional terms have to be taken into account when performing the spin summation. In the polarized case, when we take the square of the matrix element in eqn (11.11) we obtain

$$\sum_{\sigma\sigma'} p_\sigma \left| \sum_l \exp(i\mathbf{q}\cdot\mathbf{R}_l)\langle \sigma's' | \mathbf{s}_n \cdot \mathbf{s}_{e\perp}^l | \sigma s\rangle \right|^2$$
$$= \sum_{lm} \langle s' | \tfrac{1}{4}(\mathbf{s}_e^l \cdot \mathbf{s}_{e\perp}^m) | s\rangle \exp\{i\mathbf{q}\cdot(\mathbf{R}_l - \mathbf{R}_m)\} \tag{11.19}$$
$$+ \sum_{\sigma\sigma'} p^\sigma \tfrac{1}{2}\langle \sigma's' | \mathbf{s}_n \cdot \sum_l (\mathbf{s}_{e\perp}^l \times \mathbf{s}_{e\perp}^m) | \sigma s\rangle.$$

In the unpolarized case, the second term linear in s_n did not survive. Using the well-known vector identities for spin and ordinary vectors, the second term reduces to

$$\sum_{\sigma\sigma'} p_\sigma \langle \sigma's' | \sum_l (\mathbf{s}_e^l \cdot \mathbf{q})(\mathbf{q}\cdot\mathbf{s}_n) | \sigma s\rangle \tag{11.20}$$

which, on noting that

$$\sum_{l} (\mathbf{s}_e^l \cdot \hat{\mathbf{q}}) \approx NS\hat{q}_z \tag{11.21a}$$

can be written in a compact form as

$$\tfrac{1}{4} NS\hat{q}_z(\hat{\mathbf{q}} \cdot \hat{\mathbf{P}}) \tag{11.21b}$$

where $\hat{\mathbf{P}}$ is the unit polarization vector of the incoming neutron. Thus for the case of polarized neutrons the differential scattering cross-section becomes

$$\begin{aligned}
\frac{d^2\sigma}{d\Omega d\omega} = &\left(\frac{e^2 g_n}{m_e c^2}\right) \frac{SN}{2} \frac{k'}{k} \sum_g \left| F(q)\right|^2 \\
&\times [\delta(\omega - \omega_\lambda)(1 + n_\lambda^0)\{1 + \hat{q}^2 + 2\hat{q}_z(\hat{\mathbf{q}} \cdot \hat{\mathbf{P}})\} \\
&+ \delta(\omega + \omega_\lambda)n_\lambda^0\{1 + \hat{q}_z^2 - 2\hat{q}_z(\hat{\mathbf{q}} \cdot \hat{\mathbf{P}})\}]\Delta(\mathbf{q} + \lambda + \mathbf{g}).
\end{aligned} \tag{11.22}$$

A derivation of the extra terms for the case of polarized neutrons was first given by Saenz (1960, 1962) in a somewhat different form. The extra polarization-dependent terms have been experimentally observed by Samuelsen, Riste, and Steinsvoll (1963).

A few words about the use of neutron scattering studies on magnetically ordered solids are now in order. We have noticed that the inelastic neutron scattering involves transfer of energy momentum to the spin system. It is thus possible to map the dispersion relation of the various magnon modes of a magnetic solid (Brockhouse and Watanabe 1962).

Intensity measurement gives an idea of the strength of the exchange coupling, in particular the $2JSa^2$ parameter. At elevated temperatures, measurements of temperature-dependent widths and shifts of the neutron peaks reveal the anharmonic effects involving magnons. Neutron-scattering experiments also provide a powerful means of probing the spin–spin correlation function (cf. eqn (11.13)) particularly near the magnetic critical point (see Marshall and Lowde 1968).

11.3. Magnetic properties through neutron scattering

In the preceding chapters we have given a theoretical description of the origin and nature of elementary excitations and their interactions in magnetically ordered solids. The purpose of the present section is to describe the experimental situation in relation to the theoretical ideas developed earlier. More specifically, these involve the measurement of the magnetic moment and its order as well as the excitation lifetime.

11.3.1. *Magnetic moment distribution and magnetic ordering*

As previously remarked, the best probe for determining the magnetic moment distribution and ordering is by coherent elastic neutron diffraction (see Fig. 11.1). As in the case of X-ray structure determination, this involves the atomic form factor and the static structure factor. The main difference, however, is that the scattering arises from both the nuclei and the uncompensated electron spins of the paramagnetic atoms.

The atomic form factor is in general a Fourier transform of the electron charge or the spin density as the case may be. We have seen that the distribution of unpaired valence electrons and their spins is more spread out than the core electronic charge density (cf. Chapter 1). Therefore, the magnetic form factor as revealed by neutrons will fall off more rapidly as a function of momentum transfer (scattering angle) than the X-ray form factor. To be more specific the magnetic form factor can be written as

$$F(\mathbf{q}) = \int_{WS} \exp(i\mathbf{q} \cdot \mathbf{r}) \{ n\uparrow |\phi\uparrow(r)|^2 - n\downarrow |\phi\downarrow(\mathbf{r})|^2 \} d^3\mathbf{r} \qquad (11.23)$$

where the integral is over the Wigner–Seitz (WS) cell. Here $n\uparrow$ and $n\downarrow$ represent the numbers of valence electrons having spin-up and spin-down

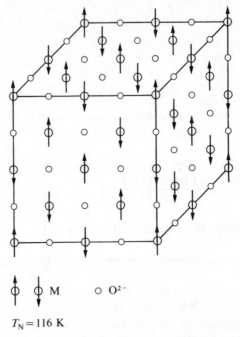

$T_N = 116$ K

FIG. 11.1. Magnetic moment ordering in MnO as revealed by neutron diffraction.

orientations respectively and $\phi\uparrow(\mathbf{r})$ and $\phi\downarrow(\mathbf{r})$ are corresponding spin-orbitals. The resultant local magnetic moment is related to $F(0)$ as

$$F(0) = n\uparrow - n\downarrow. \qquad (11.24)$$

The quantity $F(\mathbf{q})$ is directly obtained from elastic magnetic scattering of neutrons, where $q = 2k \sin \frac{1}{2}\theta$, θ being the scattering angle.

The spatial spin distribution is obtained by inverting $F(\mathbf{q})$ to the real space. For a spherically symmetric case the radial distribution $\sigma(r)$ is given by

$$\sigma(r) = \frac{2r}{\pi} \int_0^\infty qF(q)\sin(rq)dq. \qquad (11.25)$$

The spin-density profile for the entire magnetic crystal in question is, of course, obtained by the usual Fourier synthesis method of crystal structure analysis (see Izyumov and Ozerov 1970).

Measurements of the magnetic form factors from neutron scattering data have revealed interesting behaviour in magnetic crystals. For example in NiO it has been observed that there is an appreciable contraction of the moment distribution around the Ni^{2+} ion compared with free atoms (Alperin 1962). This is interpreted in terms of the molecular orbital model wherein the magnetic electrons are in the antibonding orbitals involving the metal ion d orbitals (see eqn (1.12) of Chapter 1). This has a node between the metal and the ligand ion. However, the experimental results on MnO show an expansion which remains a puzzle (see Izyumov and Ozerov 1970). Perhaps the spin-polarization mechanism involving the metal ion $4s$ orbital, which is more spread out, plays a more significant role in MnO. In this context it should be noted that for a purely covalent bond (in the absence of

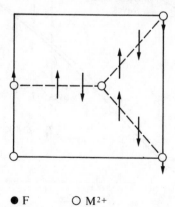

● F   ○ M^{2+}

FIG. 11.2. Spin-density distribution of valence electrons in MnF_2 as seen by neutron scattering. (After Nathans 1963.)

spin polarization) the spin density should be zero everywhere. The spin-polarization effect (i.e. the exchange interaction of the covalent electrons with the unpaired electrons of the magnetic ions) leads to a non-zero spatial spin density. Thus in MnF_2 (antiferromagnetic) the spin densities of these electrons have the same sign as the spin of the magnetic ion in the vicinity of the latter (Nathans *et al.* 1963; also see Fig. 11.2) (see Chapter 4).

There is still another way through which the covalent bonding effect can show up in neutron scattering results. This may appear as a reduced intensity of the scattering compared with the intensity calculated on the basis of a purely ionic model. The intensity of a magnetic Bragg peak is proportional to the square of the magnetic moment associated with the magnetic ions. For example in NiO (for the unit $Ni^{2+} - O^{2-} - Ni^{2+}$) the unpaired electrons are in the antibonding eg^* orbitals (see eqn (1.12)). Thus a fraction $\lambda_\sigma^2 + \lambda_s^2$ of an unpaired electron is transferred to the $2p$ and $2s$ orbitals of the oxygen ion from each of the neighbouring Ni^{2+} ions. Inasmuch as the spins of the two Ni^{2+} ions are antiparallel the above fraction of the total spin is annulled from the point of view of neutron scattering. Thus the net magnetic moment of the nickel ion is reduced from the free-ion value μ_0 to, say, $\mu_0(1 - 3\lambda_\sigma^2 - 3\lambda_s^2)$ taking into account the six

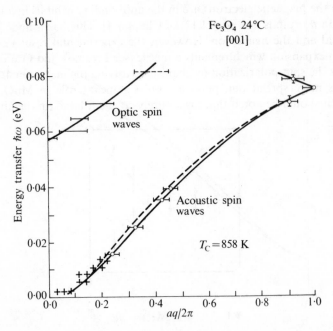

FIG. 11.3. Neutron scattering results of magnon dispersion in Fe_3O_4. (After Brockhouse and Watanabe 1962.)

ligands surrounding each magnetic ion. The corresponding reduction in the neutron scattering intensity can be measured which in turn gives an estimate for the covalency parameters. Thus for NiO, $\lambda_\sigma^2 + \lambda_s^2$ is about 6% (Owen and Thornley 1966). The neutron scattering results taken in conjunction with hyperfine magnetic resonance data can often give values of individual parameters such as λ_σ, λ_π, etc. (see Chapters 1 and 2).

11.3.2. Spin-wave dispersion relation by neutron scattering

Inelastic neutron scattering has been extensively used for the determination of the dispersion relation (i.e. the dependence of energy on the wave vector) of an excitation mode in a solid. The energy and momentum conservation requirements give rise to intensity peaks in the energy distribution of neutrons scattered coherently in a given direction. The positions of these peaks are related to the energy of the quantum of excitation mode and to the direction of the momentum of the excitation mode in question. In most of the experimental conditions the scattering cross-section is predominantly due to the absorption or emission of a single quantum of an excitation

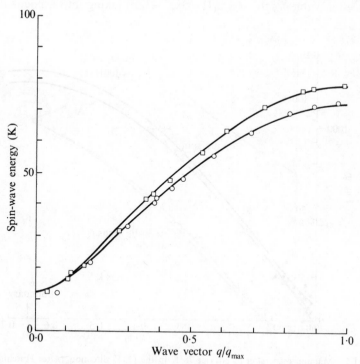

FIG. 11.4. Magnon dispersion in MnF_2 as studied by neutron scattering: □ propagation in the $\langle 001 \rangle$ direction; ○ propagation in the $\langle 100 \rangle$ direction. (After Okazaki et al. 1964.)

mode (e.g. one phonon or one magnon). The measurement of the energy and momentum transfers gives information about the dispersion relation of the mode in question via eqns (11.4). The momentum conservation relation, of course, contains the modulo reciprocal lattice vector, i.e. $\mathbf{k} - \mathbf{k}' = \boldsymbol{\lambda} + \mathbf{g}$.

In Figs. 11.3 and 11.4 we have reproduced the experimental dispersion relations in Fe_3O_4 (ferrimagnetic) and MnF_2 (antiferromagnetic) along some symmetry directions measured by neutron scattering as discussed above and the dispersion curves are in general agreement with theory (cf. Chapter 5). A recent neutron scattering study of the spin-wave dispersion relations has been made for the NiO system by Hutchings and Samuelsen (1972). NiO is a f.c.c. antiferromagnet with four interpenetrating magnetic sublattices. This work settles the old question as to whether the nearest-neighbour (nn) exchange interaction J_1 (>0) via 90° Ni^{2+} —— O^{2-} —— Ni^{2+} superexchange is dominant or the usual 180° next-nearest-neighbour (nnn) interaction J_2 (<0) involving Ni^{2+} —— O^{2-} —— Ni^{2-}. The estimates show that $J_2 = -211$ K (antiferromagnetic) and $J_1 = 15 \cdot 9$ K (ferromagnetic). These results support the conclusion that NiO is a weakly covalent insulator and that the exchange is through covalency and the overlap effect (see Chapter 4).

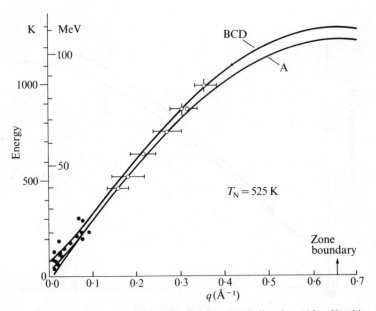

FIG. 11.5. Magnon dispersion in NiO at 78 K in the [111] direction. (After Hutchings and Samuelsen 1972.) Here A, B, C, D refer to different reciprocal lattice domains. See original paper for further details.

In Fig. 11.5 the observed spin-wave dispersion at 78 K in the $\langle 111 \rangle$ direction for NiO is shown along with the calculated curves. The important point brought out by the experimental work of Hutchings and Samuelsen is that there is a steep initial slope of order 250 meV Å and a high maximum energy (~ 117 meV) and a lower zone boundary energy in certain directions. For further details of this work reference should be made to the original paper.

12

LOW–TEMPERATURE THERMAL CONDUCTIVITY OF MAGNETIC INSULATORS

In this chapter we shall discuss the thermal energy transport in magnetic insulaors arising from the various interaction processes involving magnons and phonons. We shall not deal with magnetically ordered metals and alloys because the spin–phonon contributions are masked by the dominant contributions of the conduction (itinerant) electrons.

It should be noted that magnons and phonons provide two independent parallel paths for the transport of energy. Thus the total thermal conductivity K is the sum of magnon (K_m) and phonon (K_{ph}) parts. In this model the expression for thermal conductivity is given by (Carruthers 1961, Callaway and Boyd 1964):

$$K = \frac{1}{3} \sum_r \frac{\Omega_v}{8\pi^3} \int \frac{\partial(E_k^r n_k^r)}{\partial T} v_g^r(\mathbf{k}) l_r(\mathbf{k}) \mathrm{d}^3 \mathbf{k} \tag{12.1}$$

where the index r denotes the excitation branch, polarization and type of excitation (phonons or magnons), $v_g^r(\mathbf{k})$ and $l_r(\mathbf{k})$ are the group velocity and the mean free path respectively, $\mathbf{k}$ is the wave vector of the excitation, E_k^r is the energy, and n_k^r is the occupation number. In eqn (12.1) the temperature derivatives of $E_k^r n_k^r$ represent the specific heat term. This equation can be recast in terms of the relaxation frequency on noting that

$$v_g^r(\mathbf{k}) = \frac{1}{\hbar} \operatorname{grad}_k E_k^r$$

$$l_r(\mathbf{k}) = v_g^r(\mathbf{k}) \tau_k^r$$

Thus, we can write for the rth component

$$K_r = \frac{\Omega_v k_B}{3(2\pi)^3 \hbar^2} \int \left(\frac{E_k^r}{k_B T} \right)^2 \frac{\exp(E_k^r/k_B T)}{\{\exp(E_k^r/k_B T) - 1\}^2} (\nabla_k E_x^r)^2 \tau_k^r \mathrm{d}k^3 \tag{12.2}$$

where the relaxation frequencies $1/\tau_k^r$ refer to the various excitations described below.

The relaxation frequency $1/\tau_\lambda^m$ for the magnon mode will comprise the following contributions:

$$\frac{1}{\tau_\lambda^m} = \frac{1}{\tau_\lambda^{mb}} + \frac{1}{\tau_\lambda^{md}} + \frac{1}{\tau_\lambda^{mm}} + \frac{1}{\tau_\lambda^{mp}} \tag{12.3}$$

where the various terms are, respectively, the relaxation frequencies for magnon–boundary, magnon–defect, magnon–magnon, and magnon–phonon scattering processes.

Likewise the phonon relaxation frequence $1/\tau_q^p$ is given by

$$\frac{1}{\tau_q^p} = \frac{1}{\tau_q^{pb}} + \frac{1}{\tau_q^{pd}} + \frac{1}{\tau_q^{pp}} + \frac{1}{\tau_q^{pm}} \tag{12.4}$$

where the superscripts have the same meaning as for eqn (12.3) except that they refer to phonons. Expression (12.1) can easily be specialized to the case of magnons and phonons.

In view of the fact that the dispersion relations for the lowest magnon modes for ferromagnetic and for antiferromagnetic systems differ, we shall present the calculations for each type of ordering separately.

12.1. Low-temperature thermal conductivity of ferromagnetic insulators

Let us consider various terms of $1/\tau_\lambda^m$. The magnon–boundary contribution can be written as

$$\frac{1}{\tau_\lambda^{mb}} = \frac{v v_g^m(\lambda)}{L_C^m} = \frac{4 v J S a^2 \lambda}{\hbar L_C^m} \tag{12.5}$$

where v is the dimensionaless number and L_C^m is the Casimir length (some average length of the order of the cube root of volume). This is only important at very low temperatures when the mean free path is comparable with the sample size and the boundary scattering is not specular but diffuse as in Casimir's (1938) theory.

The magnon–defect (magnetic) scattering which is assumed to be of the Rayleigh type, is given by

$$\frac{1}{\tau_\lambda^{md}} = A_R^m (E_\lambda^m)^4 \tag{12.6}$$

where A_R^m is the Rayleigh scattering parameter for magnons and is independent of temperature and frequency. This Rayleigh-type energy dependence is implicitly related to the linear magnetic polarization of the magnetic point defect. It should be noted that, strictly speaking, the dependence on the wave vector comes via the energy (frequency) dependence of the scattering process together with the approximate dispersion relation. Only for a linear dispersion relation, e.g. phonons, antiferromagnons, etc., could one obtain the well-known k^4 (wave vector) dependence. For quadratic dispersion, we see that $1/\tau_\lambda^{md} \alpha |\lambda|^8$. It is obviously negligible in the long-wavelength region.

The magnon–magnon mean free path has been calculated by Dyson

(1956). He shows that this is proportional to $T^{-5/2}$. However, it must be emphasized that magnon–magnon scattering *per se* cannot contribute to thermal resistance as the process always conserves the total crystal momentum of the magnon system. Further, the Umklapp magnon–magnon processes are exponentially unimportant at low temperatures. They can contribute only indirectly by modifying the scattering of magnons by defects etc. in that they convert two long-wavelength magnons into one short-wavelength magnon. The latter in turn can be scattered more effectively by a defect. However, this situation is only true for high temperatures and clean samples when the magnon–magnon mean free path is short compared with the magnon–defect mean free path. On the other hand, other scattering processes dominate for dirty samples in low-temperature regions. Therefore, we shall not pursue magnon–magnon contributions any further.

However, there will be a magnon contribution to thermal conductivity due to their scattering by phonons. The relevant relaxation frequency can be calculated by making use of the two-magnon one-phonon interaction processes given earlier for ferromagnets (see Chapter 8). A straightforward calculation under gross approximations gives (Bhandari and Verma 1966)

$$\frac{1}{\tau_\lambda^{mp}} = \frac{32aS^2 J_M{}^2 q_D{}^5}{5\pi\rho v_s \theta_C \theta_D} T^2 \lambda^{-2} \tag{12.7}$$

where it is assumed that $E_\lambda > k_B T$.

Similarly, for the phonon part of the thermal conductivity we need the corresponding relaxation frequencies. Thus for phonon–boundary scattering we have

$$\frac{1}{\tau_q^{pb}} \approx \frac{v_s}{L_p{}^C} \tag{12.8}$$

where $L_p{}^C$ is the Casimir length for phonons. This is independent of wave vector.

The phonon–defect scattering is given by the Rayleigh-like formula

$$\frac{1}{\tau_q^{pd}} \approx A_R{}^p (\hbar\omega_q)^4 \propto q^4 \tag{12.9}$$

for acoustic phonons (i.e. $\omega_q = v_s q$).

As in the case of magnons, the normal phonon–phonon scattering processes will not contribute. The phonon–magnon contribution can be extracted from the same interaction processes by averaging over the magnon variables. One obtains (after gross approximations)

$$\frac{1}{\tau_q^{pm}} = \frac{32aS^2 (J_M)^2}{\pi\rho v_s \theta_C \theta_D} \lambda_{max} T^2 q^2. \tag{12.10}$$

By making use of these expressions Bhandari and Verma (1966) have calculated K_m and K_{ph}. Their calculated thermal conductivity $K = K_m + K_{ph}$ for YIG seems to be in good agreement with experiment. They have however, scaled several adjustable parameters. Strictly speaking, they should have used the magnon–phonon interaction terms derived for a ferrimagnet (Joshi and Sinha 1964). This is important inasmuch as the wave-vector dependence may turn out to be different for

$$\frac{1}{\tau_\lambda^{mp}} \quad \text{and} \quad \frac{1}{\tau_q^{pm}}.$$

In the following section we shall discuss the calculation for the ferrimagnetic and antiferromagnetic systems.

12.2. Two-sublattice antiferromagnetic systems

The central point to note is that for simple antiferromagnets (e.g. MnF_2) no magnon component of heat current is observed experimentally down to 1 K (Nettleton 1964). In fact, the magnon–magnon relaxation time is very short and they equilibrate very quickly.

Hence magnon occupation numbers can be replaced by the equilibrium Bose distribution. Thus the heat current is primarily carried by phonons while magnons contribute indirectly via magnon–phonon interaction processes. As pointed out before, the contribution to the relaxation frequency $1/\tau_q^p$ is calculated for various scattering processes. Nettleton (1964), after making use of the interaction terms given by Upadhyaya and Sinha (1963), obtain

$$\frac{1}{\tau_q^{pm}} = (QT)q^4 \tag{12.11}$$

where

$$Q = \frac{4\hbar^2 v_s S^2 J_M{}^2}{\pi \rho k_B{}^3 \theta_C{}^4 (\theta_C/\theta_D)^2} \left(1 - \frac{\theta_C{}^2}{\theta_D{}^2}\right)^2 \\ \times \left(\tan^{-1}\frac{\theta_C}{\theta_D} - \frac{C}{X}\right) \tag{12.12}$$

for $\theta_C < \theta_D$. The total $1/\tau_q^p$ is the sum arising from boundary, defects and magnon scattering processes. The computed K_{ph} (Nettleton 1964) is in very good agreement with the low-temperature data for MnF_2. However, similar calculations for MnO show poor agreement. It should be noted that MnO is a more complicated system in that there are four magnetic sublattices.

Thus the magnon–phonon interaction terms may have a more complicated structure.

12.3. Two-sublattice ferrimagnets

We confine our attention to the acoustic spin-wave branch and the acoustic phonons in the low-temperature region. The magnon–phonon interaction terms were given in Chapter 8. The q dependence of $1/\tau_q^{pm}$ is (Joshi and Sinha 1966)

$$\frac{1}{\tau_q^{pm}} = Rf(q) \qquad (12.13)$$

where

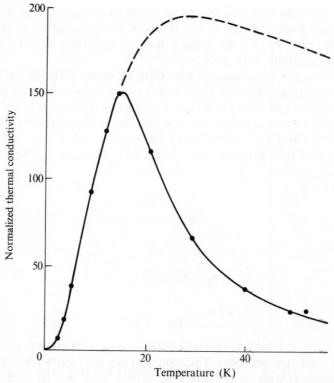

FIG. 12.1. A comparison of theoretical (broken curve) and experimental (solid curve) values for the temperature-dependent thermal conductivity in MnF_2. (After Nettleton 1964).

$$R = \frac{J_M{}^2(S_A + S_B)^2 T}{\pi \rho k_B v_s \theta_C{}^2 z^2} \tag{12.14}$$

and

$$f(q) = q^2(e^\xi - 1)\exp\left\{-\frac{(\xi + \beta)^2}{4\beta}\right\} \tag{12.15}$$

with

$$\xi = \frac{\hbar \omega_q}{k_B T}, \qquad \beta = \frac{\theta_D{}^2}{\theta_C T}.$$

The overall expression is further simplified to

$$\frac{1}{\tau_\xi{}^{mp}} = Q_1 \xi^3$$

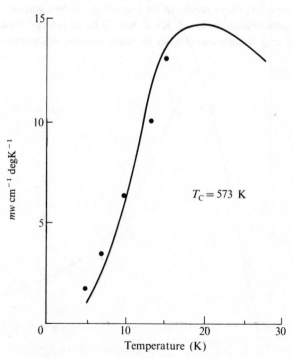

$T_C = 573$ K

FIG. 12.2. Theoretical (solid curve) and experimental (points) values for thermal conductivity of MnFe₂O₄. (After Joshi and Sinha 1967.)

where

$$Q_1 = \frac{6k_B J_M{}^2 (S_A + S_B)^2 T^3 e^{-\beta/4}}{\pi \rho \hbar^3 v_s{}^3 \theta_C{}^2 z^2}. \tag{12.16}$$

Taking account of the boundary and defect scatterings, we obtain

$$\frac{1}{\tau_\xi{}^{mp}} = A + Q_1 \xi^3 + P\xi^4 \tag{12.17}$$

and hence

$$K_{ph} = \frac{k_B{}^4 T^3}{2\pi^2 \hbar^3 v_s} \int_0^{\theta_D/T} \frac{\xi^4}{A + Q_1 \xi^3 + P\xi^4} \frac{e^\xi d\xi}{(e^\xi - 1)^2}. \tag{12.18}$$

This expression has been numerically integrated. For $MnFe_2O_4$ the agreement with experiment is fairly good (see Joshi and Sinha 1966).

In Figs. 12.1 and 12.2 the calculated curves and the experimental values of thermal conductivity in MnF_2 (antiferromagnetic) and $MnFe_2O_4$ (ferrimagnetic) are shown. The agreement before the Umklapp peak is satisfactory. These results thus support the magnon–phonon processes discussed here. For $MnFe_2O_4$ there seems to be a small deviation starting in the very low-temperature region (below 5 K). It would be of interest to have careful experimental and theoretical studies in these regions on samples of known purity.

13

INTERACTION OF LIGHT WITH MAGNONS

In addition to the direct magnetic dipole interaction with a spin system (as in magnetic and spin-wave resonance etc.), electromagnetic radiation can interact with magnons through various processes involving electric dipole and electric quadrupole transitions. In fact, two-magnon absorption lines have been observed in antiferromagnetic insulators and have been found to be of electric dipole type. Phenomenologically, the interaction involves a spin-dependent electric polarization of the medium. We shall, however, adopt a microscopic viewpoint. It is well known that the coupling of light with matter involves certain selection rules such as the conservation of parity, spin angular momentum, and linear momentum. In the case of interactions with spin waves (magnons) in magnetically ordered systems, this puts serious restrictions on the possible mechanisms. One can classify these mechanisms under the following two categories: one-centre (single magnetic ion) and two-centre (a pair of magnetic ions) mechanisms.

13.1. Interaction mechanisms

In the single-ion mechanism, apart from the pure magnetic dipole process, one has to invoke spin–orbit coupling to make the electric dipole transition possible. Only then we can satisfy the spin and the parity selection rules. This will give rise to one-magnon two-photon scattering processes in ferromagnetic and antiferromagnetic insulators analogous to the Brillouin scattering which involves acoustic phonons. For this process to be allowed the ground state of the magnetic ion must not be orbitally quenched. In most of the ferromagnetic or ferrimagnetic insulators the ground state of the magnetic ions is orbitally quenched (e.g. Mn^{2+}, Eu^{2+}, etc.). The above process is, however, inherently weak. Accordingly, not much experimental work is available on ferromagnets. On the other hand, optical absorption in antiferromagnetic insulators has been extensively studied. For such systems no single-ion mechanism can give rise to an electric dipole transition. The reason is that excitons and magnons are constructed from single-ion transitions of even parity. However, in the systems which have been experimentally studied (e.g. MnF_2 and $KMnF_3$) parity is a good quantum number. One is thus forced to invoke a two-ion mechanism to explain the observed results. The most important mechanism of this type involves off-diagonal exchange excitation between two magnetic ions (Tanabe, Moriya, and Sugano 1965). In physical terms this mechanism connects the ground state of two neighbouring magnetic ions on the two sublattices to an excited state in which one of the ions is excited to an odd-parity spin-reversed state while the other ion simply reverses its spin. This interaction thus admixes an odd-parity excited state with an even-parity ground state. This results in electric dipole transition moments which will couple with the electric vector of the radiation field.

As an example let us consider a pair of ions in the ground state where the up and the down spins are in the orbitals ϕ_a and ϕ_b. The transition electric dipole moment is given by

$$\langle \phi_a\uparrow\phi_b\downarrow|\mathbf{P}_{\text{eff}}|\phi_b\uparrow\phi_a\downarrow\rangle$$

$$= \sum_\mu \frac{\langle \phi_a\uparrow\phi_b\downarrow|\mathbf{P}|\phi_\mu\uparrow\phi_b\downarrow\rangle\langle\phi_\mu\uparrow\phi_b\downarrow|V|\phi_b\uparrow\phi_a\downarrow\rangle}{\Delta E(\phi_\mu\leftarrow\phi_a)}$$

$$+ \sum_\nu \frac{\langle \phi_a\uparrow\phi_b\downarrow|P|\phi_a\uparrow\phi_\nu\downarrow\rangle\langle\phi_a\uparrow\phi_\nu\downarrow|V|\phi_b\uparrow\phi_a\downarrow\rangle}{\Delta E(\phi_\nu\leftarrow\phi_b)} \tag{13.1}$$

plus terms obtained by interchanging $\mathbf{P}$ and V, where $\mathbf{P}$ is the electric dipole moment operator and V is the interelectronic Coulomb operator e^2/r_{12}; ϕ_μ and ϕ_ν correspond to the odd-parity excited-orbital states. The above equation can be written in terms of the spin operators S_a and S_b and has the form

$$\mathbf{P}_{\text{eff}} = \pi_{ab}(\mathbf{S}_a \cdot \mathbf{S}_b). \tag{13.2}$$

This gives an interaction with the electromagnetic field of the form (see the review article by Loudon 1968)

$$H_{ab}(\text{2-magnon}) = \{\mathbf{E}\cdot(\pi_{ab}+\pi_{ba})\}(S_a^- S_b^+) \tag{13.3}$$

where S_a^- and S_b^+ can be developed in magnon variables (see Chapter 5). This mechanism will always give two-magnon absorption. These magnons will belong to the two different branches for reasons of spin conservation.

There will be additional interaction terms for situations where one of the atoms goes to the excited (e) state and the other remains in the ground (g) state, but with a change in spin:

$$H_{ab}^{eg} = \sum_{\sigma\sigma'} \{(\mathbf{E}\cdot\pi_{ba}^{eg})C_{\mu a\sigma'}^{+}C_{ga\sigma}S_b^+ \langle\sigma'|s_a^-|\sigma\rangle$$

$$+ (\mathbf{E}\cdot\pi_{ba}^{eg})C_{\nu b\sigma'}^{+}C_{gb\sigma}S_a^- \langle\sigma'|s_b^+|\sigma\rangle\} \tag{13.4}$$

where $C_{\mu a\sigma}^{+}$ and $C_{ga\sigma}$ are the electron creation and annihilation operators for the excited and the ground states. It is clear that the above process gives one-magnon sidebands.

In physical terms a one-magnon sideband is a composite excitation comprising a purely electronic excitation (a Frenkel exciton) and a magnon.

Thus in an antiferromagnetic crystal such as MnF_2, where $3d$ electrons on the Mn^{2+} ions are tightly bound, we have a Frenkel exciton which is a phased linear combination of intraionic orbital excitation coupled by the weak interionic interaction. These excitons form a narrow band centred at the energy of the single-ion excitation in the absence of interionic coupling. Thus the electric dipole type of one-magnon sideband can be looked upon as a phased linear superposition of transitions of pairs of ions wherein one ion goes to the excited state with change of spin and other simply undergoes spin flip. The interaction of light through this kind of pair excitation is shown in Fig. 13.1 (see Sell 1968 for experimental results).

In addition to the mechanism discussed above there are other processes, albeit weaker. This is analogous to the Dexter (1962) mechanism which involves interaction of the electric dipole moment of one ion with the electric quadrupole moment of the other ion. For an antiferromagnetic system (e.g. FeF_2) this was invoked by Halley and Silvera (1965). This model includes the magnon, phonon, photon, and exciton fields in the zeroth order. The interaction Hamiltonian comprises the spin–orbit, magnon–phonon, electric dipole, electric quadrupole, and crystal-field effects. Let us consider two electronic states of the ion which are of opposite parity. They will couple with the external electromagnetic field through the interaction

$$H_{ed} = \left(-\frac{e}{mc} \right) \mathbf{A} \cdot \mathbf{p}$$

where $\mathbf{A}$ is the vector potential and $\mathbf{p}$ is the momentum operator. The above excited state (exciton at ion a) goes to another exciton state via spin–orbit coupling giving a spin–dependent dipole moment. This state will interact via quadrupole–dipole coupling with the exciton state of ion b which in turn is coupled to the ground state of ion b via spin–orbit coupling giving another spin-dependent term. The interaction is of fourth order in the perturbation. More specifically, the effective transition matrix element can be written as

$$\langle \phi_{bg} | H_{so} | \phi_{b\lambda} \rangle \langle \phi_{b\lambda} | H_{qd} | \phi_{av} \rangle \langle \phi_{av} | H_{so} | \phi_{a\mu} \rangle \langle \phi_{a\mu} | H_{ed} | \phi_{ag} \rangle | \Delta E_{a\mu} \Delta E_{av} \Delta E_{a\lambda}. \tag{13.5}$$

This can be recast in a form which will give an effective Hamiltonian which has the same form as the two-magnon process discussed earlier. Here H_{so}, H_{qd}, and H_{ed}, denote the spin–orbit, quadrupole–dipole, and electric dipole interaction terms respectively. The subscripts on the ϕ's (e.g. aλ) denote the excited states at respective atoms. The above interaction appears to be weak owing to the high order of the perturbation involved. It is known that spin–orbit and quadrupole–dipole interactions are inherently weak effects.

For ionic antiferromagnets it is possible to have another two-magnon

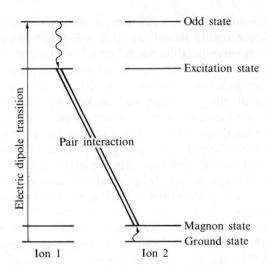

F$_{IG}$. 13.1. Schematic representation of the pair transition causing an electric dipole magnon sideband. (After Sell 1968.)

absorption process. This involves the interaction of the radiation field with the infrared active transverse optical phonons, which in turn interacts with the spin moment via the 'near-zone' magnetic field associated with TO phonon modes in ionic crystals. This is a ramification of the spin–phonon mechanism developed earlier (Kumar and Sinha 1967a,b). This mechanism also gives a two-magnon absorption process.

13.2. Formulation based on symmetry considerations

In the foregoing, we have discussed some of the plausible microscopic mechanisms of the interaction of light with magnetic insulators. It is convenient to develop a general formalism which describes the absorption and the scattering of light in terms of a spin-dependent electric dipole moment and the spin-dependent polarizability, respectively, in magnetic crystals entirely from symmetry viewpoints. In the presence of the electromagnetic field the Hamiltonian for the electric dipole type of interaction can be written as

$$H_{ed} = -\mathbf{E} \cdot \mathbf{P} \tag{13.6}$$

where $\mathbf{E}$ is the electric field vector and $\mathbf{P}$ is the dielectric polarization associated with the spin system and is given by (see Moriya 1968):

$$\mathbf{P} = \sum_j \mathbf{P}_j + \sum_{j,l} \mathbf{P}_{jl} + \ldots \tag{13.7}$$

Here P_j is the electric dipole moment at the magnetic site j and P_{jl} is the electric dipole moment for the pair (j, l). The most general bilinear form in spin variables consistent with the transformation properties under the symmetry group of the system is given by

$$P_j{}^\alpha = \sum_{\beta\gamma} K_j{}^{\alpha,\beta\gamma} S_{j\beta} S_{j\gamma} \tag{13.8}$$

and

$$P_{jl}{}^\alpha = \pi_{jl}{}^\alpha (\mathbf{S}_j \cdot \mathbf{S}_l) + \sum_{\beta\gamma} \Gamma_{jl}{}^{\alpha,\beta\gamma} \tfrac{1}{2} (S_{j\beta} S_{l\gamma} + S_{j\gamma} S_{l\beta})$$
$$+ D_{jl}{}^{\alpha,\beta} [\mathbf{S}_j \times \mathbf{S}_l]_\beta \tag{13.9}$$

where the greek indices denote Cartesian components. It can be seen that there is no term linear in the spin operators which could violate time-reversal symmetry.

A few words about the symmetry properties of the coefficients involved will be relevant for future discussion. The quantity $\mathbf{P}$ is a polar vector and invariant under time reversal. Thus $\mathbf{P}_j$ (linear Stark term) vanishes identically if the magnetic ion is at a centre of inversion in the crystal. In eqn (13.9) the tensor coefficients $\pi_{jl}{}^\alpha$ and $\Gamma_{jl}{}^{\alpha,\beta\gamma}$ are symmetric with respect to interchange of the indices jl, and D_{jl} is antisymmetric. It follows, therefore, that if the midpoint of the pair (j, l) is a centre of inversion, $\pi_{jl}{}^\alpha$ and, $\Gamma_{jl}{}^{\alpha,\beta\gamma}$ must vanish identically but $D_{jl}{}^{\alpha,\beta}$ will not.

In fact the bulk of experimental work has been done on the transition-metal fluorides (e.g. FeF_2) which have rutile-type structure. For this structure the magnetic ions are at a centre of inversion; however, the midpoint of the two nearest-neighbour magnetic ions is not a centre of inversion. Accordingly, $\mathbf{P}_j{}^\alpha$ vanishes but $\mathbf{P}_{jl}{}^\alpha$ survives. Inasmuch as $\pi_{jl}{}^\alpha$ arises from the off-diagonal exchange mechanism, it is inherently predominant when allowed by symmetry.

13.3. Two-magnon absorption in antiferromagnets at $T = 0$

When the spin operators in eqns (13.8) and (13.9) are expanded in terms of magnon operators (along with the usual canonical transformations for an antiferromagnet) one obtains the magnon interaction terms. For this purpose it is convenient to write the electric vector of the radiation field in the second-quantized representation. This is given by (in a transverse gauge, i.e. div $\mathbf{A} = 0$)

$$\mathbf{E}(\mathbf{r}) = i \sum_{\mathbf{\kappa},p} \sqrt{\frac{2\pi\hbar\omega_\kappa}{\Omega_v}} \exp(i\mathbf{\kappa} \cdot \mathbf{r}) \mathbf{e}_{\kappa p} (a_{\kappa p} - a_{-\kappa p}{}^+) \tag{13.10}$$

where ω_κ is the photon frequency for wave vector κ, $e_{\kappa p}$ is the polarization vector, and $a_{\kappa p}$ and $a_{\kappa p}{}^+$ are the photon annihilaton and creation operators. Assuming that for the two-sublattice antiferromagnet in question only the term $\pi_{jl}{}^\alpha(S_j \cdot S_l)$ is dominant and $\pi_{jl}{}^\alpha$ vanishes for the pair belonging to the same sublattice, we obtain the magnon–photon interaction term H_{m-pt} as

$$H_{m-pt} = i \sum_{\lambda\mu\kappa} \left(\frac{2\pi\hbar\omega}{\Omega_v}\right)^{1/2} \frac{S}{2} \left\{ e_{\kappa p} \cdot \pi\left(\frac{\lambda-\mu}{2}\right) \right\}$$
$$\times a_{\kappa p} \alpha_\lambda{}^+ \beta_\mu{}^+ \Delta(\kappa-\mu-\lambda) + \text{h.c.} \tag{13.11}$$

where

$$\pi(\lambda) = \sum_l \exp(i\lambda \cdot r_{jl})\pi_{jl} = -\pi(-\lambda) \tag{13.12}$$

for the centre-of-inversion case. It should be noted that, strictly speaking, the above expression for magnon–photon interaction is valid near the zone boundary only in that the magnons of the two branches (α and β) in this region describe spin waves on the respective sublattices. Because of the high density of states this is the region which makes the maximum contribution to the above process. The absorption coefficient for the two-magnon process is easily calculated using time-dependent perturbation theory. Recalling that the photon wave vector κ has a vanishingly small magnitude, we obtain the absorption coefficient $K(\omega)$ for the incident photon of frequency ω involving simultaneous creation of two magnons, one of each branch, as (at $T=0$)

$$K(\omega) = \sum_\lambda \frac{8\pi^2\omega}{c\hbar\Omega_v} S^2 \langle \pi_E(\lambda)\pi_E(\lambda) \rangle \delta(\omega - 2\omega_\lambda)$$
$$= \left(\frac{4\pi^2 S^2}{c\hbar\Omega_v}\right) \rho\left(\frac{\omega}{2}\right) \langle \pi_E(\lambda)\pi_E(\lambda) \rangle \omega_\lambda = \omega/2. \tag{13.13}$$

where $\pi_E(\lambda)$ is the component of $\pi(\lambda)$ in the direction of E and

$$\rho(\omega) = \sum_\lambda \delta(\omega - 2\omega_\lambda)$$

i.e., the two-magnon density of states. The two-magnon excitation process is very weak for very-long-wavelength magnons. This is clear from eqn (13.12). The major contribution will come from a region of large density of states near the Brillouin zone boundary and the critical points of Van Hove (1953) type which arise from locally flat regions of the frequency as a function of wavevector where the group velocity ($\nabla_\lambda\omega$) vanishes. Also, owing to the fact that $\pi(\lambda)$ can be anisotropic, the absorption of polarized light will depend strongly on the direction of polarization with respect to the crystal axes.

Thus for systems such as MnF_2, FeF_2, etc., where the magnetic ions are distributed at sites having body-centred tetragonal structure, and taking π_{jl} for the nearest neighbours only, i.e. atoms at $(\pm \frac{1}{2}a, \pm \frac{1}{2}a, \pm \frac{1}{2}c)$ and the atom at $(0, 0, 0)$, we obtain for the absorption coefficient for $\mathbf{E}$ parallel to the c axis

$$K_{\parallel}(\omega) = \frac{256\pi^2 \omega S^2}{c\hbar\Omega_v} \sum_{\lambda} \pi_z^{\;2} \sin^2\left(\lambda_x \frac{a}{2}\right) \sin^2\left(\lambda_y \frac{a}{2}\right) \sin^2\left(\lambda_z \frac{c}{2}\right) \delta\left(\omega - 2\omega_\lambda\right)$$

$$(13.14a)$$

which shows that the major contribution comes from the points $(\pm \pi/a, \pm \pi/a, \pm \pi/c)$ of the Brillouin zone. Similarly for $\mathbf{E}$ perpendicular to the c axis

$$K_{\perp}(\omega) = \frac{256\pi^2 \omega S^2}{c\hbar\Omega_v} (\pi_x^{\;2} + \pi_y^{\;2}) \times \sin^2\left(\lambda_x \frac{a}{2}\right) \sin^2\left(\lambda_y \frac{a}{2}\right) \cos^2\left(\lambda_z \frac{c}{2}\right) \delta(\omega - 2\omega_\lambda).$$

$$(13.14b)$$

In this case the contribution will come mainly from the points $(\pm \pi/a, \pm \pi/a, 0)$ of the Brillouin zone.

Experimental observation of two-magnon absorption has been reported for systems such as MnF_2, FeF_2, CoF_2, $MnCO_3$, etc. (see Allen, Loudon, and Richards 1966, Richards 1967). There seems to be qualitative agreement between theory and experiment. It is interesting to note that the two-magnon absorption peak does not shift on the application of an external magnetic field. This is expected because the two magnons involved belong to two different branches and they have opposite Zeeman shifts.

13.4. Magnon sidebands

As was shown in eqn (13.4), magnon sidebands appear from exciton–magnon absorption of light and involve orbital excitation of one of the pair of atoms. The absorption coefficient turns out to be

$$K(\omega) \alpha \sum_{\lambda} \{|\pi_{ab}^{\;eg}(\lambda)|^2 + |\pi_{ba}^{\;eg}(\lambda)|^2\} \cosh^2\theta_\lambda \delta(\omega - \omega_\lambda).$$

$$(13.15)$$

Magnon sidebands have been observed in antiferromagnets and ferrimagnets. They cannot be observed in ferromagnetic insulators unless the system has large non-uniaxial anisotropy. For details reference should be made to the paper by Tanabe and Gondaira (1967).

Fig. 13.2 shows the experimental results of one-magnon sidebands observed in MnF_2 together with the theoretical assignment. The various ab-

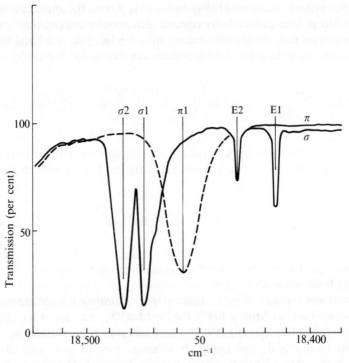

FIG. 13.2. Experimental results of one-magnon side bands in MnF_2 together with theoretical assignments; fine structure of ${}^6A_{1g}({}^6S) \rightarrow {}^4T_{1g}({}^4G)$ transition at 2.2 K. (After Sell 1968.)

sorption peaks are the fine structure of the ionic transition ${}^6A_{1g}({}^6S) \longrightarrow {}^4T_{1g}({}^4G)$ of Mn^{2+}. The relatively weak lines designated by E1 and E2 are attributed to purely magnetic dipole type exciton transition. On the other hand, the strong lines designated as $\sigma 1$ and $\pi 1$ are electric dipole type spin-wave sidebands of E1 and similarly $\sigma 2$ corresponds to E2. Here σ and π polarizations refer to spin-wave excitations at the centers and the boundaries of the Brillouin zone.

13.5. Scattering of light by magnons

Physically, the scattering of light arises from the spin-dependent polarizability of the magnetic crystal. At low temperatures this can be expanded in terms of magnon operators giving rise to one-magnon and two-magnon processes.

In the one-magnon process only magnons of wave vector $\lambda \sim 0$ can participate. However, for the two-magnon process the magnons involved must have nearly equal and opposite wave vectors. The actual computation of the differential extinction coefficient will require details of the specific magnetic system. The spin-dependent dynamic electric polarizability $\alpha_q(\omega)$ can be written in a general form as (Moriya 1968)

$$\alpha_q(\omega) = \frac{1}{\Omega_v} \sum_j \alpha_j(\omega) \, \exp(-i\mathbf{q} \cdot \mathbf{R}_j)$$

$$+ \frac{1}{\Omega_v} \sum_{j,l} \alpha_{jl}(\omega) \, \exp(-i\mathbf{q} \cdot \mathbf{R}_{jl}) \tag{13.16}$$

where

$$\alpha_j(\omega) = \sum_\mu \alpha_{j\mu}(\omega) \, S_{j\mu} + \sum_{\mu\nu} \alpha_{j\mu\nu}(\omega) \, S_{j\mu} S_{j\nu} + \ldots \tag{13.17}$$

and

$$\alpha_{jl}(\omega) = \sum_{\mu\nu} \alpha_{jl\mu\nu}(\omega) \, S_{j\mu} S_{l\nu} + \ldots \tag{13.18}$$

In the above $\alpha_j(\omega)$ and $\alpha_{jl}(\omega)$ are the polarizabilities associated with the single ion and the pair of ions respectively. For antiferromagnetic transition-metal fluorides the components of the polarizability tensor for the single ion at the corner site is (from symmetry considerations)

$$\alpha_j = \begin{pmatrix} 0 & 0 & 0 \\ 0 & 0 & ia_4 \\ 0 & -ia_4 & 0 \end{pmatrix} S_\xi + \begin{pmatrix} 0 & 0 & -ia_5 \\ 0 & 0 & 0 \\ ia_5 & 0 & 0 \end{pmatrix} S_\eta + \begin{pmatrix} 0 & ia_6 & 0 \\ -ia_6 & 0 & 0 \\ 0 & 0 & 0 \end{pmatrix} S_\zeta. \tag{13.19}$$

The differential extinction coefficient for the incident radiation of wave vector $\boldsymbol{\kappa}$ parallel to the η axis polarized along ξ and the scattered radiation of wave vector $\boldsymbol{\kappa}'$ in the $\eta\xi$ plane polarized along the η direction is given by

$$\frac{\mathrm{d}^2 h}{\mathrm{d}\Omega\mathrm{d}\omega} = \frac{\omega_0 \omega^3}{c} \frac{\hbar}{\pi g^2 \mu B^2} \left[\exp\left\{ \frac{\hbar(\omega - \omega_0)}{k_B T} \right\} - 1 \right]^{-1}$$

$$\times \{ a_+{}^2 \chi_{\xi\xi}''(q, \omega - \omega_0) + a_-{}^2 \overline{\chi}_{\xi\xi}''(q, \omega - \omega_0) \} \ldots \tag{13.20}$$

where

$$q = 2\kappa \sin\left(\frac{\theta}{2}\right)$$

θ being the scattering angle, and

$$a_\pm = \frac{a_4 \pm a_5}{2}$$

and $\chi''(q, \omega)$ and $\overline{\chi}''(q, \omega)$ are the imaginary parts of the magnetic susceptibility for the uniform and the staggered fields respectively. The above expression follows from the fluctuation–dissipation theorem. For a quantitative estimate one has to evaluate the susceptibilities involved in expression (13.19). The susceptbilities can be evaluated by various approximate methods such as the molecular field and Green function methods (Moriya 1968, Fleury 1973). It should be noted that the positive and negative values of $\omega - \omega_0$ correspond respectively to anti-Stokes and Stokes lines. The susceptibilities contain information about various magnon processes. Thus in the first-order process a photon is scattered by the emission or absorption of a magnon whereas in the second order process the scattering involves the absorption or emission of two magnons of nearly equal and opposite momenta over the entire Brillouin zone. It should be noted that

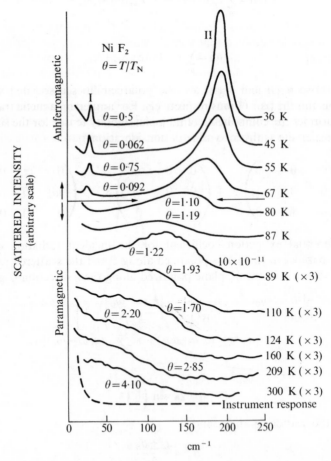

FIG. 13.3. The Magnon spectra of NiF$_2$ below and above the Neel temperature. (After Fleury 1973.)

the susceptibilities are also temperature dependent. Accordingly, the extinction coefficient is found to decrease with increasing temperature. Estimates for FeF_2 show that the extinction coefficient is of the order of 10^{-12}–10^{-10} cm^{-1} sr^{-1}.

The two-magnon scattering processes arise from the terms bilinear in the ionic spin operators. On going over to spin-wave representation, we obtain

$$\alpha_{\mu\nu}(\omega) = \sum_{\lambda} \alpha_{\mu\nu}(\omega, \lambda)\alpha_{\lambda}\beta^{-}_{\lambda} + \text{h.c.} \tag{13.21}$$

with

$$\alpha_{\mu\nu}(\omega, \lambda) = \sum_{j} \alpha_{jl\mu\nu}(\omega) \exp(i\lambda \cdot \mathbf{R}_{jl}).$$

Although the form above looks similar to the two-magnon absorption process, it should be noted that the selection rules for the scattering process are different.

For ferromagnetic insulators such as EuO the magnon–photon (Brillouin) scattering mechanisms are forbidden for reasons of parity and spin selection rules. However, one can envisage an indirect scattering mechanism wherein light is scattered primarily by the density fluctuation of the lattice due to phonons. The latter are in turn renormalized by the

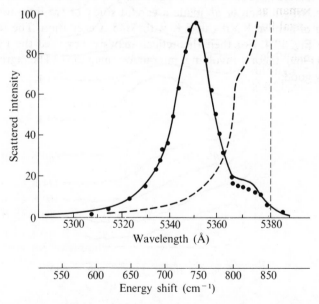

FIG. 13.4. Two-magnon Raman spectra for $KNiF_3$. The broken and the solid lines denote the non-interacting and interacting magnon spectra respectively. (After Chinn et al. 1971.)

magnetoelastic interaction with spin waves. The scattered intensity $I(q, \omega)$ is given by (Krishnasami and Kumar 1972)

$$I(\mathbf{q}, \omega) \sim \left(\frac{\partial \varepsilon}{\partial \rho}\right)^2 \left(\frac{\hbar \rho q}{2\pi v_s}\right) \coth\left(\frac{\hbar \omega}{2k_B T}\right)$$

$$\times \left[\frac{\chi''(\mathbf{q}, \omega)}{\{\hbar\omega - \hbar\omega_q + \chi'(\mathbf{q}, \omega)\}^2 + \chi''^2(\mathbf{q}, \omega)} + (\mathbf{q}, \omega \rightarrow -\mathbf{q}, -\omega)\right]$$

(13.22)

where $\hbar\omega$ and $\hbar\mathbf{q}$ are the energy momentum transfers in the scattering process and $\chi'(\mathbf{q}, \omega)$ and $\chi''(\mathbf{q}, \omega)$ are the real and imaginary parts of the complex 'susceptibility' function $\chi(\mathbf{q}, \omega)$ given by

$$\chi(\mathbf{q}, \omega) = |\phi_q|^2 \sum_\lambda \frac{\langle n_\lambda \rangle - \langle n_{\lambda-q} \rangle}{\hbar\omega - \hbar\omega_\lambda + \hbar\omega_{\lambda-q} + i\eta}$$

where $\eta \rightarrow 0^+$. The estimated width of the Brillouin components for EuO is of the order of 10 kHz.

A considerable number of experimental results are available on two-magnon Raman as well as one-magnon Brillouin light scattering from transition-metal fluoride antiferromagnets such as MnF_2, FeF_2, CoF_2, and NiF_2 (for a recent review see Fleury 1973) and $KNiF_3$ and K_2NiF_4 (Chinn, Zeiger, and O'Connor 1971).

In Fig. 13.3 we have shown one-magnon (I) and two-magnon (II) scattering peaks for NiF_2. Chinn *et al.* made a careful study of two-magnon Raman scattering of light in $KNiF_3$ at 5 K with 5145 Å excitation. The results are shown in Fig. 13.4. For their theoretical analysis they used the Elliott and Thorpe (1969) theory involving interaction magnons. The agreement is extremely good.

14

CONDUCTION-ELECTRON MAGNON
INTERACTION IN FERROMAGNETIC
INSULATORS

In recent years there has been considerable activity, both experimental and theoretical, on the transport and the optical properties of magnetic semi-conductors (see Methfessel and Mattis 1968). This rapid advance has been made possible by the preparation of magnetic materials which are fer-romagnetic insulators in the pure state (resistivity $\sim 10^{10}$ Ω cm). The pure insulators are used for studying optical properties in relation to band structure determination. One can also dope the samples by appropriate impurities to study the transport properties of the carriers thus produced in the conduction (valence) band. As the carrier concentration (degeneracy) can be varied effectively over a large range, one can expect interesting transport behaviour in these systems. Before we describe the interaction processes, it will be helpful to discuss a few typical examples.

Two families of such systems have been extensively studied. The first family comprises rare-earth (R) chalcogenides RX, which have a rocksalt structure, where X stands for O^{2-}, S^{2-}, Se^{2-} or Te^{2-}. Interesting optical, magnetic, and electronic transport phenomena have been discovered in europium chalcogenides (when doped with trivalent La, Gd, etc.). The second family has the spinel structure. Some examples are $CdCr_2S_4$, $CdCr_2Se_4$, $HgCr_2S_4$ and $HgCr_2Se_4$, the dopants being In, Ag, etc.

In the rare-earth chalcogenides, the following transport properties have been observed in the low-carrier-concentration region (von Molnar 1970). In the paramagnetic region, the resistivity increases exponentially as one approaches the ferromagnetic ordering temperature. There is a resistivity peak near the ferromagnetic Curie temperature (see Fig. 14.1). They also show giant magnetoresistance in this temperature region. The magnetoresis-tance effects persist far beyond T_c, even up to $2T_c$. Hall effect measurements in Gd-doped EuSe shows that the exponential increase of resistivity is not due to the change of carrier concentration but to the mobility change. This is corroborated by photoconductivity measurements on this system.

The characteristic optical property of these magnetic semiconductors is the large shift of the absorption edge towards lower energies as the temperature is lowered through the magnetic ordering temperature or with increasing external magnetic field. This is referred to as the red shift of the absorption edge (Dimmock 1970). For example, in EuO ($T_c \sim 69.4$ K), the optical energy gap diminishes from about 1.18 eV at 80 K to about 0.95 eV

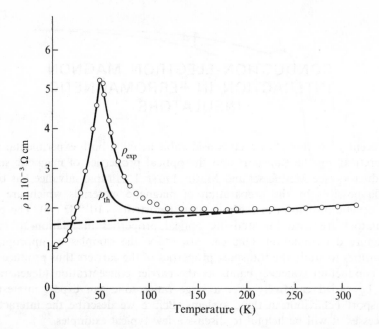

FIG. 14.1.   Resistivity peak near the ferromagnetic Curie temperature in Eu_{95} $Gd_{0.05}$ S. (After von Molnar 1970 and reference therein.)

at 0 K (see Fig. 14.2). The above absorption is connected with the atomic transition $4f^7 \rightarrow 4f^6 5d$ of Eu^{2+}. Similar observations regarding the transport and optical properties have been made in the spinel-type ferromagnetic chalcogenides (see Haas 1970).

Before considering a formal explanation in terms of interactions involving free carriers and the excitation of the spin system, we shall briefly discuss some physical descriptions. These are based on the model which proposes that the doped system has free carriers which interact with the localized magnetic moments through the usual s–d (f) exchange interaction. The resistivity of the sample will accordingly consist of three additive components; the residual resistivity ρ_0 (temperature independent, arising from elastic impurity scattering), the lattice resistivity ρ_L (temperature dependent, arising from phonon scattering), and the spin-disorder resistivity ρ_M (temperature dependent, arising from scattering of the carriers with the localized spins). The last component, i.e. ρ_M, is very sensitive to the magnetic ordering. The exponential increase of the resistivity as T_c is approached from above is associated with the spin-disorder resistivity. The above critical behaviour reflects the short-range spin–spin correlation which is strongly temperature dependent in the critical region.

The red shift of the absorption edge can be explained on the basis of a

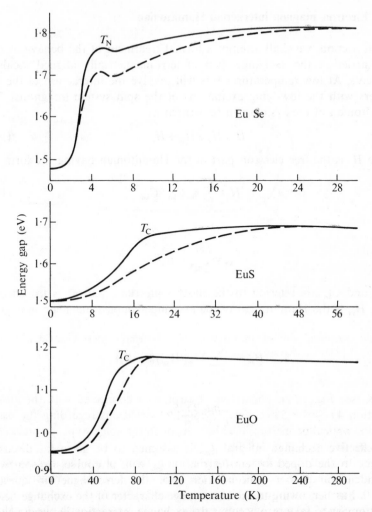

FIG. 14.2. Shift of the absorption edge in europium chalcogenides as a function of magnetic ordering: solid curves, $H = 0$; broken curves, $H = 10$ kG. (After Dimmock 1970, and Busch and Wachter 1968).

band model of the conduction electrons. Below T_c the spin system orders leading to a spin splitting of the conduction band. This results in a shift of the band edge. This shift is a function of the magnetic order and hence is dependent on temperature and the external magnetic field. Another possible interpretation is in terms of a magnetic excition model (Kasuya and Yanase 1968) in which the excited electron is localized near the cation and depends entirely on the temperature-dependent spin correlation of the excited electron with the nearest-neighbour magnetic ions. This also gives a spin-dependent lowering of the excitation energy.

14.1. Electron–magnon interaction Hamiltonian

In this section, we shall attempt a formal treatment of the behaviour of a free carrier in the exchange field of ferromagnetically aligned localized moments. At low temperatures this will involve the interaction of the free carriers with the low-lying excitations of the spin system (magnons). The Hamiltonian of the system can be written as

$$H = H_e + H_m + H_{e-m} \qquad (14.1)$$

where H_e is the free electron part of the Hamiltonian having the form

$$H_e = \sum_{\mathbf{k}\sigma} \varepsilon_{\mathbf{k}\sigma} C_{\mathbf{k}\sigma}^{+} C_{\mathbf{k}\sigma} \qquad (14.2)$$

with

$$\varepsilon_{\mathbf{k}\sigma} = \frac{\hbar^2 k^2}{2m^*} - \mu_B B \sigma; \qquad (14.3)$$

$C_{\mathbf{k}\sigma}^{+}$ and $C_{\mathbf{k}\sigma}$ are referred to the Bloch state $|\mathbf{k}\sigma\rangle$ and m^* is the effective mass. H_m is the Hamiltonian of the exchange-coupled magnetic ions given by

$$H_m = -\sum_{mn} 2J_{mn}(\mathbf{R}_{mn})(\mathbf{S}_m \cdot \mathbf{S}_n)$$

$$\qquad (14.4)$$

$$-g\mu_B B \sum_m S_m^z.$$

The effective exchange integral J_{mn} is assumed to be given (as discussed earlier). In the doped system (extrinsic) J_{mn} will, of course, be somewhat dependent on carrier concentration. For the ferromagnet in question $J_{mn} > 0$. Further, owing to the short-range character of the exchange field it is customary to take into account the exchange interaction between nearest magnetic neighbours only. One can then write the first term of eqn (14.4) as

$$-J \sum_{m,\Delta} \mathbf{S}_m \cdot \mathbf{S}_{m+\Delta},$$

where Δ runs over the nearest neighbours; J is treated as a constant positive exchange parameter. One can go over to the magnon representation by the usual spin deviation and spin-wave transformation discussed earlier (see Chapter 5). The magnon Hamiltonian H_m then takes the form

$$H_m = \text{constant} + \sum_{\lambda} \hbar\omega_{\lambda}(a_{\lambda}^{+} a_{\lambda} + \tfrac{1}{2}) \qquad (14.5)$$

with

$$\hbar\omega_\lambda = g\mu_B B + 2z \, JS(1-\gamma_\lambda).$$

The exchange interaction between a conduction-electron spin and a localized moment can be expressed (assuming a short-range contact type interaction) as

$$H_{e-m} = \frac{-I\Omega_v}{N} \sum_{m,i} (\mathbf{S}_m \cdot \mathbf{s}_i)\delta(\mathbf{r}_i - \mathbf{R}_m) \tag{14.6}$$

where $\mathbf{r}_i$ and $\mathbf{s}_i$ are the space co-ordinate and the spin operator of the ith conduction electron; I is the exchange parameter Ω_v the crystal volume. Recasting the Hamiltonian in terms of fermion and magnon operators, we obtain (see Chapter 3)

$$\begin{aligned} H_{e-m} = & \left\{ \frac{I}{2N} \sum_{\substack{k,k' \\ \lambda,\lambda'}} \Delta(\mathbf{k}'-\mathbf{k}+\lambda'-\lambda)a_{\lambda'}{}^+a_\lambda (C_{k'\uparrow}{}^+ C_{k\uparrow} - C_{k'\downarrow}{}^+ C_{k\downarrow}) \right. \\ & \left. -\frac{SI}{2}\sum_{k\sigma} \sigma C_{k\sigma}{}^+ C_{k\sigma} \right\} \\ & -\left(\frac{2S}{N}\right)^{1/2} \frac{I}{2}\sum_{k,k'} \Delta(\mathbf{k}'-\mathbf{k}+\lambda)(C_{k\uparrow}{}^+ C_{k\downarrow}a_\lambda{}^+ + C_{k\downarrow}{}^+ C_{k\uparrow}a_\lambda) \end{aligned} \tag{14.7}$$

14.2. Band splitting in the mean-field approximations

We shall now consider a simplified treatment of the effect of electron–magnon interactions on the system of electrons and magnons. As a first approximation, the effect of the terms in braces in eqn (14.7) on the renormalization of the electron and magnon energies is taken into account. This will give a polarization of the conduction electrons owing to the ferromagnetic ordering of the localized spins. We shall now use the mean field (Hartree) approximation. Accordingly, we take the symmetrized factorization of the quantity $b_{\lambda'}{}^+; b_\lambda C_{k'\sigma}{}^+ C_{k\sigma}$ as

$$(\langle b_\lambda{}^+ b_\lambda \rangle C_{k\sigma}{}^+ C_{k\sigma} + \langle C_{k\sigma}{}^+ C_{k\sigma}\rangle b_\lambda{}^+ b_\lambda)\delta_{\lambda\lambda'}\delta_{kk'}$$

where the angular brackets denote the thermal average. Thus the renormalized conduction electron and magnon energies due to the terms in braces in eqn (14.7) become

$$\tilde{\varepsilon}_{k\sigma} = \varepsilon_{k\sigma} - \frac{I}{2}\left(S - \frac{1}{N}\sum_\lambda \langle n_\lambda\rangle\sigma\right) \tag{14.8}$$

$$\hbar\tilde{\omega}_\lambda = \hbar\omega_\lambda + \frac{I}{2N}(\langle n\uparrow\rangle - \langle n\downarrow\rangle) \tag{14.9}$$

where $\langle n\uparrow\rangle - \langle n\downarrow\rangle$ is the net spin polarization of the conduction electrons. It should be noted that eqns (14.8) and (14.9) should be solved self-consistently. The spin splitting of the conduction band is contained in eqn (14.8). Writing the saturation magnetization $M(0) = g\mu_B SN$ and $M(T) = g\mu_B N(S - I/N \sum \langle n_\lambda\rangle)$, we can write

$$\tilde{\varepsilon}_{k(\pm)} = \varepsilon_{k(\pm)} \pm \frac{M(T)}{2M(0)} IS. \tag{14.10}$$

The red shift observed in going from above the Curie temperature to very low temperature should thus be equal to $\frac{1}{2}IS$. The experimental value of the shift in EuO is about 0.2 eV. Thus I should be of the order of 0.1 eV.

14.3. Renormalized single-particle energy and lifetime

The Hamiltonian, after incorporating the above mean field approximation, reduces to

$$H = H_e + H_m + H_{em}^{(r)} \tag{14.11}$$

where the residual interaction $H_{em}^{(r)}$ is given by

$$H_{em}^{(r)} = -\frac{1}{2}\left(\frac{2S}{N}\right)^{1/2} I \sum_{k\lambda} (C_{k+\lambda\downarrow}^+ C_{k\uparrow} a_\lambda + C_{k-\lambda\uparrow}^+ C_{k\downarrow} a_\lambda^+). \tag{14.12}$$

The residual interaction terms involve emission or absorption of a magnon together with spin-flip scattering of a conduction electron. Its effect on the single particle energies is as follows. In the low-temperature region we obtain

$$\tilde{\varepsilon}_{k\uparrow}^{(r)} = \tilde{\varepsilon}_{k\uparrow} + \frac{SI^2}{2N}\sum_\lambda \frac{\langle 1 - n_{k+\lambda\downarrow}\rangle + \langle n_\lambda\rangle}{\tilde{\varepsilon}_{k\uparrow} - \tilde{\varepsilon}_{k+\lambda\downarrow} + \hbar\tilde{\omega}_\lambda}. \tag{14.13}$$

$$\tilde{\varepsilon}_{k\downarrow}^{(r)} = \tilde{\varepsilon}_{k\downarrow} + \frac{SI^2}{2N}\sum_\lambda \frac{\langle 1 - n_{k-\lambda\uparrow}\rangle + \langle n_\lambda\rangle}{\tilde{\varepsilon}_{k\downarrow} - \tilde{\varepsilon}_{k-\lambda\uparrow} - \hbar\omega_\lambda}. \tag{14.14}$$

The above renormalized single-particle energies for the up and down spins have to be used for evaluating the effective masses. The lifetime (damping) of the carriers is given by the imaginary part of the correction to the single particle energy:

$$\frac{1}{\tau_{k\uparrow}} = \frac{\pi}{\hbar}\frac{SI^2}{N}\sum_\lambda (\langle 1 - n_{k+\lambda\downarrow}\rangle + \langle n_\lambda\rangle) \\ \times \delta(\tilde{\varepsilon}_{k\uparrow} - \tilde{\varepsilon}_{k+\lambda\downarrow} + \hbar\omega_\lambda) \tag{14.15}$$

$$\frac{1}{\tau_{k\downarrow}} = \frac{\pi SI^2}{\hbar 2N} \sum_{\lambda} (\langle 1 - n_{k-\lambda\uparrow} \rangle + \langle n_{\lambda} \rangle) \times \delta(\tilde{\varepsilon}_{k\downarrow} - \tilde{\varepsilon}_{k-k\uparrow} - \hbar\omega_{\lambda}). \quad (14.16)$$

The analytical evaluation of the above integrals has not been done in a closed form except for the case of $T = 0$. Some authors have made numerical computations at finite temperatures (Woolsey and White 1970). The essential conclusions derived are as follows.

For small carrier concentrations (low level of doping, i.e. $n \sim 10^{20}$ cm^{-3}) there is a large, well-defined spin-up Fermi surface lying below the band edge of the spin-down band. Therefore, the latter is completely empty at very low temperatures. Under these conditions the modified dispersion relation of the spin-up electrons near the Fermi surface is flat. With increasing temperature the energy correction becomes larger and is always negative. This follows directly from expressions (14.13) and (14.14). For larger doping, when a well-defined spin-down Fermi surface exists, one obtains a non-zero energy correction for the spin-up electron even at $T = 0$. This follows from the fact that an electron in the spin-down band (which is now populated) can emit a magnon by flipping its spin and the magnon can be re-absorbed by a spin-up electron. In this case the energy correction will show two logarithmic singularities as a function of wave vector below the Fermi surface. This indicates a breakdown of perturbation theory. At a finite temperature, of course, the singularities are smoothed out. It should be noted that the order of correction is typically 10^{-2}–10^{-3} eV near the Fermi surface. The effective mass $m_\sigma^* = \hbar^2 k/(\partial \tilde{\varepsilon}_k^{(r)}/\partial k)$ (away from the band edge of spin-up and spin-down electrons) is a sensitive function of doping, wave vector, and temperature. For example, for a certain choice of parameters (see Woolsey and White 1970 for details) and at the Fermi surface the spin-up mass increases beyond $n \sim 4 \times 10^{20}$ cm^{-3} and the spin-down mass decreases rapidly.

For $T \ll T_c$, the mobility at the Fermi surface

$$\mu_\sigma = \frac{e\tau_\sigma(k_F)}{m^*} \quad (14.17)$$

is a sensitive function of the lifetime and the effective mass as given by eqns (14.15) and (14.16). The mobility averaged over the two sub-bands decreases rapidly with increasing temperature.

14.4. Spin-disorder resistivity

In the critical region there is no long-range magnetic order. Thus one cannot treat the problem in terms of magnon co-ordinates. One is in the regime of spin-disorder resistivity due to violent long-range fluctuations of magnetization near T_c (de Gennes and Friedel 1958). The critical scattering of electrons from short-range correlated spins can be expressed as (Takada 1971),

$$\frac{1}{\tau} = \text{constant} \int_{-1}^{+1} \langle \mathbf{S}(\mathbf{q}) \cdot \mathbf{S}(-\mathbf{q}) \rangle (1 - \cos \theta) \mathrm{d}(\cos \theta) \qquad (14.18)$$

where $\cos \theta = [1 - q^2/2k_F^2]$, $\mathbf{q}$ being the momentum transfer to the conduction electron; $\langle \mathbf{S}(\mathbf{q}) \cdot \mathbf{S}(-\mathbf{q}) \rangle$ represents the spin–spin correlation function in momentum space. This is one of the most active fields of research at the moment. A simplified treatment is, however, possible in terms of the Ornstein–Zernike correlation function of Yukawa form. One then obtains the resistivity via $\rho = m^*/ne^2\tau$ as

$$\rho(T) = \rho_c - b \left| \frac{T}{T_c} - 1 \right| \left| \ln \left| \left(\frac{T}{T_c} - 1 \right) \right| \right|^{-1}. \qquad (14.19)$$

For $b > 0$, we obtain a concave cusp at $T = T_c$ (Fisher and Langer 1968).

Finally it should be noted that the s–d exchange interaction has been treated essentially as a perturbation leading to renormalization of single-particle energies and damping. When the coupling constant I is large, there is the possibility of formation of magnetic polarons which are bound states of electrons and magnons. This radically modifies the transport and the optical absorption properties of the system (see Richmond 1970, Izyumov and Medvedev 1971).

BIBLIOGRAPHY

ABRAGAM, A., and BLEANEY, B. (1970). *Paramagnetic resonance*. Clarendon Press, Oxford.

AKHIEZER, A. I. (1946). *J. Phys. (Moscow)* 10, 217.

AKHIEZER, A. I., BARYAKHTER, V. G., and PELETMINSKII, S. V. (1968). *Spin waves*, North-Holland, Amsterdam.

ALEXANDER, S., and ANDERSON, P. W. (1964). *Phys. Rev. A* **133**, 1594.

ALLEN, S. J., LOUDON, R., and RICHARDS, P. L. (1966). *Phys. Rev. Lett.* **16**, 463.

ALPERIN, H. (1962) *J. phys. Soc. Japan* **17** (BIII), 12.

ANDERSON, P. W. (1952). *Phys. Rev.* **86**, 694.

——(1959). *Phys. Rev.* **115**, 2.

——(1963). *Solid State Phys.* **14**, 99.

——(1964). In *transition metal compounds* (ed. E. R. Schatz. Gordon and Breach, New York.

ANDERSON, P. W., and SUHL, H. (1955). *Phys. Rev.* **100**, 1788.

ARAI, T. (1962). *Phys. Rev.* **126**, 471.

BAKRE, R. V., JOSHI, A. W., and SINHA, K. P. (1967). *Ind. J. pure and appl. Phys.* **5**, 205.

BHANDARI, C. M., and VERMA, G. S. (1966). *Phys. Rev.* **152**, 731.

BLOCH, F. (1930). *Z. Phys.* **61**, 206.

—— (1946). *Phys. Rev.* **70**, 460.

BLOCH, M. (1962). *Phys. Rev. Lett.* **9**, 286.

—— (1963). *J. appl. Phys.* **34**, 1151.

BORN, M., and HUANG, K. (1954). *Dynamical theory of crystal lattices*. Clarendon Press, Oxford.

BOROVIK-ROMANOV, A. S., and KALINKINA, I.N. (1961). *Zh. eksper. teor. Fiz.* **41**, 1694.

BROCKHOUSE, B. N., and WATANABE, H. (1962). Phys. Lett. **1**, 189.

BUSCH, G., and WACHTER, P. (1968). **26**, 1.

CALLAWAY, J., and BOYD, R. (1964). *Phys. Rev. A* **134**, 1655.

CALLEN, H. B. (1963). *Phys. Rev.* **130**, 890.

CARRUTHERS, P., (1961). *Rev. mod. Phys.* **33**, 92.

CASIMIR, H. B. G. (1938). *Physica* **5**, 495.

CASIMIR, H. B. G. and DU PRE, F. K. (1938). *Physica* **5**, 507.

CHARAP, S. H., and BOYD, E. L., (1964). *Phys. Rev. A* **133**, 811.

CHINN, S. R., ZEIGER, H. J., and O'CONNOR, J. R. (1971). *Phys. Rev. B* **3**, 1709.

DARBY, M. I. (1969). *Am. J. Phys.* **37**, 354.

DEXTER, D. L. (1962). *Phys. Rev.* **126**, 1962.

DIMMOCK, J. O. (1970). *IBM J. Res. Dev.* **14**, 107.

DIRAC, P. A. M. (1929). *Proc. R. Soc. A* **123**, 714.

DOUGLASS, R. L. (1960). *Phys. Rev.* **132**, 2398.

DYSON, F. J. (1956). *Phys. Rev.* **102**, 1217, 1230.

DZIALOSHINSKII, I. E. (1958). *J. Phys. Chem. Solids* **4**, 241.

ELLIOTT, R. J., and LOWDE, R. D. (1955). *Proc. R. Soc. A* **230**, 46.

ELLIOTT, R. J., and THORPE, M. P. (1969). *J. Phys C* **2**, 1630.

FISHER, M. E. (1974). *Rev. mod. Phys.* **46**, 597.

FISHER, M. E., and LANGER, J. S. (1968). *Phys. Rev. Lett.* **20**, 665.

FLEURY, P. (1973). *Proc. Conf. on Magnetism*, Moscow (Academy of Science, U.S.S.R.) vol I, p. 81.

GENKIN, V. N., and FAIN, V. M. (1962). *Sov. Phys.–JETP* **14**, 1086.

DE GENNES, P. G. (1963). In *Magnetism*, Vol. 3 (eds. G. T. Rado and H. Suhl). Academic Press, New York, p. 155.

DE GENNES, P. G., and FRIEDEL, J. (1958). *J. Phys. Chem. Solids* **4**, 71.

GLASSER, M. L., and MILFORD, F. J. (1963). *Phys. Rev.* **130**, 1783.

GONDAIRA, K., and TANABE, Y. (1966). *J. Phys. Soc. Japan* **21**, 1527.

GOODENOUGH, J. B. (1963). *Magnetism and the chemical bond*. Interscience, New York.

GOSSARD, A. C., JACCARINO, V., and REMEIKA, J. P. (1961). *Phys. Rev. Lett.* **7**, 122.

GRIFFITHS, J. S. (1961). *The theory of transition metal ions*. Cambridge University Press, Cambridge.

HAAS, C. (1970). *IBM J. Res. Dev.* **14**, 282.

HALL, T. P. P., HAYES, W., STEVENSON, R. W. H., and WILKENS, J. (1963a). *J. Chem. Phys.* **38**, 1977;

—— (1963b) *J. Chem. Phys.* **39**, 35.

HALLEY, J. W., and SILVERA, I. (1965). *Phys. Rev. Lett.* **15**, 654.

HALPERN, V. (1966). *Proc. R. Soc. A* **291**, 113.

HARRIS, A. B. (1963). *Phys. Rev.* **132**, 2398.

HEISENBERG, W. (1928). *Z. Phys.* **49**, 619.

HEITLER, W., and LONDON, F. (1927). *Z. Phys.* **44**, 455.

HELLER, P., and BENEDEK, G. B. (1962). *Phys. Rev. Lett.* **8**, 428.

HERRING, C. (1962). *Rev. Med. Phys.* **126**, 471.

HOOPER, H. O., and de GRAAF, A. M. (1973). *Amorphous magnetism*, Plenum Press, New York.

HOLSTEIN, T., and PRIMAKOFF, H. (1940). *Phys. Rev.* **58**, 1098.

HUTCHINGS, M. T., and SAMUELSEN, E. J. (1972). *Phys. Rev. B* **6**, 3447.

INGLIS, D. R. (1934). *Phys. Rev.* **46**, 135.

IZYUMOV, Y. A., and MEDVEDEV, M. V. (1971). *Sov. Phys.–JETP* **32**, 302.

IZYUMOV, Y. A., and OZEROV, R. (1970) *Magnetic neutron diffraction*. Plenum Press, New York.

JACCARINO, V., and SHULMAN, R. G. (1957). *Phys. Rev.* **107**, 1196.

JOSHI, A. W., and SINHA, K. P. (1965). *Proc. Int. Conf. on Magnetism, Nottingham, 1964*. Institute of Physics and Physical Society, London, p. 411.

—— (1966). *Proc. phys. Soc.* **88**, 685.

—— (1967). *Proc. phys. Soc.* **91**, 97.

KADANOFF, L. P. (1966), *Physics (N.Y.)* **2**, 263.

KANAMORI, J. (1959). *J. Phys. Chem. Solids* **10**, 87.

KASUYA, T. (1956). *Prog. theor. Phys.* **16**, 45.

KASUYA, T., and LE CRAW, R. C. (1961). *Phys. Rev. Lett.* **6**, 223.

KASUYA, T., and YANASE, A. (1968). *J. appl. Phys.* **39**, 430; (1968) *J. Phys. Soc. (Japan)* **25**, 1025.

KEFFER, F. (1966). *Handb. Phys.* **18**, 2.

KIM, D. J., and NAGAOKA, Y. (1963). *Prog. theor. Phys.* **30**, 743.

KITTEL, C. (1963). *Qantum theory of solids*, Wiley, New York, (1971) *Introduction to Solid-state physics*, Wiley, New York.

KOIDE, S. and OGUCHI, T. (1963). *Adv. chem. Phys.* **5**, 189.

KOIDE, S., SINHA, K. P., and TANABE, Y. (1959). *Prog. Theor. Phys.* **22**, 647.

KONDO, J. (1957). *Prog. theor. Phys.* **18**, 541.

KOTHARI, L. S., and SINGWI, K. S. (1959). *Solid State Phys.* **8**, 105.

KOUVEL, J. S., and BROOKS, H. (1954). *Tech. Rep. No.* 198, Cruft Laboratory, Harvard University, Cambridge, Mass.

KOWALSKA, A., MOUSTAFA, R., and SOKALSKI, K. (1972). *Acta Phys. polon. A* **42**, 721.

KRAMERS, H. A. (1934). *Physica* **1**, 182.

KRISHNASAMI, K., and KUMAR, N. (1972). *Phys. Lett. A* **41**, 220.

KRONIG, R. de L. (1939). *Physica* **6**, 33.

KUBO, R. (1953). *Rev. mod. Phys.* **25**, 344.

KUMAR, N., and SINHA, K. P. (1966). *Ind. J. Phys.* **40**, 62.

—— (1967a). *Physica* **34**, 387.

—— (1967b). *Physica* **35**, 456.

LANDAU, L. D., and LIFSHITZ, E. M. (1958). *Quantum mechanics.* Pergamon Press, Oxford.

—— (1969). *Statistical physics.* Pergamon Press, Oxford.

LARSON, G. H., and JEFFRIES, C. D. (1966). *Phys. Rev.* **141**, 461; **145**, 311.

LEVY, P. M. (1975). In *Magnetic oxides*, Part I (ed. D. J. Craik). Wiley, London.

LE CRAW, R. C., and SPENCER, E. G. (1962). *J. phys. Soc. Japan*, (Suppl. B1) **17**, 401.

LOOPSTRA, B. O., VAN LEAR, B., and BREEL, D. J. (1968). *Phys. Lett. A* **26**, 526.

LOUDON, R. (1968). *Adv. Phys.* **17**, 243.

LOVESEY, S. W. (1972). *J. Phys. C* **5**, 2769.

LOW, G. (1963). *Proc. phys. Soc.* **82**, 992.

LOWDIN, P. O. (1962). *Rev. mod. Phys.* **34**, 80.

MA, S. K. (1976). *Modern theory of critical phenomena*, W. A. Benjamin, London.

MARSHALL, W., and LOWDE, R. D. (1968). *Rep. Prog. Phys.* **31**, 705.

MATTIS, D. (1965). *The theory of magnetism.* Harper and Row, New York.

METHFESSEL, S., and MATTIS, D. C. (1968). *Handb Phys.* **18** (7) 389.

MIZUNO, Y., and IZUYAMA, T. (1959). *Prog. theor. Phys.* **22**, 344.

VON MOLNAR, S. (1970). *IBM J. Res. Dev.* **14**, 269.

MORGENTHALER, F. R. (1960). *J. appl. Phys.* **31**, 955.

MORIYA, T. (1960). Phys. Rev. **120**, 91.

MORIYA, T. (1968). *J. appl. Phys.* **39**, 1042.

NAGAI, O. (1969). *J. appl. Phys.*, **40**, 1116.

NAGAI, O., and TANAKA, T. (1969). *Phys. Rev.* **188**, 821.

NATHANS, R., ALPERIN, H., PICKART, S., and BROWN, P. (1963). *J. appl. Phys.* **34**, 1182.

NAVARRO, R., and DE JORGH, L. J. (1976) *Physica* (*Utrecht*) **84B**, 229.

NEEL, L. (1932). *Ann. Phys.* (*Paris*) **18**, 5; see also *Ann. Phys.* (*Paris*), **232**, (1935).

—— (1948). *Ann. Phys.* (*Paris*) **3**, 137.

NESBET, R. K. (1958). *Ann. Phys.* (*N.Y.*), **4**, 87.

NETTLETON, R. E. (1964). *Phys. Rev. A* **135**, 1023.

OGUCHI, T. (1960). *Phys. Rev.* **117**, 117.

OKAZAKI, A., TURBERFIELD, K. C., and STEVENSON, R. W. (1964). *Phys. Lett. A* **8**, 9.

ORBACH, R., (1961). *Proc. phys. Soc.* **77**, 829.

—— (1962). In *Fluctuation, relaxation and resonance in magnetic systems* (ed. D. ter Haar). Oliver and Boyd, Edinburgh.

ORNSTEIN, L. S. and ZERNIKE, F. (1914). *Proc. Sect. sci. K. med Akad. Wet.* **17**, 793.

OWEN, J., and THORNLEY, J. H. M. (1966). *Rep. Prog. Phys.* **29**, 675.

PEIERLS, R. E. (1956). *Quantum theory of solids.* Clarendon Press, Oxford.

PHILLIPS, J. C. (1959). *J. Phys. Chem. Solids* **11**, 226.

PRYCE, M. H. L. (1950). *Proc. Phys. Soc. (London)* **A63**, 25.

PYTTE, E. (1965). *Ann. Phys. (N.Y.)* **32**, 377.

RAINFORD, B., HOUMANN, J. G., and GUGGENHEIM, H. J. (1972). *5th IAEA Symp. on Neutron Inelastic Scattering, Grenoble, France.* International Atomic Energy Agency, Vienna.

REZENDE, S. M., and WHITE, R. M. (1976). *Phys. Rev. B* **14**, 2939.

RICHARDS, P. L. (1967). *J. appl. Phys.* **38**, 1500.

RICHMOND, P. (1970). *J. Phys. C* **3**, 2402.

RIMMER, D. (1965). *Proc. Int. Conf. on Magnetism, Nottingham,* 1964. Institute of Physics and Physical Society, London, p. 337.

—— (1969): *J. Phys. C* **2**, 329.

RUDERMAN, M. A., and KITTEL, C. (1954) *Phys. Rev.* **96**, 99.

RUELLE, D. (1969). *Statistical mechanics,* Benjamin, New York.

SAENZ, A. W. (1960). *Phys. Rev.* **119**, 1542.

—— (1962). *Phys. Rev.* **125**, 1940.

SAMUELSON, E. J., RISTE, T., and STEINSVOLL, O. (1963). *Phys. Lett.* **6**, 47.

SCHLOMANN, E., GREEN, J. J., and MILANO, U. (1960). J. Appl. Phys. **31**, 386s.

SELL, D. D. (1968). *J. appl. Phys.* **39**, 1030.

SHUKLA, G. C., and SINHA, K. P. (1967). *Can. J. Phys.* **45**, 2719.

SINHA, K. P. (1961). *Ind. J. Phys.* **35**, 484.

——(1973). In *Electrons in crystalline solids.* International Atomic Energy Agency, Vienna.

SINHA, K. P., and UPADHYAYA, U. N. (1962). *Phys. Rev.* **127**, 432.

SINHA, K. P., and LE CRAW, R. C. (1971). *J. Phys. Chem. Solids* **32**, 373.

SLATER, J. C. (1930). *Phys. Rev.* **35**, 509.

—— (1953). *Quarterly Progress Report,* July 15, Oct. 15, M.I.T., Cambridge, Mass.

SLICHTER, C. P. (1963). *Principles of magnetic resonance.* Harper and Row, New York.

SPARKS, M. (1964). *Ferromagnetic relaxation theory.* McGraw-Hill, New York.

STEVENS, K. W. H. (1953). *Proc. R. Soc. A* **219**, 542.

——, (1976). *Phys. Rep.* **24C**, 1–75.

TAKADA, S. (1971). *Prog. theor. Phys.* **46**, 15.

TANABE, Y. and GONDAIRA, K. (1967). In *Optical properties of ions in crystals* (eds. A. M. Crosswhite and H. W. Moos). Interscience, New York, p. 279.

TANABE, Y., MORIYA, T., and SUGANO, S. (1965). *Phys. Rev. Lett.* **15**, 1023.

TYABLIKOV, S. V. (1959). *Ukr. Math. Zh.,* **11**, 287.

UPADHYAYA, U. N., and SINHA, K. P. (1963). *Phys. Rev.* **130**, 939.

VAN HOVE, L., (1953). *Phys. Rev.* **89**, 1189.

VAN KRANENDONK, J., VAN VLECK, J. H. (1958). *Rev. mod. Phys.* **30**, 1.

VAN VLECK, J. H. (1932). *The theory of electric and magnetic susceptibilities.* Oxford University Press, Oxford.

—— (1937). *Phys. Rev.* **52**, 1195.

—— (1939). *J. Chem. Phys.* **7**, 72.

—— (1940). *Phys. Rev.* **57**, 426.

—— (1948), *Phys. Rev.* **74**, 1168.

VONSOVSKII, S. V. (1946). *Zh. eksper. teor. Fiz.* **16**, 981.

VONSOVSKII, S. V., and IZYUMOV, Y. A. (1963), *Sov. Phys. Uspekhi* **78**, 723.

VONSOVSKII, S. V., and KARPENKO, B. V. (1968). *Handb, Phys.* **18** (1), 265.

WALLACE, D. C. (1967). *Phys. Rev.* **153**, 547.

WILSON, K. G. (1971). *Phys. Rev. B* **4**, 3174, 3184.

—— (1973). *Conf. Prog. on Magnetism and Magnetic Materials* (ed. C. D. Graham and J. J. Rhyne). American Institute of Physics, New York, No. 10 (Part I), p. 843.

WILSON, K. G., and KOGUT, J. (1974). *Phys. Rep. C* **12**, 75.

WOOLSEY, R. B., and WHITE, R. M. (1970). *Phys. Rev.* **1**, 4474.

YOSIDA, K. (1957). *Phys. Rev.* **106**, 893.

ZENER, C. (1951). *Phys. Rev.* **81**, 440.

AUTHOR INDEX

SUBJECT INDEX